About Pearson

Pearson is the world's learning company, with presence across 70 countries worldwide. Our unique insights and world-class expertise comes from a long history of working closely with renowned teachers, authors and thought leaders, as a result of which, we have emerged as the preferred choice for millions of teachers and learners across the world.

We believe learning opens up opportunities, creates fulfilling careers and hence better lives. We hence collaborate with the best of minds to deliver you class-leading products, spread across the Higher Education and Test Preparation spectrum.

Superior learning experience and improved outcomes are at the heart of everything we do. This product is the result of one such effort.

Your feedback plays a critical role in the evolution of our products and you can contact us - reachus@pearson.com. *We look forward to it.*

CLASS

6

Trishna's

PEARSON IIT FOUNDATION

Mathematics

Seventh Edition

2025

Pearson

Photo Credits

Chapter 1 Opener: 123dartist / Shutterstock
Chapter 2 Opener: doomu / Shutterstock
Chapter 3 Opener: Chekyravaa / Shutterstock
Chapter 4 Opener: Marques / Shutterstock
Chapter 5 Opener: EreborMountain / Shutterstock
Chapter 6 Opener: travellight / Shutterstock
Chapter 7 Opener: R. MACKAY PHOTOGRAPHY, LLC / Shutterstock
Chapter 8 Opener: Gábor Páll / 123RF
Chapter 9 Opener: Studio 8 / Pearson Education Ltd
Chapter 10 Opener: Nataliiap / Shutterstock
Chapter 11 Opener: littleredshark / Shutterstock

ISBN 978-93-6159-226-3

First Impression

Published by Pearson India Education Services Pvt. Ltd, CIN: U72200TN2005PTC057128.
Head Office: 1st Floor, Berger Tower, Plot No. C-001A/2, Sector 16B, Noida - 201 301,
Uttar Pradesh, India.
Registered Office: Featherlite, 'The Address' 5th Floor, Survey No 203/10B, 200 Ft MMRD Road,
Zamin Pallavaram, Chennai – 600 044.
Website: in.pearson.com, Email: companysecretary.india@pearson.com

Compositor: Saksham Printographics, Delhi
Printed in India by Saurabh Printers Pvt. Ltd.

Brief Contents

Preface *xi*
Chapter Insights *xv*

Chapter 1 **Numbers** 1.1
Chapter 2 **Factors and Multiples** 2.1
Chapter 3 **Fractions and Decimals** 3.1
Chapter 4 **Powers and Roots** 4.1
Chapter 5 **Ratio and Proportion** 5.1
Chapter 6 **Percentages and their Applications** 6.1
Chapter 7 **Algebra** 7.1
Chapter 8 **Geometry** 8.1
Chapter 9 **Mensuration** 9.1
Chapter 10 **Statistics** 10.1
Chapter 11 **Sets** 11.1

Contents

Preface *xi*

Chapter Insights *xv*

CHAPTER 1: NUMBERS **1.1**

Hindu–Arabic System **1.3**

Notation and Numeration 1.3

Expanded Form 1.3

Face Value and Place Value of Digits **1.4**

Numbers to be Remembered 1.4

International System of Numeration 1.4

Comparison of Numbers **1.4**

Successors and Predecessors 1.4

Integers **1.5**

Integers as Directed Numbers 1.6

Representation of Integers on the Number Line 1.6

Multiplication of Integers 1.7

Division of Integers 1.8

Absolute Value of an Integer 1.9

Simplification **1.9**

Classroom Wing *1.11*

Competition Wing *1.14*

Hints and Explanations *1.17*

CHAPTER 2: FACTORS AND MULTIPLES **2.1**

Factors and Multiples **2.3**

Even Numbers 2.4

Odd Numbers 2.4

Prime Numbers 2.4

Sphenic Numbers 2.4

Composite Numbers 2.4

Twin Primes 2.4

Co-primes 2.4

Greatest Common Divisor or Highest Common Factor **2.5**

Prime Factorization Method 2.5

Division Method 2.6

Least Common Multiple **2.6**

Prime Factorization Method 2.6

Relationship between LCM and GCD 2.7

Divisibility **2.7**

Tests of Divisibility 2.8

Classroom Wing *2.10*

Competition Wing *2.12*

Hints and Explanations *2.15*

CHAPTER 3: FRACTIONS AND DECIMALS **3.1**

Fractions **3.3**

Types of Fraction 3.3

Comparison of Fractions 3.4

Addition of Fractions 3.4

Multiplication of Fractions 3.4

Division of Fractions 3.5

Decimal Numbers **3.6**

Comparison of Decimal Numbers 3.6

Addition and Subtraction of Decimals 3.7

Multiplication and Division of Decimal Numbers 3.7

Classroom Wing *3.9*

Competition Wing *3.12*

Hints and Explanations *3.15*

CHAPTER 4: POWERS AND ROOTS **4.1**

Laws of Exponents **4.3**

Squares and Square Roots **4.4**

Methods for Finding the Square Root of a Number 4.5

Cubes and Cube Roots **4.6**

Methods for Finding Cube Root of a Number 4.6

Classroom Wing *4.8*

Competition Wing *4.10*

Hints and Explanations *4.12*

CHAPTER 5: RATIO AND PROPORTION **5.1**

Ratio **5.3**

Terms of a Ratio 5.3

Properties of a Ratio 5.3

Simplest Form of a Ratio 5.3

Proportion **5.4**
Direct and Inverse Proportions 5.5
Classroom Wing *5.6*
Competition Wing *5.8*
Hints and Explanations *5.11*

CHAPTER 6: PERCENTAGES AND THEIR APPLICATIONS **6.1**

Percentages **6.3**
Expressing x% as a Fraction 6.4
Expressing the Fraction a/b as a Decimal and as a Percentage 6.4
Percentage, a Relative Value 6.4

Profit, Loss and Discount **6.6**
Profit and Loss 6.6
Cost Price 6.6
Selling Price 6.6
Discount 6.7
Overheads 6.7

Simple Interest **6.8**
Principal or Sum 6.8
Amount 6.8
Rate of Interest 6.8
Simple Interest 6.8
Formula for the Computation of Simple Interest 6.8
Classroom Wing *6.11*
Competition Wing *6.14*
Hints and Explanations *6.16*

CHAPTER 7: ALGEBRA **7.1**

Algebraic Expressions **7.3**
Constant 7.3
Variable 7.3
Algebraic Expression 7.3
Terms 7.3
Polynomial 7.4
Value of an Expression 7.4

Operations on Polynomials **7.5**
Addition of Polynomials 7.5
Subtraction of Polynomials 7.6
Multiplication of a Polynomial with a Monomial 7.6
Division of a Polynomial by a Monomial 7.7

Equations **7.7**
Algebraic Expressions 7.7
Mathematical Sentence 7.7
Mathematical Statement 7.8
Open Sentences 7.8
Linear Equation 7.8
Simple Equation 7.8
Properties of Equality 7.8
Solving an Equation in One Variable 7.8
Classroom Wing *7.11*
Competition Wing *7.14*
Hints and Explanations *7.16*

CHAPTER 8: GEOMETRY **8.1**

Basic Concepts **8.3**
Plane 8.3
Line 8.3
Line Segment 8.3
Ray 8.3
Coplanar Lines 8.4
Intersecting Lines 8.4
Angle 8.4
Perpendicular Lines 8.5
Complementary Angles 8.5
Supplementary Angles 8.5
Adjacent Angles 8.5
Linear Pair 8.5
Vertically Opposite Angles 8.5
Concurrent Lines 8.5
Parallel Lines 8.5
Transversal 8.6

Triangles **8.7**
Types of Triangles 8.7
Constructions 8.8

Circles **8.11**
Chord 8.11
Secant 8.11
Tangent 8.11
Arc 8.12
Circumference 8.12
Angle Subtended by a Pair of Points 8.12
Segment of a Circle 8.12
Sector of a Circle 8.12
Quadrant 8.12

Symmetry **8.13**
Classroom Wing *8.16*
Competition Wing *8.21*
Hints and Explanations *8.24*

CHAPTER 9: MENSURATION **9.1**

Plane Figures **9.3**

Units of Measurement 9.3

Rectangle 9.4

Square 9.4

Solids **9.5**

Prism 9.5

Pyramid 9.6

Cuboid 9.6

Cube 9.7

Classroom Wing *9.9*

Competition Wing *9.11*

Hints and Explanations *9.14*

CHAPTER 10: STATISTICS **10.1**

Data **10.3**

Some Basic Definitions 10.3

Tabulation or Presentation of Data 10.3

Types of Data 10.4

Statistical Graphs 10.4

Some Important Terms Related to Data Collection and Record 10.8

Classroom Wing *10.9*

Competition Wing *10.12*

Hints and Explanations *10.15*

CHAPTER 11: SETS **11.1**

Set **11.3**

Elements of a Set 11.4

Cardinal Number of a Set 11.4

Representation of Sets 11.4

Types of Sets 11.5

Operation on Sets 11.5

Venn Diagrams 11.6

Some Formulae on the Cardinality of Sets 11.7

Classroom Wing *11.9*

Competition Wing *11.12*

Hints and Explanations *11.14*

Preface

"If you have a great ambition, take as big a step as possible in the direction of fulfilling it. The step may only be a tiny one, but trust that it may be the largest one possible for now."

Mildred McAfee

The *Pearson IIT Foundation* Series has been created keeping in mind the learner's ambition to excel in a competitive examination like IIT-JEE. The series can be used in addition to the books being studied in school to attain that extra edge required to strengthen the concepts and prepare well for future endeavours.

Why Start Early with Pearson IIT Foundation

Classes VI to X are the base years of a learner's academic life. In these years learner explore their interests and determine the goals they wish to attain. *Pearson IIT Foundation* series is filled with interactive learning that not only nurtures a learner's interest in science and mathematics but also strengthens their concepts.

The series uses real-life examples and application-based problems to teach theoretical concepts. The objective of this series is to help learners cultivate an analytical mind.

Most of the lessons to be learnt are introduced to the learners in the books for class VI. As they get promoted to higher classes, new topics are added to these lessons. This additive method helps the learners' span their learning over four standards, from VI-X. Thus, learners are not overwhelmed by the introduction of completely new lessons every time they are promoted to a new class.

While their learning is being spanned across five years, so is their ability to resolve doubts for further conceptual clarity. For instance, they can use concepts learnt in class VI to solve questions in class VII. If, in case, they get stuck while answering a question, the learners can infer for themselves that they might be lacking in conceptual clarity. They can then approach their teachers, requesting them to explain the concept once again. This helps the learner to clarify their concepts while revising the lessons previously learnt.

Since classes VI-X are deemed to be a student's formative years, we, at Pearson, aim to provide a foundation level course which serves more than just a standard curriculum.

Here is how it makes a difference to a learner's overall learning...

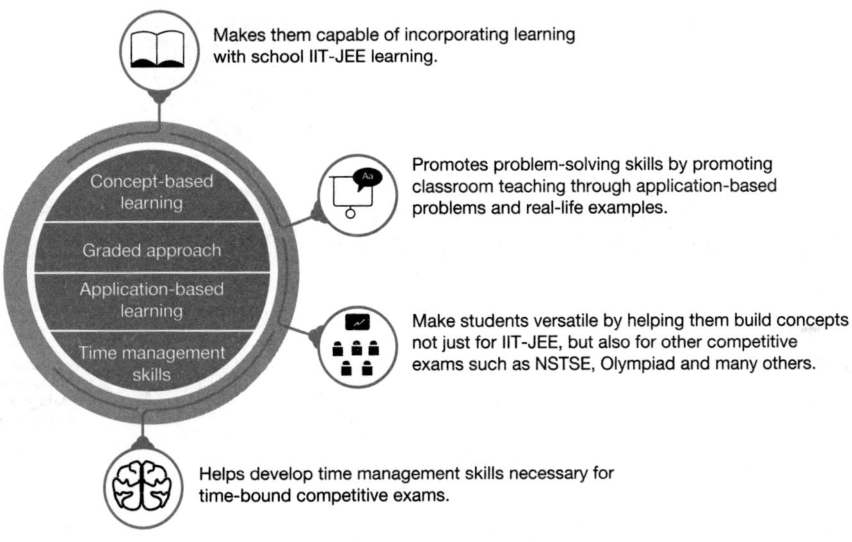

Other Uses of the Series

Instead of limiting themselves to IIT-JEE, a learner can also use this series to prepare for several other competitive examinations such as NSTSE, National and International Olympiads, NEET, BITSAT, etc. This series offers a level of concept learning that empowers learners to handle the challenging nature of questions posed in these examinations. Moreover, this will also allow the learners to have an early insight into their key strengths as well as improvement areas and help them work on themselves.

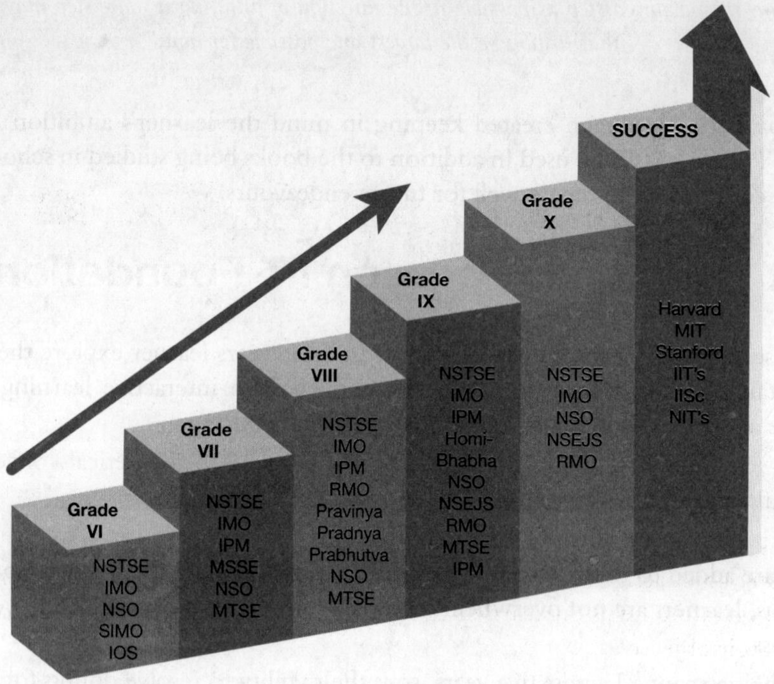

[IMO: International Mathematics Olympiad; NSO: National Science Olympiad, IOS: International Olympiad of Science, NSTSE: National Level Science Talent Search Examination, MTSE: Maharashtra Talent Search Examination, RMO: Regional Mathematical Olympiad, PPP: Pravinya Pradnya Prabhutva, NSEJS: National Standard Examination in Junior Science, IIT: Indian Institute of Technology, IISc: Indian Institute of Science, NIT: National Institute of Technology.]

Highlights of the Series

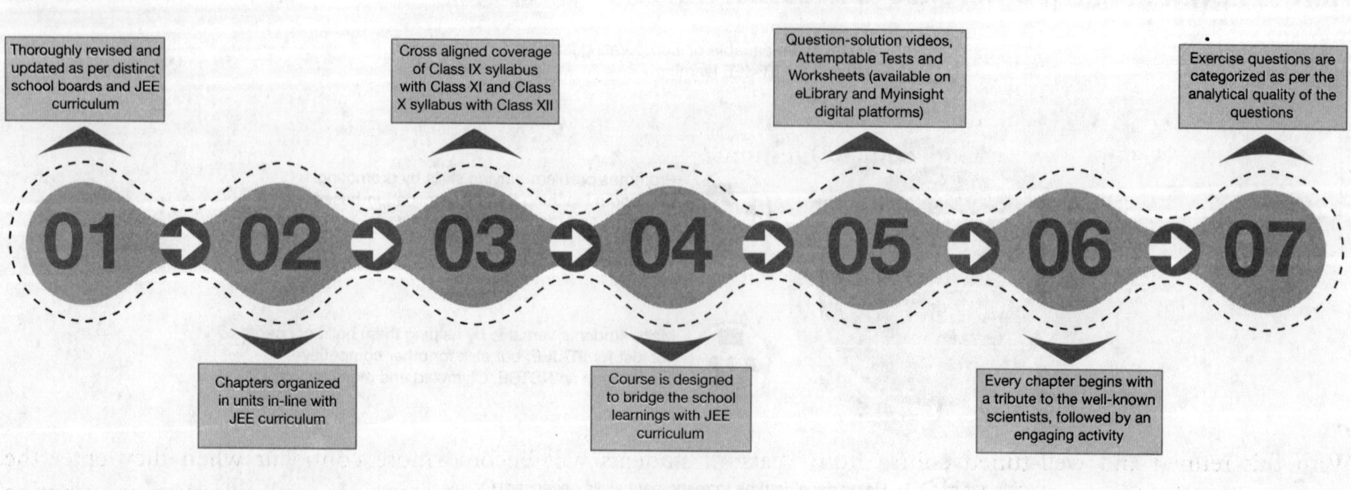

Pearson IIT Foundation series provides a perfect blend of learning through theory and practice questions with a fusion of school and JEE curriculum. It is imperative to note that this series would be as profound as you want it to be. Therefore, to get maximum benefit from this book, we recommend following the given study plan.

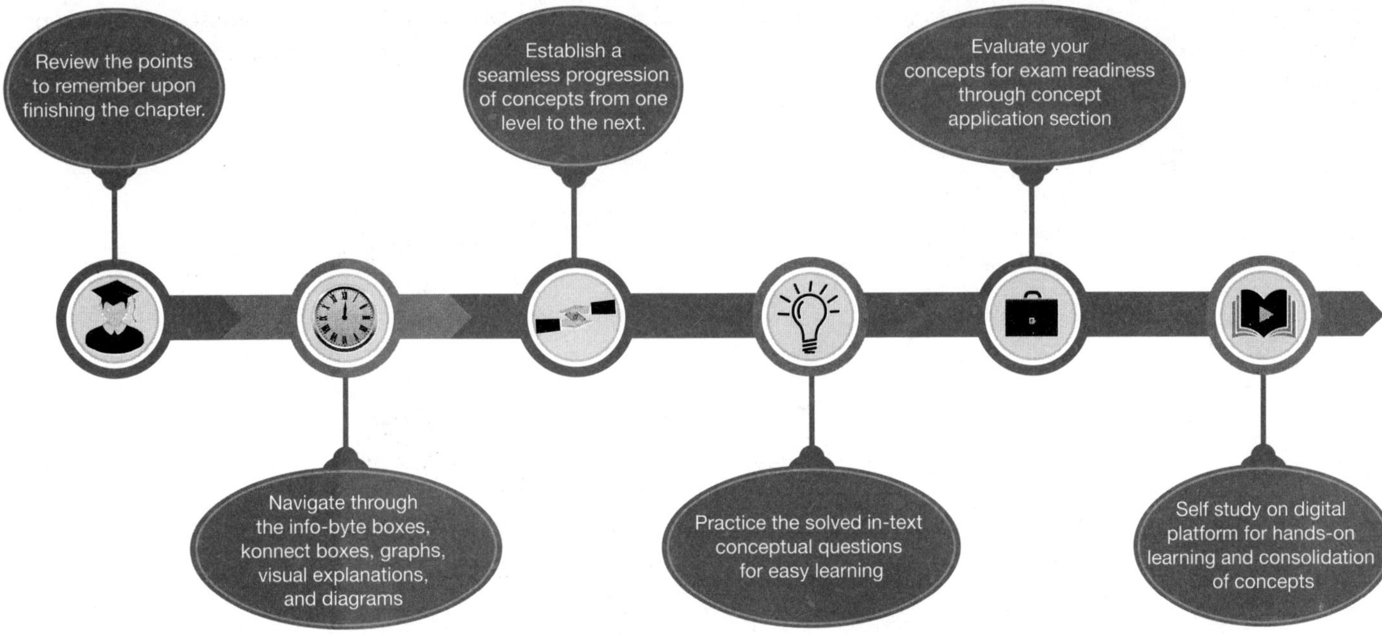

To provide a graded learning approach, the exercise part of each chapter is categorized by using four icons for question tagging. The question categorization helps the learners assess their own problem-solving and analytical skills and motivates them to improve to reach their objectives.

The following icons are used to categorize the questions with specific meanings:

Real-life Situations Questions: 

Analytical Questions: 

Conceptual Questions: 

Value-based Questions: 

With this refined and well-tuned course from Pearson, students will become more confident when they enter the competitive world for actual IIT-JEE preparation. The effort put in today will transform into a valuable asset, contributing to success in future competitive examinations.

Chapter Insights

Remember

Before beginning this chapter, you should be able to:

- Recall multiplication tables
- Perform multiplication and division of tables

Remember section will help them to memorize and review the previous learning on a particular topic

Key Ideas

After completing this chapter, you should be able to:

- Know types of fractions
- Understand comparison of fractions

Key points will help the students to identify the essential points in a chapter

Scientific Crypt

A Tribute to Carl Friedrich Gauss (1777-1855)

Johann Carl Friedrich Gauss was a renowned German mathematician and physicist, whose contributions to number theory, probability theory, and electromagnetism, not only reshaped the landscape of academia but also paved the way for the modern age of discovery.

Born on April 30, 1777, in Brunswick, Germany, Gauss demonstrated extraordinary mathematical talent from a young age. His early achievements include discovering a method for quickly summing the integers from 1 to 100 in his primary school years.

Carl Friedrich Gauss revolutionized mathematics with his proofs of the fundamental theorem of algebra, advancements in number theory, and pioneering work in planetary motion and statistical methods. Overcoming skepticism from established mathematicians due to his innovative ideas, especially in the realm of number theory and with limited resources, he persevered to create innovative solutions that transformed the field despite challenges.

FUN TIME

CROSSWORD

Scientific Crypt provides information about well-known scientists related to the chapter. The engaging activity is also given in the form of a crossword to keep the learners interested.

INTRODUCTION

We have studied numbers, addition, subtraction, multiplication and division of numbers in previous classes. Now, we will expand our knowledge on a system of numbers, integers and operations on numbers. Before beginning the study of numbers in detail, take a look on the table given below for the numerals ranging from small to large numbers.

Introduction section helps to lay the foundation of the following chapter and leads the way for further learning

Profit, Loss and Discount

The concept of percentage finds numerous applications in commercial Mathematics. When we go shopping, we frequently come across terms like sale, discount, price, etc. Let us understand the basic terms related to profit, loss and discount.

Profit and Loss

When a person buys an article for a certain price and then sells it for a different price, he makes a **profit** or incurs a **loss**.

Concepts are explained in a well-structured and lucid manner

Konnect boxes are some add-on information of related topic

Konnect

Every number is a factor of itself. So, the number 7 has 7 as one of its factors. This goes for every single number out there.

Info Bytes!

Name of the popular search engine 'Google' came from the mis-spelling of the word 'googol'.

Info bytes are interesting trivia and facts that engage young minds and keep the grey cells ticking!

EXAMPLE 2.7 Find the LCM of 24 and 40.

SOLUTION

2	24, 40
2	12, 20
2	6, 10
	3, 5

$\therefore$ The LCM of 24 and 40

$= 2 \times 2 \times 2 \times 3 \times 5$

$= 120$

Examples are given in the form of in-text exercises to reinforce the concepts learnt in a particular chapter

Illustrative examples solved in a logical and step-wise manner

POINTS TO REMEMBER

- ✔ When two or more natural numbers are multiplied, then their product is called the multiple of either of the numbers. Each of those numbers is called a factor of the product.
- ✔ A positive integer which is the product of three distinct prime factors is called a sphenic number.
- ✔ The natural numbers which ha two factors are called composite
- ✔ Prime numbers differing by 2 a primes
- ✔ Every pair of two natural numb common factor other than 1 is co-primes

Points to remember summarises the concepts and topics presented in each chapter

PRACTICE QUESTIONS CLASSROOM WING

Very Short Answer Type Questions

Direction for questions from 1 to 5: **Select the correct alternative from given choices.**

1. The number of 3-digit numbers that can be formed using the digits 3, 5 and 7 without repetition is ______.
   (a) 3 (b) 4
   (c) 5 (d) 6

2. The sum of the successor and the predecessor of 100 is

Direction for questions from 11 to 14: **Select the corre alternative from given choices.**

11. Which of the following statement is true?
    (a) The product of two negative integers is negative.
    (b) The sum of a negative integer and a positive inte ger is always positive.
    (c) The product of two positive and two negative inte gers is positive.
    (d) The product of any number of negative integers negative.

Short Answer Type Questions

25. Simplify: 6 ÷ 6 ÷ 6 ÷ 6 ÷ 6
26. List out the integers between the absolute valu −20 and 10.
27. Write the following in figures.
    (i) Six crore six lakh and six thousand
    (ii) Seven arab five crore three hundred and one

Essay Type Questions

59. Find the difference between the greatest 5-digit nur ber and the greatest 3-digit number formed using t digits 9, 7, 3, 4, 0 when the repetition is not allowe

Different typologies of questions have been included in the *Classroom Wing* which help students to develop the problem-solving skill

Competition Wing at the end of the chapter incorporated for competitive examination inline with JEE syllabus

Graded as per complexity: Level 1; Level 2; and Level 3

PRACTICE QUESTIONS COMPETITION WING

Level 1: Apply Your Concepts

Direction for questions from 1 to 5: **Fill in the blanks.**

1. The sum of the predecessor and the successor of 0 is ______.
2. The local value (place value) of the digit '3' in the number 2356 is
3.

8. If P is a 3-digit number and Q is the number formed by reversing the digits of P, then find the difference between the place value of the digits in the tenth place.
   (a) 1 (b) 9
   (c) 0 (d) Cannot say

hopkeeper brought 12 dozen eggs out of which ozen eggs are sold and 9 eggs are damaged. After

Level 2: Review Your Concepts

13. The cost of a pen is the largest two-digit nu (in ₹). The cost of a text book and geometry respectively are the successor and predecessor c cost of the pen. Find the sum of the costs of the book and geometry box (in ₹).
    (a) 197 (b) 198
    (c) 200 (d) 201

Level 3: Assess Your Concepts

16. A small-scale industry made different kinds of bulbs. The details are as follows:

Type of Bulbs (in watts)	60 w	90 w	120 w
No. of Bulbs	240	180	120

These bulbs are packed in cartons. Each carton contains same number of bulbs and only one variety. Find the minimum number of bulbs required to pack these bulbs.
(a) 6 (b) 7
(c) 8 (d) 9

Short Answer Type Questions

25. Simplify: 6 ÷ 6 ÷ 6 ÷ 6 ÷ 6
26. List out the integers between the absolute values of −20 and 10.
27. Write the following in figures.
    (i) Six crore six lakh and six thousand
    (ii) Seven arab five crore three hundred and one
    (iii) Eighty eight crore ninety nine lakh fifty five thousand and seventy four
28. Find the difference between the place values of the two 5's in 895435.
29. Write all the possible three-digit numbers using the digits 5, 0 and 7 without repetition of the digits.
30. X is the number of two-digit numbers formed by 3, 5, or 7, when the repetition is allowed. Y is the number of two-digit numbers formed by 3, 5, or 7, when the repetition is not allowed. Find by how much X exceeds

(iii) 36 m below sea level
(iv) 12°C rise in temperature
(v) 5°C fall in temperature

35. Arrange the following integers in ascending order.
    (i) 3, −5, 0, −2, −7, −1, 4
    (ii) −15
36. Write
    (i) −8
    (ii) 42
37. Write the ele
    (i) In
    (ii) In
    (iii) If
    (i)

31. Write all the possible 4-digit even numbers using the digits 5, 8, 9 and 4 when the repetition is not allowed.
32. Write the expanded form of twenty four lakh seventy five thousand and fifty six.
33. How many whole numbers are there between 321 and 543 which do not change, when the order of the digits is reversed?
34. Represent the following as integers.
    (i) Gain of ₹28
    (ii) Loss of ₹48

The icons are used for categorisation of the questions in Classroom Wing and Competition Wing

Hints and Explanations

CLASSROOM WING

Very Short Answer Type Questions

1. Non-renewable
2. Renewable
3. Ignition temperature
4. Geothermal
5. Nuclear fusion
6. Calorific
7. Hydrocarbons
8. Peat
9. Infrared radiations
10. (a) Nuclear fission is the process in which a heavy
22. Petrol – presence of hydrogen.
23. A device that converts wind energy to mechanical or electrical energy.
24. A device which directly converts solar energy into electrical energy.

Short Answer Type Questions

Note: This is how you should frame your answer covering.

25. Wind mill, turbine.
26. (i) Solid fuels
    (ii) Liquid fuels
    (iii) Gaseous fuels

Hints and Explanations for key questions of classroom wing and competition wing along with highlights on the common mistakes that students usually make in the examinations

Competition Wing

Level 1: Apply Your Concepts

Explanation for questions from 1 to 5:

1. Calorific value.
2. Hydrocarbons
3. Ignition temperature
4. Solar energy.
5. The minimum temperature at which the substance begins to burn.

Explanation for questions from 6 to 10:

6. False. Ignition temperature is the minimum temperature at which a substance begins to burn, not melt.
7. True.
8. False. Tidal energy is renewable as it relies on the gravitational effects of the moon and sun, which are repetitive and consistent.
9. True.
10. False. This description is for nuclear fusion.

Explanation for questions from 21 to 27:

21. (b). Nuclear fission involves the splitting of a heavy nucleus, while nuclear fusion involves the combination of lighter nuclei.

Explanation for questions from 36 to 44:

36. Silver is the metal which is used for connecting wires that connect solar cells in a solar panel, due to its large conductivity.
37. The most suitable fuel burns completely and does not release (expel) any carbon particles with smoke.
38. Solar energy provides wind energy, light energy and heat energy.
39. In case of box-type solar cooker, more energy will be trapped by using a box, whose inner surfaces are painted black and which cannot conduct more energy to the surroundings. Now from the given options, if we choose a double wall plastic box, whose inner surfaces are painted black, then the efficiency will be more.
40. The net output = output – input = 1000 – 200 = 800 J.
41. A good source of energy should have large, net energy output. Among the given options, a source of energy which has input energy of 100 J and an output energy of 12,500 J is the best source of energy, because the net energy output is (12,500-100) J = 12,400 J.
42. More is the velocity of wind, more will be the kinetic energy of blades of a windmill due to which more amount of electrical energy can be produced. That is, the output of a windmill increases with increase in the

WORKSHEET
CHAPTER 2: DYNAMICS

DW

Directions for questions from 1 to 5:
Select the correct alternative from the following options.

1. A bullet of mass 100 g moving with a velocity of 100 m s^{-1} is stopped by a plank. If the bullet travels a distance of 10 cm in the plank before it comes to rest, find the average force exerted by the plank.
   (a) 100 N (b) 1000 N
   (c) 2500 N (d) 5000 N
2. Find the power developed by an engine in filling water

a rough surface, the total work done by the frictional force is zero.

8. The orbital velocity of a satellite is inversely proportional to the radius of the orbit.
9. When a stone is tied to a string and rotated in a circular path, the work done by the tension of the string is zero.
10. A satellite revolving in an orbit closer to the surface of the earth has more speed than one which is moving in an orbit of higher radius.

DW: Downloadable worksheets supplementing textual exercises for hand-on learning

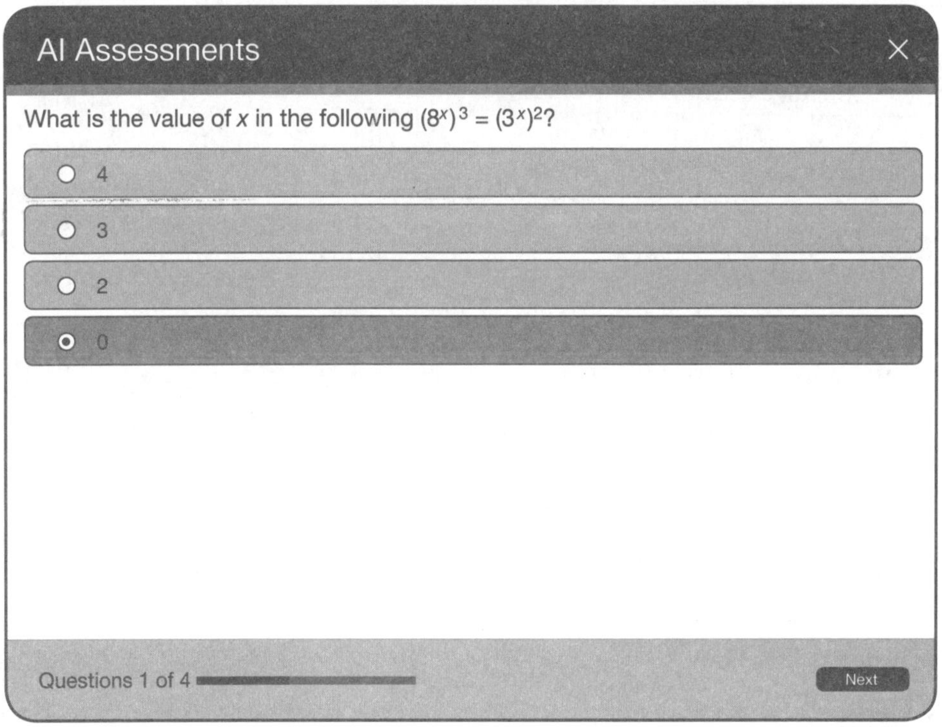

AT

AT: Attemptable Tests for assessing understanding of concepts and getting a clear picture of your exam readiness

17. Find the greatest 4-digit number which is common multiple of 12, 16, and 24.

(a) 9984 (b) 9980

(c) 9999 (d) 9890

18. Ranga and Pranav are good friends from their childhood. They play a game in which they select a number from 1 to 1000. Ranga selects every 12th number and Pranav selects every 27th number. What are the numbers selected by the friends in common?

(a) 8 (b) 9

(c) 10 (d) 11

Video icon: Audio and visual learning to difficult questions for effective learning and retention

CHAPTER
1

Numbers

Remember

Before beginning this chapter, you should be able to:

- Recall digits and numbers
- Perform addition, subtraction, multiplication and division of numbers

Key Ideas

After completing this chapter, you should be able to:

- Understand Hindu-Arabic system
- Describe face value and place value of digits
- Work on integers
- Describe properties of numbers and perform operations on numbers
- Apply BODMAS rule

Scientific Crypt

A Tribute to Sir Isaac Newton (1642-1727)

Sir Isaac Newton (1642–1726/27), one of the most influential scientists in history, was an English mathematician, physicist, astronomer, and author who played a central role in the Scientific Revolution and Enlightenment. His book "Philosophiæ Naturalis Principia Mathematica" (1687) laid the foundation for classical mechanics and universal gravitation, which dominated science for centuries.

Born on December 25, 1642, in Woolsthorpe-by-Colsterworth, a hamlet in Lincolnshire, England, his education began at The King's School in Grantham, where he displayed an inclination for mathematics and natural philosophy. He later studied at Trinity College, University of Cambridge.

Isaac Newton's revolutionary theory of gravitation is often linked to an apple falling from a tree. This simple observation sparked his profound exploration into the fundamental laws of motion and the universe, leading to the development of his revolutionary theory of universal gravitation.

Isaac Newton's influential work, 'Mathematical Principles of Natural Philosophy,' not only laid the foundation for classical mechanics but also integrated prior discoveries. His wide-ranging contributions extended from optics to the co-development of calculus with Leibniz, encompassing his revolutionary laws of motion. In mathematics, he advanced power series, the binomial theorem, root approximation techniques, and the categorization of cubic plane curves.

FUN TIME

CROSSWORD

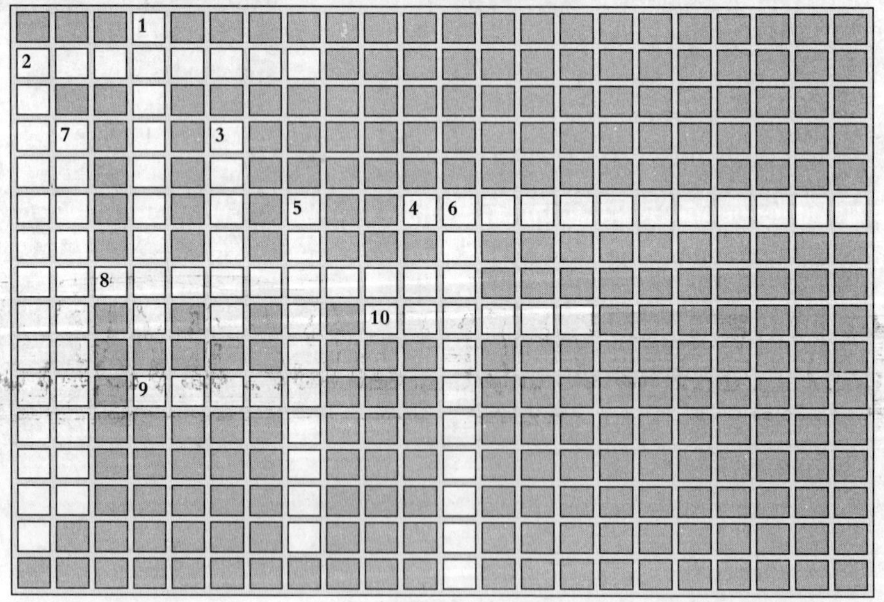

Across

2. The representation of a number in figures.
4. Zero joined the party of counting numbers to form this group.
8. How a number is represented in words.
9. The nation credited with introducing the concept of zero as a digit.
10. A special rule that dictates the order of mathematical operations.

Down

1. The actual worth of a digit as it appears in a number.
2. All the numbers you'd use if you started counting from one.
3. Another term to refer to the number that signifies nothing.
5. A digit's worth determined by its position in a number.
6. A numeral system that spans from 0 to 9.
7. Always one step behind the given number.

INTRODUCTION

We have studied numbers, addition, subtraction, multiplication and division of numbers in previous classes. Now, we will expand our knowledge on a system of numbers, integers and operations on numbers. Before beginning the study of numbers in detail, take a look on the table given below for the numerals ranging from small to large numbers.

Hindu-Arabic System

As we know, we use 0, 1, 2, 3, 4, 5, 6, 7, 8 or 9 to write any number. The system where we use 0, 1, 2, ..., 9 to write any number is known as **Hindu–Arabic System**.

Table 1.1 Use of 10 digits from 0 to 9 to describe all numbers

Place Name	Numeral	No. of Digits
Ten Crores	10,00,00,000	9 digits
Crores	1,00,00,000	8 digits
Ten Lakhs	10,00,000	7 digits
Lakhs	1,00,000	6 digits
Ten Thousands	10,000	5 digits
Thousands	1,000	4 digits
Hundreds	100	3 digits
Tens	10	2 digits
Ones	1	1 digit

Info Bytes!

Ancient India made a significant contribution to the Hindu-Arabic numeral system with the zero ('0'). It's not just a number; it's a symbol for 'nothing.' Its invention transformed calculations and paved the way for the development of algebra.

Notation and Numeration

Notation is the representation of a number in figures. **Numeration** is the representation of number in words.

Table 1.2 Notation and Numeration

Number	Number in Words
23,576	Twenty three thousand five hundred and seventy six.
5,48,907	Five lakh forty eight thousand nine hundred and seven.
12,00,50,056	Twelve crore fifty thousand and fifty six.

Expanded Form

When we write any number, for example, 123, what it actually displays is 100 + 20 + 3. In simple words, '100 + 20 + 3' is an expanded form of 123. When we expand a number, we show the value of each digit. This is called its **expanded form**.

EXAMPLE 1.1 Expand 88,456

SOLUTION

88,456 = 8(10000) + 8(1000) + 4(100) + 5(10) + 6(1) = 80000 + 8000 + 400 + 50 + 6

Face Value and Place Value of Digits

The actual value of a digit in a number is called **face value** of the number. The **place value** of a digit in a number is the digit times the value of the place.

Example: The face value and place value for 20,980 are given in table 1.3.

Table 1.3 Face and place values of digits

Digit	Face Value	Place Value
2	2	2(10000) = 20,000
9	9	9(100) = 900
8	8	8(10) = 80

Konnect

The place value of a digit is based on the position of the digit, whereas the face value of a digit remains same irrespective of the places of the digit.

Numbers to be Remembered

1. 1 Googol = 10^{100}
2. 1 Googolplex = 10^{googol}
3. 1 Arab = 10^9
4. 1 Kharab = 10^{11}
5. 1 Vrinda = 10^{22}
6. 1 Padma = 10^{32}
7. 1 Samudra = 10^{52}

Info Bytes!

Name of the popular search engine 'Google' came from the mis-spelling of the word 'googol'.

International System of Numeration

This system is same as the Indian system up to five digits. The smallest 6-digit number 100000 is called **one hundred thousand**. The comma is placed to mark ones and thousands. Hence, it is written as 100,000.

Table 1.4 International system of numeration

Millions		Thousands		Ones	
100,000,000 9 digits	Hundred millions	100,000 6 digits	Hundred thousands	100	Hundreds
10,000,000 8 digits	Ten millions	10,000 5 digits	Ten thousands	10	Tens
1,000,000 7 digits	Millions	1,000 4 digits	Thousands	1	Ones

Comparison of Numbers

To understand the concept of comparison of numbers, following points must be kept in mind:

1. For a given number line, the numbers lying on the right hand side of the number are greater.
2. Among the given numbers, the number which has more number of digits is the greatest number.
3. If the number of digits of different numbers is same, then we shall compare the left most digits of the numbers. The number which has greater digit in the same place is the greatest number.

Successors and Predecessors

The successor of a number is the number that is 1 more than the given number, whereas predecessor of a number is the number which is 1 less than the given number.

Example: The successor of 9,00,000 is 9,00,001 and the predecessor of 9,00,003 is 9,00,002.

EXAMPLE 1.2 Compare 91,752 and 4,847

SOLUTION

Now, 91,752 has five-digits and 4,847 has four-digits. Therefore, 91,752 us greater than 4,872.

EXAMPLE 1.3 Compare 91,752 and 92,847

SOLUTION

The given numbers have same number of digits. If we compare the left most digits, the digits which are in the ten thousands place are equal.

Now let us compare the digits which are in thousands place. As 2 is greater than 1, we conclude that 92,847 is greater than 91,752.

EXAMPLE 1.4 Find the number of all the three-digit numbers in Hindu–Arabic System.

SOLUTION

The greatest three-digit number is 999. The greatest two-digit number is 99.

The number of all the three-digit numbers = 999 – 99 = 900.

EXAMPLE 1.5 List out all the three-digit numbers formed by using the digits 2, 7 and 9.

SOLUTION

Hundreds Place	Numbers
2	279 and 297
7	729 and 792
9	927 and 972

Integers

In the lower classes, we have studied natural numbers and whole numbers. In this chapter, we shall learn what integers are and also the properties of integers and operations on integers.

1. **Natural numbers:** All counting numbers are **natural numbers**.

   Example: 1, 2, 3, 4, ... are natural numbers.

2. **Whole numbers:** Zero and natural numbers together are called **whole numbers**.

   Example: 0, 1, 2, 3, 4, ... are whole numbers

3. **Integers:** All the numbers .... –3, –2, –1, 0, 1, 2, 3, ... are **integers**.

> **Info Bytes!**
> The only integer that is neither positive nor negative is zero (0).

Integers as Directed Numbers

We have seen situations where we use integers in opposite sign.

Let us see some situations where we use integers in opposite sign.

1. If the distance above sea level is represented by positive number, then the distance below sea level is represented by negative integer.
   Example: 65 m above sea level is represented by +65 m and 33 m below sea level is represented by –33 m.
2. If the temperature above freezing point is represented by positive number, then the temperature below freezing point is represented by negative integer.
   Example: 13°C above freezing point is represented by +13°C and 15°C below freezing point is represented by –15°C.
3. If profit made on selling an article is represented by a positive number, then loss incurred on selling an article is represented by a negative number.
   Example: ₹45 profit is represented by ₹+45 and ₹36 loss is represented by ₹–36.

Representation of Integers on the Number Line

A line on which numbers are represented is known as the **number line**. Some integers are represented on the number line given in figure 1.1.

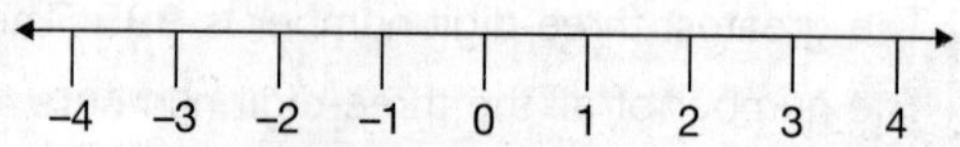

Figure 1.1 Number Line

We observe the following points about the number line.

1. As we move from left to right, the integers are in the ascending order.
   .... $-4 < -3 < -2 < -1 < 0 < 1 < 2 < 3$ ....
   As we move from right to left, the integers are in the descending order.
2. When we add a positive integer, the result obtained is to the right of the given integer.
   Example: 0 + 2 = 2, 2 is to the right of 0. 2 + 1 = 3, 3 is to the right of 2. 1 + 4 = 5, 5 is to the right of 1.
3. When we add a negative integer to a given integer, the result obtained is to the left of the given integer.
   Example: 2 + (–3) = –1, –1 is to the left of 2. 4 + (–3) = 1, 1 is to the left of 4.
4. When we subtract a positive integer, from a given integer, the result obtained is to the left of the given integer.
   Example: 3 – 2 = 1, 1 is to the left of 3. 3 – 2 = 1, 1 is to the left of 2.
5. When we subtract a negative integer from a given integer, the result obtained is to the right of the given integer.
   Example: 3 – (–4) = 7 and 7 is to the right of 3.
6. The sum of two positive integers is a positive integer.
   Example: 3 + 5 = 8; 6 + 5 = 11
7. The sum of two negative integers is a negative integer.
   Example: (–5) + (–4) = –9; (–5) + (–6) = –11
8. The sum of a positive integer and a negative integer may be positive, negative or zero.
   Example: (i) 6 + (–3) = 3; (ii) 5 + (–7) = –2; (iii) 6 + (–6) = 0

Let us learn the addition and subtraction of integers with the help of the given examples.

EXAMPLE 1.6 Arrange the following in ascending order: –5, –9, 11, –3, 8, 14, –11, 5.

SOLUTION

–11, –9, –5, –3, 5, 8, 11, 14.

EXAMPLE 1.7 Add 5 to –3 and show the addition on the number line.

SOLUTION

When a positive integer is added, we should move towards the right on the number line.

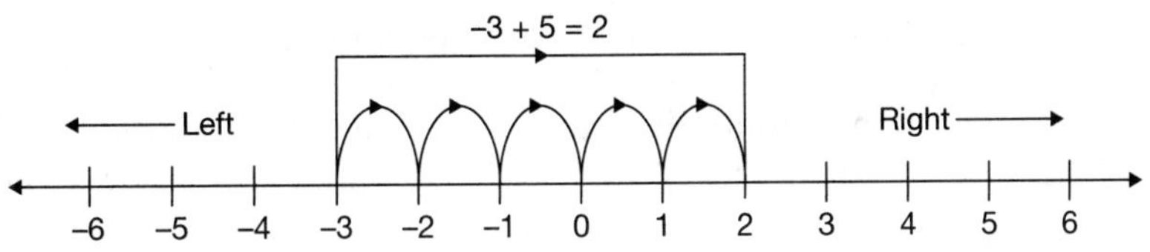

EXAMPLE 1.8 Find the value of 4 + (–5) using number line.

SOLUTION

When a negative integer is added, we should move towards the left on the number line.

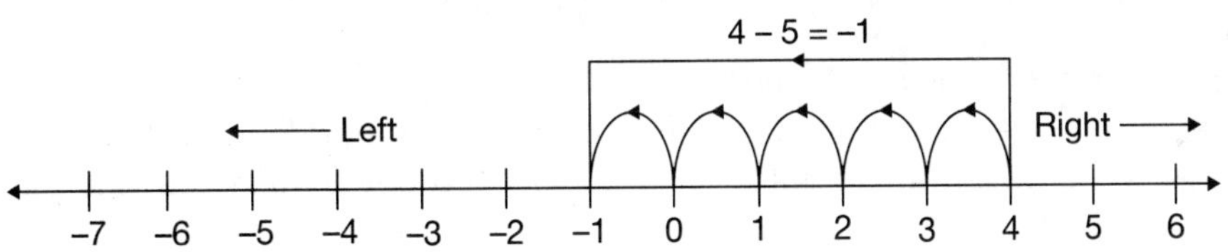

EXAMPLE 1.9 Evaluate: 45 – 93 + 43 – 28 + (–25) – (–53)

SOLUTION

45 – 93 + 43 – 18 + (–25) – (–53) = 45 – 93 + 43 – 18 –25 +53

= 45 + 43 + 53 – 93 – 18 – 25 = 141 – 136 = 5

Multiplication of Integers

1. The product of two positive integers p and q is also a positive integer.
   Example: $4 \times 5 = 20$ and $6 \times 4 = 24$.
2. The product of a positive integer and a negative integer is negative.
   Example: $5 \times (-6) = -30$ and $(-8) \times 6 = -48$.
3. The product of two negative integers is a positive integer.
   Example: $(-7) \times (-2) = 14$ and $(-6) \times (-7) = 42$.

4. The product of three negative integers is a negative integer.
Example: $(-3) \times (-5) \times (-2) = (-15) \times (-2) = -30$.

5. The product of four negative integers is a positive integer.
Example: $(-1) \times (-2) \times (-3) \times (-6) = 36$.

Division of Integers

We know that $2 \times 4 = 8$. We can write that as $8 \div 4 = 2$ or $8 \div 2 = 4$. Thus, we can say that division is an inverse operation of multiplication.

1. When we divide a positive integer by another positive integer, we get a positive number, which need not be an integer.

   Example: $7 \div 5 = \frac{7}{5}$ or $1\frac{2}{5}$. We observe that division is not closed for integers.

2. When a negative integer is divided by a positive integer, we get a negative number.
Example: $-12 \div 4 \Rightarrow -12/4 = -3$. When 12 is divided by 4, the quotient is 3 and we get a negative sign before 3.

3. When a positive integer is divided by a negative integer, we get a negative number.
Example: $30 \div (-10)$ can be written as $-(30/10) = -3$.

4. When a negative integer is divided by a negative integer, we get a positive number.
Example: $(-40) \div (-4)$ can be written as $(40/4) = 10$.

5. For two integers p and q, $(p \div q) \neq (q \div p)$.
Example: $3 \div 1 = 3$ and $1 \div 3 = 1/3$.
$3 \neq \frac{1}{3}$. We observe that division is not commutative for integers.

6. When a positive integer p is divided by 1, the result is p. $p \div 1 = p$.
Example: $3 \div 1 = 3$, $12 \div 1 = 12$ and $0 \div 1 = 0$. However, $1 \div 0$ is not defined. There is no integer which when multiplied by zero gives one. It is important to note that $0 \div 0$ is not defined. Any integer (or any number) when multiplied by zero gives zero.

EXAMPLE 1.10 Evaluate: **(I)** $4875 \div 125$ **(II)** $8844 \div 22$

SOLUTION

(I) $4875 \div 125 \Rightarrow \frac{4875}{125} = \frac{975}{25} = \frac{195}{5} = 39$

(II) $8844 \div 22 \Rightarrow \frac{8844}{22} = \frac{804}{2} = 402$

EXAMPLE 1.11 Showick covers a certain distance in 180 minutes. He covers half of the distance in 3/5 of the time. Find the time taken to cover the remaining distance.

SOLUTION

Total time taken = 180 minutes

Time taken to cover the remaining distance = $= \left(1 - \frac{3}{5}\right) \times 180 = \frac{2}{5} \times 180 = 72$ minutes

EXAMPLE 1.12 Raj and Simran went on a vacation to Ooty. They documented the temperature changes over their trip as follows. Initially, it was 12°C, then there was a 3° rise in the temperature. Later, there was a 5° fall, followed by a 1° rise, 4° fall, and finally, a 2° rise. What was the temperature at the end of their observations?

SOLUTION

Initial temperature: 12°C

A 3° rise from 12°C: 12°C + 3°C = 15°C

A 5° fall from 15°C: 15°C - 5°C = 10°C

A 1° rise from 10°C: 10°C + 1°C = 11°C

A 4° fall from 11°C: 11°C - 4°C = 7°C

A 2° rise from 7°C: 7°C + 2°C = 9°C

So, by the end of their observations, the temperature was 9°C.

Alternate Method:

The above situation can be represented by the following numerical expression:

12°C + 3°C – 5°C + 1°C – 4°C + 2°C = 18°C – 9°C = 9°C

Absolute Value of an Integer

The **absolute value** of an integer is the numerical value regardless of its sign (+ or –). The absolute value of an integer x is denoted by $|x|$.

Example: $|-13| = 13$; $|13| = 13$; $|0| = 0$.

Simplification

To simplify arithmetic expressions, which involve various operations like brackets, multiplication, addition, etc., a particular sequence of operations has to be followed. For example: $2 + 3 \times 4$ has to be calculated by multiplying 3 with 4 and the result is 12. Now, 12 is added to 2 to produce an output result of 14. This is because in arithmetic operations, multiplication should be done first before addition is taken up.

The hierarchy of arithmetic operations is given by a rule called **BODMAS** rule. The operations have to be carried out in the following order, in which they appear in the word BODMAS, where different letters of the word BODMAS stand for the following operations:

B Brackets	**O** Of	**D** Division	**M** Multiplication	**A** Addition	**S** Subtraction

There are four types of brackets:

1. **Vinculum:** This is represented by a bar on the top of the numbers.

   Example: $2 + 3 - \overline{4 + 3}$. Here, the figures under the vinculum have to be calculated as 4 + 3 first and the 'minus' sign before 4 is applicable to 7. Thus the given expression is equal to 2 + 3 – 7 which is equal to –2.

2. **Simple Brackets:** These are represented by ( ).

3. **Curly Brackets:** These are represented by { }.

4. **Square Brackets:** These are represented by [ ].

The brackets in an expression have to be opened in the order of vinculum, simple brackets, curly brackets and square brackets, i.e., [{ ($\overline{\quad}$) }] to be opened from inside to outwards.

After brackets is O in the BODMAS rule that stands for 'of' which means multiplication.

Info Bytes!

Simplification forms the core of how modern-day computers function. When you see stunning graphics in video games or use an app, the computer is performing millions of simplifications to provide you with that experience.

Example: $\frac{1}{2}$ of 4 will be equal to $\frac{1}{2} \times 4$ which is equal to 2.

After O, the next operation is D it stands for division. This is followed by M which stands for multiplication. After multiplication, A that stands for addition will be performed. Then, S meant for subtraction is performed.

EXAMPLE 1.13 Simplify: $9 \times 4 - 5 + 18 \div 6$

SOLUTION

$9 \times 4 - 5 + 18 \div 6 = 9 \times 4 - 5 + 3 = 36 - 5 + 3 = 34$

EXAMPLE 1.14 Simplify: $26 \div 2 - 3 \times 8 + 9$

SOLUTION

$26 \div 2 - 3 \times 8 + 9 = 13 - 3 \times 8 + 9 = 13 - 24 + 9 = 22 - 24 = -2$

EXAMPLE 1.15 Simplify: $92 - [18 + 16 \div 4\{26 - (14 - \overline{7-3})\}]$

SOLUTION

$92 - [18 + 16 \div 4\{26 - (14 - \overline{7-3})\}]$
$= 92 - [18 + 16 \div 4\,\{26 - (14 - 4)\}] = 92 - [18 + 16 \div 4\,\{26 - 10\}]$
$= 92 - [18 + 16 \div 4 \times 16] = 92 - [18 + 4 \times 16]$
$= 92 - [18 + 64] = 92 - [82] = 10$

EXAMPLE 1.16 If *P* means multiplication, *Q* means division, *R* means addition and *S* means subtraction, then find the value of 36*P*48*Q*16*R*15*S*23.

SOLUTION

36*P*48*Q*16*R*15*S*23
$= 36 \times 48 \div 16 + 15 - 23 = 36 \times 3 + 15 - 23 = 108 + 15 - 23 = 100$

POINTS TO REMEMBER

- ✔ Notation is the representation of a number in figures. Numeration is the representation of number in words.
- ✔ The actual value of a digit in a number is called face value of the number
- ✔ The place value of a digit in a number is the digit times the value of the place.
- ✔ All counting numbers are natural numbers.
- ✔ Zero and natural numbers together are called whole numbers.
- ✔ A line on which numbers are represented is known as the number line.
- ✔ The hierarchy of arithmetic operations is given by a rule called BODMAS rule.

PRACTICE QUESTIONS CLASSROOM WING

Very Short Answer Type Questions

Direction for questions from 1 to 5: **Select the correct alternative from given choices.**

1. The number of 3-digit numbers that can be formed using the digits 3, 5 and 7 without repetition is ______.
   (a) 3 (b) 4
   (c) 5 (d) 6

2. The sum of the successor and the predecessor of 100 is ______.
   (a) 198 (b) 199
   (c) 200 (d) 201

3. The difference between the greatest and the smallest numbers formed by all the digits 2, 3, 5, and 7 is $XYZX$, where X, Y, Z are digits, then X is ______.
   (a) 5 (b) 8
   (c) 9 (d) 10

4. The difference of the face value and place value of 8 in 4875 is ______.
   (a) 792 (b) –792
   (c) 92 (d) –92

5. Which of the following is a non-negative number?
   (a) $|2-3|$ (b) $|-3|-|-4|$
   (c) $|-4|-|4|$ (d) Both (a) and (c)

Direction for question 6: **Match the Column A with the Column B.**

6.

	Column A		Column B
(a)	Arab	(p)	10^9
(b)	Mahasamudram	(q)	10^{11}
(c)	Kharab	(r)	10^{52}
(d)	Googol	(s)	10^{100}

Direction for questions from 7 to 10: **Fill in the blanks.**

7. The absolute value of 0 is ______.

8. The predecessor of the greatest non-positive numbers is ______.

9. $4 + (-8) - 7 =$ ______.

10. The sum of two integers is –6 and one of them is 7, then the other is ______.

Direction for questions from 11 to 14: **Select the correct alternative from given choices.**

11. Which of the following statement is true?
    (a) The product of two negative integers is negative.
    (b) The sum of a negative integer and a positive integer is always positive.
    (c) The product of two positive and two negative integers is positive.
    (d) The product of any number of negative integers is negative.

12. Which of the following is true?
    $A: -12 + (-15)$ $B: -16 - (12)$ $C: -14 - (-12)$
    (a) $B > C > A$ (b) $A + B > C$
    (c) $C > A > B$ (d) $A < B < C$

13. Which of the following properties are true?
    (A) $(14) \div (-2) = 7$ (B) $(-14) \div 2 = -7$
    (C) $(-14) \div (-2) = 7$
    (a) A, B (b) B, C
    (c) A, C (d) A, B, C

14. Which of the following statements is true?
    (a) If there is a drop of 4°C from –10°C, the result is –6°C
    (b) 525 m above sea level is denoted as –525 m
    (c) $|-5| - |-3| = |-8|$
    (d) The absolute value of an integer is never less than the integer itself.

Direction for question 15: **Match the Column A with Column B.**

15.

	Column A		Column B
(a)	(–2) (–3) (–5)	(p)	–30
(b)	6 (–2) (–3)	(q)	–36
(c)	(–15) (–2)	(r)	30
(d)	(–9) (–2) (–2)	(s)	36

Direction for questions from 16 to 19: **Fill in the blanks.**

16. $8 - \overline{3 - 2} =$ ______.

17. $6 \div 3 + 3 =$ ______.

18. $5 \times 2 + 4 =$ ______.

19. $9 \times (-13) - 13 =$ ______.

Direction for questions from 20 to 23: **Select the correct alternative from given choices.**

20. $15 \div 3 \times 5 - 10 =$ ______.
(a) 15 (b) –9 (c) –3 (d) 20

21. $5 \div 5 \div 5 =$ ______.
(a) 5 (b) $\frac{1}{5}$
(c) 25 (d) $\frac{1}{25}$

22. Which of the following is false?
(a) $2 \times 7 - 7 = 0$ (b) $2 + 3 \times 2 = 10$
(c) $16 \div 8 + 8 = 1$ (d) All of these

23. Which of the following is true?
(a) $4 \div 4 + 1 = 2$
(b) $5 - 2 \times 3 = 9$
(c) Both (a) and (b)
(d) None of these

Direction for question 24: **Match the Column A with the Column B.**

24.

	Column A		Column B
(a)	$3 \times 2 - 8 \div 4$	(p)	14
(b)	$4 \div 2 + 3 \times 4$	(q)	12
(c)	$18 - 9 \div 3 \times 5$	(r)	4
(d)	$72 - 15 \times 20 \div 5$	(s)	3

Short Answer Type Questions

25. Simplify: $6 \div 6 \div 6 \div 6 \div 6$

26. List out the integers between the absolute values of –20 and 10.

27. Write the following in figures.
(i) Six crore six lakh and six thousand
(ii) Seven arab five crore three hundred and one
(iii) Eighty eight crore ninety nine lakh fifty five thousand and seventy four

28. Find the difference between the place values of the two 5's in 895435.

29. Write all the possible three-digit numbers using the digits 5, 0 and 7 without repetition of the digits.

30. X is the number of two-digit numbers formed by 3, 5, or 7, when the repetition is allowed. Y is the number of two-digit numbers formed by 3, 5, or 7, when the repetition is not allowed. Find by how much X exceeds Y.

31. Write all the possible 4-digit even numbers using the digits 5, 8, 9 and 4 when the repetition is not allowed.

32. Write the expanded form of twenty four lakh seventy five thousand and fifty six.

33. How many whole numbers are there between 321 and 543 which do not change, when the order of the digits is reversed?

34. Represent the following as integers.
(i) Gain of ₹28
(ii) Loss of ₹48
(iii) 36 m below sea level
(iv) 12°C rise in temperature
(v) 5°C fall in temperature

35. Arrange the following integers in ascending order.
(i) 3, –5, 0, –2, –7, –1, 4
(ii) –15, –12, 11, –13, 10, 5, –9

36. Write the following in descending order.
(i) –8, 6, –9, 13, –23, 14, –16, 25
(ii) 42, –43, 64, –86, 120, –115

37. Write the statements given below in symbols and list the elements.
(i) Integers lying between –15 and – 8.
(ii) Integers greater than –5 and less than 1.
(iii) If A and B are the number of elements in the sets (i) and (ii), respectively, then find the value of $|-(A - B)|$.

38. Find the value of
(i) $|-15| + |12|$ (ii) $-|13| - |-7|$
(iii) $|17| - |-9|$

39. P is an integer in meters representing "17 m below sea level". Q is an integer in ₹ representing "withdrawal of ₹27". R is an integer in ₹ "representing a gain of ₹43".
Find the following.
(i) $|P| - |R|$
(ii) $||Q| - |R||$
(iii) $|P| + |Q|$

40. A is neither positive nor negative, $B = -|-8|$, C is the absolute value of −12. Find the value of
    (i) $A + B + C$
    (ii) $|B + C|$
    (iii) Compare $2B$, A and $3C$

41. Do the following simplification and show it on the number line.
    $3 + 5 - 6 - 4$

42. Evaluate:
    (i) $14625 \div 25$
    (ii) $15120 \div 144$

43. An integer P is added to another integer Q, then the result is R. If R is −12 more than P, then find Q. Also find R when P is 42.

44. A basket contains 120 fruits from which 15 are sold and 42 are spoiled. After removing the spoiled fruits, 36 new fruits are placed in the basket. Find the number of fruits in the basket finally.

Direction for questions from 45 to 54: **Simplify the following.**

45. $45 - 26 \div 13 \times 6 + 10$

46. $65 \div 5 - 15 \times 3 + 27 \div 9 \times 3 - 24 \div 8 + 7$

47. $[\{12 - \overline{14 - 8} + 7\} - 15]$

48. $52 - [48 \div 12 \times 6\ \{6 - (8 \times 3 - \overline{6 - 4})\}]$

49. $242 - [360 - 248 \div \{180 + 7 \times (2 - \overline{26 - 16})\}]$

50. $25 + [14 - 18 + \{12 \text{ of } 5 - (16 \div 4 \times 3 - 2)\}]$

51. $[78 - \{75 - (76 - \overline{72 - 75})\}]$

52. $\{16 - (4 + 18 \div 6 - \overline{7 - 5}) \times 5]$

53. $[3077 - 85\{32 \div 8 \times (24 - \overline{36 - 18})\}]$

54. $4940 \div [\{12 + 16\ (48 - (8 - \overline{15 + 6}))\}]$

55. If P, Q, R and S represents '×', ÷, + and – respectively, then find the value of $60Q15P35S25R45$.

56. Which integer should be placed in the place of x in $13 + 56 \div (16 - x) + 7 \times [-3]$ such that the result is zero?

57. Write the expanded form of the following and write in words.
    (i) 32,008 (ii) 7,00,050 (iii) 9,01,020

58. Write the following numbers in figures.
    (i) Seventy nine crore seven hundred and seven
    (ii) Eighty nine lakh sixty four thousand and two
    (iii) Four arab thirty two crore sixty eight lakh thirty four thousand and seventy three

Essay Type Questions

59. Find the difference between the greatest 5-digit number and the greatest 3-digit number formed using the digits 9, 7, 3, 4, 0 when the repetition is not allowed.

60. How many whole numbers are there between 601 and 829 which do not change, when the order of the digits is reversed?

PRACTICE QUESTIONS COMPETITION WING

Level 1: Apply Your Concepts

***Direction for questions from 1 to 5:* Fill in the blanks.**

1. The sum of the predecessor and the successor of 0 is ______.

2. The local value (place value) of the digit '3' in the number 2356 is ______.

3. The digit whose place value is always the same regardless of its position or place in a given number is ______.

4. The difference between the place value and face value of the digit '6' in the number 9867 is ______.

5. The number of 4-digit numbers in the Hindu-Arabic system is ______.

***Direction for questions from 6 to 10:* Select the correct alternative from given choices.**

6. Which of the following is false?
   (a) $|-5| = -5$ (b) $|5| = 5$
   (c) $|0| = 0$ (d) All of these

7. The sum of the place values of 2's in 2332 is ______.
   (a) 1998 (b) 2000
   (c) 2002 (d) 1996

8. If P is a 3-digit number and Q is the number formed by reversing the digits of P, then find the difference between the place value of the digits in the tenth place.
   (a) 1 (b) 9
   (c) 0 (d) Cannot say

9. A shopkeeper brought 12 dozen eggs out of which 2 dozen eggs are sold and 9 eggs are damaged. After removing the damaged eggs, 8 eggs are replaced. Find the remaining number of eggs with the shopkeeper finally.
   (a) 8 dozen (b) 119
   (c) 10 dozen (d) 121

10. If A, B, C and D represents ×, ÷, + and – respectively, then find the value of $90B3A5D3C9$.
   (a) 12 (b) 24
   (c) 156 (d) 30

11. If $3x + 4y = 80$, where $3x$ and $4y$ are two-digit numbers in which 3 and 4 are in the tens places and x and y are in the units places, and $x \leq y$, find the possible values of (x, y).

12. Find the number of two-digit numbers formed by non-zero digits in the Hindu-Arabic System.

Level 2: Review Your Concepts

13. The cost of a pen is the largest two-digit number (in ₹). The cost of a text book and geometry box respectively are the successor and predecessor of the cost of the pen. Find the sum of the costs of the text book and geometry box (in ₹).
   (a) 197 (b) 198
   (c) 200 (d) 201

14. P is neither positive nor negative, $Q = -|-9|$ and R is the absolute value of -13. Which of the following is the value of $P + Q + R$?
   (a) 21 (b) 22
   (c) 4 (d) -4

Level 3: Assess Your Concepts

15. If x, y and z are digits, and

$$\begin{array}{r} 7\ x\ 2 \\ -\ 4\ 8\ y \\ \hline z\ 7\ 3 \end{array}$$

Then, find the value of $2x + 3y + 5z$.
   (a) 49 (b) 27
   (c) 12 (d) 39

16. Given that:

$$\begin{array}{r} 3x \\ \times\ 2y \\ \hline 7yy \\ \hline \end{array}$$

Find the value of $x + y$.

(a) 5 (b) 6
(c) 7 (d) 8

17. Bharat has a plant in his garden. In the month of March, if it gives a flower on the first day of the month, two flowers on the second day of the month, three flowers on the third of the month and it continues till the end of the month. What is the total number of flowers given by the plant in the month of March?

(a) 495 (b) 290
(c) 496 (d) 486

AT

ANSWER KEYS

Crossword

Across

2. Notation 4. Whole numbers 8. Numeration 9. India 10. BODMAS

Down

1. Face value 2. Natural numbers 3. Cipher 5. Place value 6. Hindu arabic
7. Predecessor

Classroom Wing

Very Short Answer Type Questions

1. (d) 2. (c) 3. (a) 4. (a) 5. (d) 6. (a) → (p), (b) → (r), (c) → (q), (d) → (s)
7. 0 8. −1 9. −11 10. −13 11. (c) 12. (c) 13. (b) 14. (d)
15. (a) → (p), (b) → (s), (c) → (r), (d) → (q) 16. 7 17. 5 18. 14 19. −130 20. (a) 21. (b)
22. (d) 23. (a) 24. (a) → (r), (b) → (p), (c) → (s), (d) → (q)

Short Answer Type Questions

25. 6
26. 11, 12, 13, 14, 15, 16, 17, 18, and 19
27. (i) 6,06,06,000 (ii) 7,05,00,00,301 (iii) 88,99,55,074 28. 4995 29. 507, 705, 750, 570
30. 3 33. 22 34. (i) ₹+28 (ii) ₹−48 (iii) −36 m (iv) +12°C (v) −5°C
35. (i) −7, −5, −2, −1, 0, 3, 4. (ii) −15, −13, −12, −9, 5, 10, 11.
36. (i) 25, 14, 13, 6, −8, −9, −16, −23. (ii) 120, 64, 42, −43, −86, −115.
37. (i) −14, −13, −12, −11, −10, −9 (ii) −4, −3, −2, −1, 0 (iii) 1 38. (i) 27 (ii) −20 (iii) 8
39. (i) −26 (ii) 16 (iii) 44 40. (i) 4 (ii) 4 (iii) $2B < A < 3C$ 41. −2
42. (i) 585 (ii) 105 43. −12, 30 44. 99 45. 43 46. −19
47. −2 48. 436 49. −116 50. 71 51. 82 52. −9
53. 1037 54. 5 55. 160 56. 9
57. (i) Thirty two thousand and eight. (ii) Seven lakh and fifty. (iii) Nine lakh one thousand and twenty.
58. (i) 79,00,00,707 (ii) 89,64,002 (iii) 4,32,68,34,073

Essay Type Questions

59. 96,456 60. 23

Competition Wing

Level 1: Apply Your Concepts

1. 0 2. 300 3. 0 4. 54 5. 9000 6. (a)
7. (c) 8. (c) 9. (b) 10. (c)
11. (1,9), (2,8), (3,7), (4,6), and (5,5) 12. 81

Level 2: Review Your Concepts

13. (b) 14. (c)

Level 3: Assess Your Concepts

15. (a) 16. (a) 17. (c)

Hints and Explanations

CLASSROOM WING

Very Short Answer Type Questions

1. 357, 375, 537, 573, 735, 753. Therefore, '6' three-digit numbers can be formed.

   Hence, the correct option is (d).

2. The required sum = 101 + 99 = 200.

   Hence, the correct option is (c).

3. $XYZX = 7532 - 2357 = 5175$

   $\therefore X = 5$

   Hence, the correct option is (a).

4. Given number is 4875.

   The face value of 8 is 8.

   The place value of 6 is 800, since 8 is in hundreds place.

   The required difference = 800 – 8 = 792.

   Hence, the correct option is (a).

5. $|2-3| = |-1| = 1$ is a non-negative number.

   $|-3| - |-4| = 3 - 4 = -1$ is a negative number.

   $|-4| - |4| = 4 - 4 = 0$ is a non-negative number.

   Hence, the correct option is (d).

6. (a) 1 Arab = 100 crores = $100 \times 10^7 = 10^9 \rightarrow$ **(p)**

   (b) 1 Mahasamudram = $10^{52} \rightarrow$ **(r)**

   (c) 1 Kharab = Ten thousand crores = $10^4 \times 10^7$

   $= 10^{11} \rightarrow$ **(q)**

   (d) 1 Googol = $10^{100} \rightarrow$ **(s)**

   Hence, the correct answer is

   (a) → (p), (b) → (r), (c) → (q), (d) → (s).

7. The absolute value of 0 is **0**.

8. The highest non positive numbers is 0. Hence, its predecessor is **–1**.

9. 4 + (–8) – 7

   = 4 – 8 – 7 = –11

10. The other number is –6 – 7 = –13

11. Since, $-2 \times -3 = 6$

    and $2 \times 3 = 6$

    Hence, the correct option is (c).

12. $A = -12 - 15 = -27$

    $B = -16 - 12 = -28$

    $C = -14 + 12 = -2$

    $B < A < C$.

    Hence, the correct option is (c).

13. (B) and (C) are true.

    Hence, the correct option is (b).

14. The absolute value of an integer is always greater than or equal to the integer itself.

    Hence, the correct option is (d).

15. (a) (–2) (–3) (–5) = –30 → **(p)**

    (b) 6(–2) (–3) = 36 → **(s)**

    (c) (–15) (–2) = 30 → **(r)**

    (d) (–9) (–2) (–2) = – 36 → **(q)**

    The correct match is as follows:

    (a) → (p), (b) → (s), (c) → (r), (d) → (q)

16. $8 - \overline{3-2} = 8 - 1 = 7$

17. $6 \div 3 + 3 = 2 + 3 = 5$

18. $5 \times 2 + 4 = 10 + 4 = 14$

19. $9 \times (-13) - 13 = -117 - 13 = -130$

20. $15 \div 3 \times 5 - 10 = 5 \times 5 - 10 = 15$

    Hence, the correct option is (a).

21. $5 \div 5 \div 5 = 1 \div 5 = \frac{1}{5}$

    Hence, the correct option is (b).

22. All the given statements are false.

    Hence, the correct option is (d).

23. $4 \div 4 + 1 = 1 + 1 = 2$

    Hence, the correct option is (a).

24. (a) $3 \times 2 - 8 \div 4 = 6 - 2 = 4 \rightarrow$ **(r)**

    (b) $4 \div 2 + 3 \times 4 = 2 + 12 = 14 \rightarrow$ **(p)**

    (c) $18 - 9 \div 3 \times 5 = 18 - 3 \times 5 = 18 - 15 = 3 \rightarrow$ **(s)**

    (d) $72 - 15 \times 20 \div 5 = 72 - 15 \times 4$

    $= 72 - 60 = 12 \rightarrow$ **(q)**

    The correct match is

    (a) → (r), (b) → (p), (c) → (s), (d) → (q)

Short Answer Type Questions

25. If an expression consists of the same operation, ÷, we need to simplify it from right to left.

$6 \div 6 \div 6 \div 6 \div 6 = 6 \div 6 \div 6 \div 1$

$= 6 \div 6 \div 6$

$= 6 \div 1 = 6.$

26. The absolute value of -20 is 20.

The absolute value of 10 is 10.

The integers between 10 and 20 are: **11, 12, 13, 14, 15, 16, 17, 18, and 19**.

27. (i) 6,06,06,000 (ii) 7,05,00,00,301

(iii) 88,99,55,074

28. 895435

One of the two 5's is in units place and the other is in thousands place. Their place values are 5000 and 5.

∴ The difference of the two values is 5000 – 5 = 4995.

29. 5, 0, 7 are the three-digits (given). The possible 3–digit numbers are: 507, 705, 750, 570.

30. The two-digit numbers with repetitions of the digits 3, 5, 7 are 33, 55, 77.

∴ The required numbers of numbers = 3

31. The given digits are 5, 8, 9 and 4.

Four-digit even numbers using the given digits.

(i) Ending with 4 are: 5894, 5984
9584, 9854
8954, 8594

(ii) Ending with 8 are: 5498, 5948
4958, 4598
9548, 9458

32. 2475056

= 2000000 + 400000 + 70000 + 5000 + 0 + 50 + 6

33. From 321 to 543 the numbers which cannot be changed when the order of digits reversed are 323, 333, 343, 353, 363, 373, 383, 393; 404, 414, 424, 434, 444, 454, 464, 474, 484, 494, 505, 515, 525, 535.

∴ The required total number of combination is 22.

34. (i) Gain of ₹28 → ₹+28

(ii) Loss of ₹48 → ₹–48

(iii) 36 m below sea level → –36 m

(iv) 12°C rise in temperature → +12°C

(v) 5°C fall in temperature → –5°C

35. (i) Ascending order: –7, –5, –2, –1, 0, 3, 4

(ii) Ascending order: –15, –13, –12, –9, 5, 10, 11

36. (i) Descending order: 25, 14, 13, 6, –8, –9, –16, –23

(ii) Descending order: 120, 64, 42, –43, –86, –115

37. (i) –14, –13, –12, –11, –10, –9

(ii) – 4, –3, –2, –1, 0

(iii) $A = 6$, $B = 5$

$|-(A - B)| = |-(6 - 5)| = |-1| = 1$

38. (i) $|-15| + |12| = 15 + 12 = 27$

(ii) $-|13| - |-7| = -13 - 7 = -20$

(iii) $|17| - |-9| = 17 - 9 = 8$

39. $P = -17$, $Q = -27$, $R = +43$

(i) $|P| - |R|$

$= |-17| - |43|$

$= 17 - 43 = -26$

(ii) $||Q| - |R||$

$= ||-27| - |43||$

$= 27 - 43$

$= |-16|$

$||Q| - |R|| = |-16| = 16$

(iii) $|P| + |Q|$

$= |-17| + |-27|$

$= 17 + 27$

$= 44$

40. $A = 0$, $B = -|-8| = -8$

$C = |-12| = 12$

(i) $A + B + C = 0 + (-8) + 12 = 4$

(ii) $|B + C| = |-8 + 12| = 4$

(iii) $2B = 2 \times (-8) = -16$

$A = 0$, $3C = 3 \times 12 = 36$

$2B < A < 3C$

41. $3 + 5 - 6 - 4 = 8 - 10 = -2$

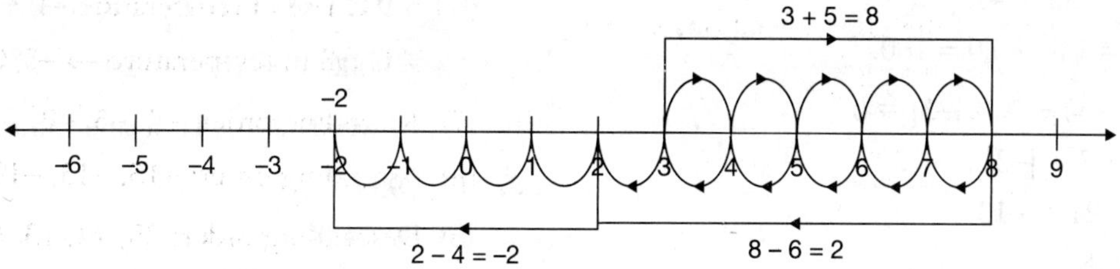

42. (i) $14625 \div 25$

$$\frac{14,625}{25} = \frac{2925}{5} = 585$$

(ii) $15120 \div 144$

$$\frac{15,120}{144} = \frac{3780}{36} = \frac{420}{4} = 105$$

43. $P + Q = R$

$P + Q = P + (-12)$

$Q = -12$

If $P = 42$, $R = P + Q = 42 + (-12) = 30$

44. The following numerical expression represents the situation explained in the problem.

$= 120 - 15 - 42 + 36$

$= 156 - 57$

$= 99$

∴ Finally, there are 99 fruits in the basket.

45. $45 - 26 \div 13 \times 6 + 10$

$= 45 - 2 \times 6 + 10 = 45 - 12 + 10 = 55 - 12 = 43$

46. $65 \div 5 - 15 \times 3 + 27 \div 9 \times 3 - 24 \div 8 + 7$

$= 13 - 15 \times 3 + 3 \times 3 - 3 + 7 = 13 - 45 + 9 - 3 + 7$

$= 22 - 48 + 7 = -19$

47. $[\{(12 - \overline{14 - 8}) + 7\} - 15]$

$= [\{(12 - 14 + 8) + 7\} - 15] = [\{6 + 7\} - 15]$

$= [13 - 15] = -2$

48. $52 - [48 \div 12 \times 6 \{6 - (8 \times 3 - \overline{6 - 4})\}]$

$= 52 - [4 \times 6 \{6 - (24 - 6 + 4)\}]$

$= 52 - [24\{6 - 22\}] = 52 - [24 \times (-16)]$

$= 52 + 384 = 436$

49. $242 - [360 - 248 \div \{180 + 7 \times (2 - \overline{26 - 16})\}]$

$= 242 - [360 - 248 \div \{180 + 7 \times (2 - 10)\}]$

$= 242 - [360 - 248 \div \{180 + (7)(-8)\}]$

$= 242 - [\{360 - 248 \div \{180 - 56\}]$

$= 242 - [360 - 248 \div 124]$

$= 242 - [360 - 2] = 242 - [358] = -116$

50. $25 + [14 - 18 + \{12 \text{ of } 5 - (16 \div 4 \times 3 - 2)\}]$

$= 25 + [-4 + \{60 - (4 \times 3 - 2)\}]$

$= 25 + [-4 + \{60 - 10\}] = 25 + [-4 + 50]$

$= 25 + 46 = 71$

51. $[78 - \{75 - (76 - \overline{72 - 75})\}]$

$= [78 - \{75 - (76 - 72 + 75)\}]$

$= [78 - \{75 - (76 + 3)\}]$

$= [78 - \{75 - 79\}] = [78 - \{-4\}] = 78 + 4$

$= 82$

52. $\{16 - (4 + 18 \div 6 - \overline{7 - 5}) \times 5\}$

$= \{16 - (4 + 3 - 2) \times 5\} = \{16 - (7 - 2) \times 5\}$

$= \{16 - 25\} = -9$

53. $[3077 - 85 \{32 \div 8 \times (24 - \overline{36 - 18})\}]$

$= 3077 - 85 \{32 \div 8 (24 - 18)\}]$

$= [3077 - 85 \{(32 \div 8 \times 6)\}]$

$= [3077 - 85 \{4 \times 6\}] = [3077 - 85 \times 24]$

$= 3077 - 2040 = 1037$

54. $4940 \div [12 + 16 \{(48 - (8 - \overline{15 + 6})\}]$

$= 4940 \div [12 + 16 \{48 - (8 - 21)\}]$

$= 4940 \div [12 + 16 \{48 + 13\}]$

$= 4940 \div [12 + 16 \{61\}]$

$= 4940 \div [12 + 976] = 4940 \div 988 = 5$

55. 60 Q15 P35 S25 R45

$= 60 \div 15 \times 35 - 25 + 45$

$= 4 \times 35 + 20 = 140 + 20 = 160.$

56. $13 + 56 \div (16 - x) + 7 \times [-3] = 0$

$56 \div (16 - x) + 7 \times [-3] = -13$

$56 \div (16 - x) - 21 = -13$

$56 \div (16 - x) = 8$

$(16 - x) = 7$

x must be 9.

57. (i) 32,008

$= 3 \times 10000 + 2 \times 1000 + 0 + 0 + 8 \times 1$

$= 30000 + 2000 + 8$

In words: Thirty two thousand and eight

(ii) 7,00,050

$= 7 \times 100000 + 0 + 0 + 0 + 5 \times 10 + 0$

$= 700000 + 50$

In words: Seven lakh and fifty.

(iii) 9,01,020

$= 9 \times 100000 + 0 + 1 \times 1000 + 0 + 2 \times 10 + 0$

$= 900000 + 1000 + 20$

In words: Nine lakh one thousand and twenty.

58. (i) 79,00,00,707

(ii) 89,64,002

(iii) 4,32,68,34,073

Essay Type Questions

59. Given digits are 9,7,3,4,0.

The greatest 5-digit number is 97430.

The greatest 3-digit number is 974.

∴ Difference of two numbers = 97430 – 974 = 96,456.

60. From 601 to 829 the numbers which cannot be changed when the order of digits reversed are 606, 616, 626, 636, 646, 656, 666, 676, 686, 696, 707, 717, 727, 737, 747, 757, 767, 777, 787, 797, 808, 818, 828.

∴ The number of numbers is 23.

COMPETITION WING

Level 1: Apply Your Concepts

1. The predecessor and the successor of 0 are -1 and 1 respectively.
   Therefore, the required sum is -1 + 1 = **0**.

2. The local value or the place value of 3 in 2356 is 3 × 100 = 300.

3. The place value of the digit '0' is always '0'.

4. 9867: Place value of '6' is 6 × 10 = 60
   Face of the digit is 6.
   Difference of the two = 60 – 6 = 54

5. The number of 4-digit numbers = 9999 – 999
   = 9000

6. $|-5| = 5$
   Hence, $|-5| = -5$ is a false statement.
   Hence, the correct option is (a).

7. Given number is 2332.
   The place values of 2's are 2000 and 2.
   The required sum is 2000 + 2 = 2002.
   Hence, the correct option is (c).

8. Let the 3-digit numbers be *xyz*, the 3-digit number after reversing the digits of *xyz* is *zyx*.
   The difference between the place values of tenth digits $= 10y - 10y = 0$
   Hence, the correct option is (c).

9. Number of eggs brought by the shopkeeper = 12 dozen = 144
   Number of eggs sold by the shopkeeper = 2 dozen = 24
   Number of eggs with the shopkeeper finally = 144 – 24 – 9 + 8 = 119
   Hence, the correct option is (b).

10. $90B3A5D3C9 = 90 \div 3 \times 5 - 3 + 9$
    $= 150 + 6 = 156$
    Hence, the correct option is (c).

11. Given that $3x + 4y = 80$, where $3x$ and $4y$ are two-digit numbers, and $x \le y$.
    As the digit in the tens place of $3x + 4y$ is 8 and 3 + 4 is 7, $x + y$ must be greater than 10.
    Therefore, (x, y) can be $(1,9)$, $(2,8)$, $(3,7)$, $(4,6)$, and $(5,5)$.

12. The given digits are 1, 2, 3, … 9.
    The required two-digit numbers are:
    11, 12, 13, 14, … 19 – There exist 9 numbers.
    21, 22, 23, 24, … 29 – There exist 9 numbers.
    31, 32, 33, 34, … 39 – There exist 9 numbers.
    ⋮
    91, 92, 93, 94, … 99 – There exist 9 numbers.
    There exist a total of 9 × 9 i.e., **81** numbers.

Level 2: Review Your Concepts

13. The largest 2-digit number = 99
    Therefore, the cost of a pen = ₹99
    The successor and predecessor of 99 are 100 and 98.
    The sum of the costs of the text book and the geometry box = 98 + 100
    = ₹198
    Hence, the correct option is (b).

14. $P = 0$, $Q = -9$, $R = 13$
    $P + Q + R = 0 - 9 + 13 = 4$
    Hence, the correct option is (c).

Level 3: Assess Your Concepts

15. We have, $2 - y = 3$
    Clearly, if y is a single digit integer, this cannot be possible. Therefore, there has to be some borrowing from x.
    Now, borrow 1 from the digit x, and we get, $12 - y = 3$ or $y = 9$.
    Since, 1 is already borrowed from x we have from the 'tens' column,
    $(x - 1) - 8 = 7$.
    Again, for single digit integer this will not work, and we will have to borrow from 7, giving
    $10 + (x - 1) - 8 = 7$.
    Now, solving for x, we have
    $10 - x - 1 - 8 = 7$
    $1 + x = 7$ or $x = 6$
    So, as we have borrowed from the hundreds column we have $(7 - 1 - 4) = z$
    This gives, $z = 2$
    We can check the answers as

$$\begin{array}{r} 7\ \mathbf{6}\ 2 \\ -\ 4\ 8\ \mathbf{9} \\ \hline \mathbf{2}\ 7\ 3 \end{array}$$

So, the desired quantity is:

$2x = 12$, $3y = 27$, and $5z = 10$

So, the value of $2x + 3y + 5z = 12 + 27 + 10 = 49$

16. Given that:

$$\begin{array}{r} 3x \\ \times 2y \\ \hline 7yy \end{array}$$

(x, y) can be $(0, 0)$, $(1, 1)$, $(5, 5)$, $(6, 6)$, and $(1, y)$, where y is any whole number.

If (x, y) is $(0, 0)$, $30 \times 20 = 600 \neq 7yy$.

If (x, y) is $(1, 1)$, $31 \times 21 = 651 \neq 7yy$.

If (x, y) is $(5, 5)$, $35 \times 25 = 875 \neq 7yy$.

As $35 \times 25 = 875$ which is more than $7yy$, (x, y) cannot be $(6, 6)$.

If $(x, y) = (1, y) = (1, 0)$, $31 \times 20 = 620 \neq 7yy$.

If $(x, y) = (1, y) = (1, 2)$, $31 \times 22 = 682 \neq 7yy$.

If $(x, y) = (1, y) = (1, 3)$, $31 \times 23 = 713 \neq 7yy$.

If $(x, y) = (1, y) = (1, 4)$, $31 \times 24 = 744 = 7yy$.

If $(x, y) = (1, y) = (1, 5)$, $31 \times 25 = 775 \neq 7yy$.

If $(x, y) = (1, y) = (1, 6)$, $31 \times 26 = 806 \neq 7yy$.

As $31 \times 26 = 806$ which is more than $7yy$, y cannot be 6, 7, 8 and 9.

Hence, $x + y = 1 + 4 = 5$.

Hence, the correct option is (5).

17. We know that the month of March has 31 days.

The total number of flowers $= 1 + 2 + 3 + 4 + \ldots + 31$.

$= (1+31) + (2+30) + (3+29) + (4+28) + \ldots$

$+ (15+17) + 16$

$= 32 + 32 + 32 + 32 + \ldots (15 \text{ times}) + 16$

$= 32 \times 15 + 16$

$= 480 + 16 = 496$.

Hence, the correct option is (c).

CHAPTER

2

Factors and Multiples

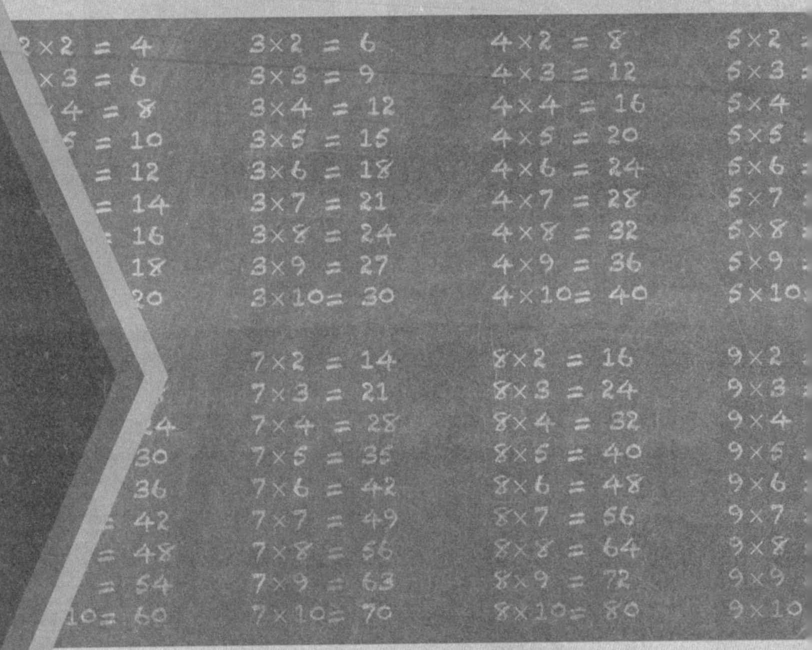

Remember

Before beginning this chapter, you should be able to:

- Recall multiplication tables
- Perform multiplication and division of tables

Key Ideas

After completing this chapter, you should be able to:

- Define even numbers, odd numbers, prime numbers, sphenic numbers, composite numbers, twin prime, co-primes
- Understand highest common factor (HCF)
- Understand least common multiple (LCM)
- Describe relationship between LCM and HCF
- Apply test of divisibility

Scientific Crypt

A Tribute to Carl Friedrich Gauss (1777-1855)

Johann Carl Friedrich Gauss was a renowned German mathematician and physicist, whose contributions to number theory, probability theory, and electromagnetism, not only reshaped the landscape of academia but also paved the way for the modern age of discovery.

Born on April 30, 1777, in Brunswick, Germany, Gauss demonstrated extraordinary mathematical talent from a young age. His early achievements include discovering a method for quickly summing the integers from 1 to 100 in his primary school years.

Carl Friedrich Gauss revolutionized mathematics with his proofs of the fundamental theorem of algebra, advancements in number theory, and pioneering work in planetary motion and statistical methods. Overcoming skepticism from established mathematicians due to his innovative ideas, especially in the realm of number theory and with limited resources, he persevered to create innovative solutions that transformed the field despite challenges.

FUN TIME

CROSSWORD

Across

2. The largest factor in the set of common factors of two or more natural numbers; it divides each of the given numbers exactly.
5. Natural numbers that have more than two factors.
6. Prime numbers that have a difference of 2 between them.
8. The smallest number which can be divided exactly by two or more given natural numbers.
11. The study of solving codes where knowledge of prime factor is applied.
12. Integers that are not divisible by 2.
13. Integers that are divisible by 2.

Down

1. A positive integer which is the product of three distinct prime factors.
3. Natural numbers that have exactly two factors.
4. A test that determines if one number can be divided by another without performing the full calculation.
7. When two or more natural numbers are multiplied, their product is referred to as this.
9. A pair of natural numbers having no common factor other than 1.
10. Each of the natural numbers involved in creating a multiple is known as this.

INTRODUCTION

Mathematics involves the study of numbers and various operations performed on them. In earlier classes, we have studied operations such as multiplication and division. We often come across terms, factors and multiples while discussing them. These two terms are directly connected to one another. Let's find out how they are related and differentiated from each other in this chapter.

Factors and Multiples

When two or more natural numbers are multiplied, then the product obtained is called the **multiple** of either of the numbers. Each of those numbers is called a **factor** of the product.

$2 \times 3 = 6$

Factors Multiple

Example: For instance, $2 \times 3 = 6$. Here, 6 is a multiple of 2 and 3. Also, 2 and 3 are two factors of 6.

Table 2.1 Multiplication Chart

X	1	2	3	4	5	6	7	8	9	10
1	1	2	3	4	5	6	7	8	9	10
2	2	4	6	8	10	12	14	16	18	20
3	3	6	9	12	15	18	21	24	27	30
4	4	8	12	16	20	24	28	32	36	40
5	5	10	15	20	25	30	35	40	45	50
6	6	12	18	24	30	36	42	48	54	60
7	7	14	21	28	35	42	49	56	63	70
8	8	16	24	32	40	48	56	64	72	80
9	9	18	27	36	45	54	63	72	81	90
10	10	20	30	40	50	60	70	80	90	100

Note:

(a) 1 is a multiple of every number.

(b) Every number is a factor of itself.

(c) Every number is a multiple of itself.

EXAMPLE 2.1

Find the factors of 18 and 20.

SOLUTION

Factors of 18: $1 \times 18 = 18$ $2 \times 9 = 18$ $3 \times 6 = 18$

So, the factors of 18 are 1,2,3,6, and 18.

Factors of 20: $1 \times 20 = 20$ $2 \times 10 = 20$ $4 \times 5 = 20$

So, the factors of 20 are 1,2,4,5,10, and 20.)

Konnect

Every number is a factor of itself. So, the number 7 has 7 as one of its factors. This goes for every single number out there.

EXAMPLE 2.2

Find the first five multiples of 7.

SOLUTION

$7 \times 1 = 7$; $7 \times 2 = 14$; $7 \times 3 = 21$; $7 \times 4 = 28$; $7 \times 5 = 55$.

$\therefore$ 7, 14, 21, 28 and 35 are the first five multiples of 7.

Even Numbers

Integers which are divisible by 2 are called **even numbers.**

Example: 0, 2, 4, 6, 8, 10, 12, ... are even numbers.

Odd Numbers

Integers that are not divisible by 2 are called **odd numbers.**

Example: 1, 3, 5, 7, 9, 11, 13, ... are odd numbers.

Prime Numbers

The natural numbers which has exactly two factors are called **prime numbers.**

Example: 2, 3, 5, 7 are some prime numbers.

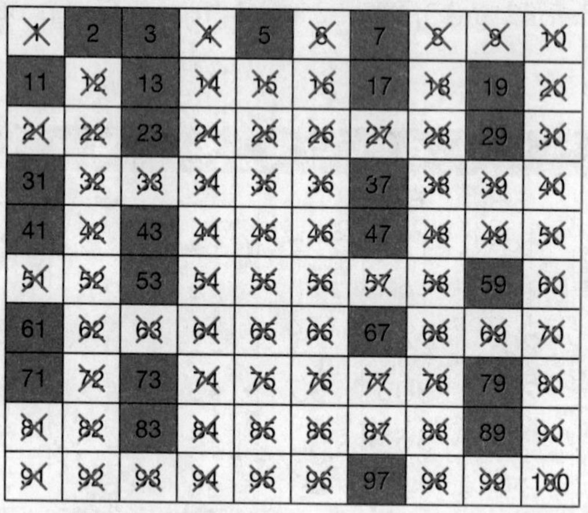

Figure 2.1 Sieve of Eratosthenes

Konnect

Sieve of Eratosthenes is used to find first 25 prime numbers by first listing out numbers between 1 and 100 in a10 × 10 grid and by removing only multiples of 2, 3, 5, and 7.

Sphenic Numbers

A positive integer which is the product of three distinct prime factors is called a **sphenic number.**

Example: $30 = 2 \times 3 \times 5$

Composite Numbers

The natural numbers which have more than two factors are called **composite numbers.**

Example: 4, 6, 8, 9, 10 are some composite numbers.

Twin Primes

Prime numbers differing by 2 are called **twin primes.**

Example: 5 and 7 are twin prime numbers.

Co-primes

Every pair of two natural numbers having no common factor other than 1 is called a **pair of co-primes** or **relative primes.**

Example: Consider the numbers 16 and 15.

The common factors of 16 and 15 is 1 only. Hence, they are relative primes.

Greatest Common Divisor or Highest Common Factor

The **highest common factor (HCF)** of two or more natural numbers is the largest factor in the set of common factors of those numbers. In other words, the HCF or greatest common divisor (GCD) of two or more numbers is the largest number that divides each of them exactly.

Info Bytes!

Knowledge of prime factor is applied in Cryptography (study of solving codes).

Prime Factorization Method

When the numbers whose GCD has to be found are relatively small, this is the best method. Here, we resolve the given numbers into their prime factors and find out the product of common factors of given numbers. This method can be easily applied to any number of numbers.

EXAMPLE 2.3 Write all the prime factors of the following.

(I) 18 **(II)** 124

SOLUTION

(I)

$$\begin{array}{r|l} 2 & 18 \\ \hline 3 & 9 \\ \hline & 3 \end{array}$$

$18 = 2 \times 3 \times 3$

$\therefore$ The prime factors of 18 are 2 and 3.

(II)

$$\begin{array}{r|l} 2 & 124 \\ \hline 2 & 62 \\ \hline & 31 \end{array}$$

$124 = 2 \times 2 \times 31$

$\therefore$ The prime factors of 124 are 2 and 31.

EXAMPLE 2.4 Find the HCF of 126 and 540 by prime factorization method.

SOLUTION

For 126:

$$\begin{aligned} 126 &= 2 \times 63 \\ &= 2 \times 7 \times 9 \\ &= 2 \times 7 \times 3 \times 3 \\ &= 2^1 \times 7^1 \times 3^2 \end{aligned}$$

For 540:

$$\begin{aligned} 540 &= 2 \times 270 \\ &= 2 \times 2 \times 135 \\ &= 2 \times 2 \times 3 \times 45 \\ &= 2 \times 2 \times 3 \times 3 \times 15 \\ &= 2 \times 2 \times 3 \times 3 \times 3 \times 5 \\ &= 2^2 \times 3^3 \times 5 \end{aligned}$$

Identifying common prime factors:

For 2: 126 has 2^1; and 540 has 2^2. Smallest exponent is 1.

For 3: 126 has 3^2; and 540 has 3^3. Smallest exponent is 2.

For 7: 126 has 7^1; and 540 doesn't have a 7 factor, so it's not considered.

For 5: 540 has 5^1; and 126 doesn't have a 5 factor, so it's not considered.

Calculating HCF: HCF $= 2^1 \times 3^2 = 2 \times 9 = 18$. Hence, the HCF of 126 and 540 is 18.

Division Method

When the numbers whose GCD has to be found are very large, it is time consuming to use prime factorization method.

In this case, we use the method of 'Long Division'. This method was proposed by Euclid and the following steps are involved in it.

Step 1: Divide the larger number by the smaller number. If the remainder is zero, then the divisor is the GCD, otherwise not.

Step 2: Let the divisor in step 1 be the dividend now and the remainder of step 1 becomes the divisor of step 2. If the remainder is zero, then the divisor is HCF. Otherwise, step 2 has to be repeated.

EXAMPLE 2.5 Find the HCF of 120, 320 and 420.

SOLUTION

Let $A = 120$, $B = 320$, $C = 420$

HCF of 120, 320

```
120) 320 (2
     240
      80) 120 (1
           80
          40) 80 (2
              80
               0
```

∴ HCF of 120, 320 is 40

```
40) 420 (10
    400
     20) 40 (2
         40
          0
```

HCF of 40, 420 is 20

∴ HCF of 120, 320 and 420 is 20.

Least Common Multiple

The **least common multiple (LCM)** of two or more natural numbers is the least of their common multiples. In other words, the LCM of two or more numbers is the least number which can be divided exactly by each of the given numbers.

> **Info Bytes!**
> LCM is always greater than or equal to the largest number of the set.

Prime Factorization Method

The given numbers are expressed as a product of prime factors. We select the common prime factors having the highest exponent. Then we multiply all such common factors with the prime factors which are not common. The product obtained is the LCM.

EXAMPLE 2.6 Find the LCM of 12 and 15 by prime factorization method.

SOLUTION

$12 = 4 \times 3 = 2^2 \times 3^1$

$15 = 3 \times 5 = 3^1 \times 5^1$

LCM (12, 15) $= 2^2 \times 3^1 \times 5^1 = 60$

```
2 | 12        3 | 15
2 |  6          |  5
  |  3
```

EXAMPLE 2.7 Find the LCM of 24 and 40.

SOLUTION

2	24, 40
2	12, 20
2	6, 10
	3, 5

$\therefore$ The LCM of 24 and 40

$= 2 \times 2 \times 2 \times 3 \times 5$

$= 120$

Relationship between LCM and GCD

The LCM and GCD of two given numbers are related to the given numbers by the following relationship.

The product of two numbers = The product of their LCM and GCD

Konnect

- If a product is divisible by two factors, then it is also divisible by the product of those two factors.
- The Euclidean algorithm, which is more than 2300 years old, is still one of the most popular ways to find the GCD of two numbers.

EXAMPLE 2.8 LCM of two numbers is 378 and their HCF is 9. If one of the numbers is 63, then find the other number.

SOLUTION

We know that LCM × HCF = The product of two numbers

Let the other number be N_2.

$378 \times 9 = 63 \times N_2$

$378 = 7N_2$

$$N_2 = \frac{378}{7} = 54$$

$\therefore$ The other number is 54.

EXAMPLE 2.9 Find the smallest number which is divisible by 18, 15 and 12.

SOLUTION

The objective is to find the smallest common multiple of 18, 15 and 12.
(LCM of 12, 15, 18)

$12 = 2^2 \times 3$

$15 = 3 \times 5$

$18 = 3^2 \times 2$

$\therefore$ LCM $= 2^2 \times 3^2 \times 5 = 180$

Divisibility

Consider two natural numbers *a* and *b*. When *a* is divided by *b*, if a remainder of zero is obtained, we say that *a* is divisible by *b*.

Example: 12 is divisible by 3 because when 12 is divided by 3, the remainder is zero. Also, we say that 12 is not divisible by 5, because 12 when divided by 5 leaves a remainder 2.

Tests of Divisibility

Test of divisibility lets us know whether a number is divisible by another or not without doing the calculations. We will now study the methods to test the divisibility of natural numbers with 2, 3, 4, 5, 6, 8, 9 and 11 without performing actual division.

Test of Divisibility by 2

A natural number is divisible by 2, if its units digit is divisible by 2, i.e., the units place is either 0, 2, 4, 6 or 8.

Example: The numbers 4096, 23548 and 34052 are divisible by 2 as they end with 6, 8 and 2, respectively.

Test of Divisibility by 3

A natural number is divisible by 3, if the sum of its digits is divisible by 3.

Example: Consider the number 21,43,251. The sum of the digits of 21,43,251 is (2 + 1 + 4 + 3 + 2 + 5 + 1), i.e., 18. As 18 is divisible by 3, the number 21,43,251 is divisible by 3.

Test of Divisibility by 4

A natural number is divisible by 4, if the number formed by its last two-digits in the same order (ten's digit and unit's digit) is divisible by 4.

Example: 4096, 53216, 548 and 4000 are all divisible by 4 as the numbers formed by taking the last two-digits in each case is divisible by 4.

Test of Divisibility by 5

A natural number is divisible by 5, if its unit's digit is either 0 or 5.

Example: The numbers 4095 and 235060 are divisible by 5, as they have 5 and 0 in their respective units' places.

Test of Divisibility by 6

A number is divisible by 6, if it is divisible by both 2 and 3.

Example: Consider the number 7,53,618. Since its units digit is 8, it is divisible by 2. Also its sum of digits is 7 + 5 + 3 + 6 + 1 + 8 = 30. As 30 is divisible by 3; 7,53,618 is divisible by 3. Hence, 7,53,618 is divisible by 6.

Test of Divisibility by 8

A number is divisible by 8, if the number formed by its last three-digits in the same order (hundreds, tens and units digits) is divisible by 8.

Example: 15,840, 5432 and 7096 are all divisible by 8 as the numbers formed by the last three-digits in each case are divisible by 8.

Info Bytes!

If the digits at ones, tens and hundreds place is 0, then the number is divisible by 1000.

Test of Divisibility by 9

A natural number is divisible by 9, if the sum of its digits is divisible by 9.

Example: Consider the number 1,25,847. The sum of digits = 1 + 2 + 5 + 8 + 4 + 7 = 27. As 27 is divisible by 9, the number 1,25,847 is divisible by 9.

Test of Divisibility by 11

A number is divisible by 11, if the difference between the sum of the digits in odd places and the sum of the digits in even places of the number is either 0 or a multiple of 11.

Example: Consider the number 95,82,540. Now, (the sum of digits in odd places) – (the sum of digits in even places) = (9 + 8 + 5 + 0) – (5 + 2 + 4) = 11, which is divisible by 11.

Hence, 95,82,540 is divisible by 11.

POINTS TO REMEMBER

- ✔ When two or more natural numbers are multiplied, then their product is called the multiple of either of the numbers. Each of those numbers is called a factor of the product.
- ✔ A positive integer which is the product of three distinct prime factors is called a sphenic number.
- ✔ The natural numbers which have more than two factors are called composite numbers.
- ✔ Prime numbers differing by 2 are called twin primes
- ✔ Every pair of two natural numbers having no common factor other than 1 is called a pair of co-primes

DW

PRACTICE QUESTIONS CLASSROOM WING

Very Short Answer Type Questions

***Direction for questions from 1 to 5:* Select the correct alternative from the given choices.**

1. Which of the following is(are) multiple(s) of both 2 and 3?
(a) 1434 (b) 792 (c) 924 (d) All of these

2. Which of the following are twin primes?
(a) (31, 33) (b) (37, 39)
(c) (41, 43) (d) (43, 45)

3. Which of the following is a composite number?
(a) 37 (b) 47 (c) 57 (d) 67

4. The HCF of which of the following pairs of composite numbers is different from that of the others? (Odd man out)
(a) 12, 18 (b) 24, 30 (c) 18, 30 (d) 18, 45

5. Which of the following is the greatest measure that can be used to measure the quantities 68 m, 102 m and 119 m?
(a) 34 (b) 51 (c) 13 (d) 17

***Direction for question 6:* Match the Column A with the Column B.**

6.

	Column A		Column B
(a)	Prime number	(p)	Divisible by only three prime numbers.
(b)	Sphenic number	(q)	'2' must be its factor.
(c)	Composite number	(r)	It has at least three factors.
(d)	Even number	(s)	It has only two factors.

***Direction for questions from 7 to 11:* Fill in the blanks.**

7. The number of factors of the least composite number is ______.

8. The HCF of any two consecutive even numbers is ______.

9. LCM $(a, b) \times$ HCF $(a, b) =$ ______.

10. The largest 3-digit number divisible by 9 is ______.

11. The smallest 4-digit number divisible by 11 is ______.

***Direction for questions from 12 to 17:* Select the correct alternative from given choices.**

12. The LCM of a and b is 220. Which of the following can be the HCF of a and b?
(a) 33 (b) 15 (c) 20 (d) 12

13. Which of the following pair of numbers have their LCM as 144?
(a) 18, 36 (b) 16, 96
(c) 24, 48 (d) 9, 16

14. The HCF of the two numbers a and b is 12. Which of the following can be the LCM of a and b?
(a) 44 (b) 65 (c) 76 (d) 96

15. Which of the following is divisible by 8, 15 and 6?
(a) 60 (b) 96 (c) 180 (d) 240

16. Which of the following is not divisible by 9?
(a) 345672 (b) 278901
(c) 46938 (d) 96435

17. Which of the following is divisible by 8?
(a) 7248882 (b) 836486
(c) 92304 (d) 726436

***Direction for question 18:* Match the Column A with the Column B.**

18.

	Column A		Column B (LCM)
(a)	6, 8, 12	(p)	72
(b)	8, 12, 18	(q)	180
(c)	12, 18, 30	(r)	288
(d)	18, 24, 32	(s)	24

***Direction for question 19 to 21:* Answer the following questions.**

19. Which of the following numbers are divisible by 5?
55, 556, 50058, 85501

20. Is 199 a prime number?

21. Which of the following pairs are co-prime?
2, 3; 8, 9; 21, 22

Short Answer Type Questions

22. List out all the common factors of the following pairs of numbers.
    (i) 120 and 160 (ii) 52 and 32

23. List out all the 2-digit prime numbers which are greater than 50.

24. Express the following as the product of prime numbers.
    (a) 36 (b) 75

25. List out the numbers which are coprime to 16 which are less than 16.

26. The LCM of two numbers is 4. Find the possible HCF of the numbers.

27. Find the greatest number that divides 80 and 115 leaving remainders 8 and 7 respectively.

28. Find the LCM of 30, 75 and 120 by prime factorization method.

29. Find the LCM of 48, 60 and 280 by synthetic division method.

30. The product of two numbers is 1680 and the LCM of two numbers is 420. Find their HCF.

31. Find the greatest 3-digit number which is divisible by 16, 18 and 24.

32. Find the smallest number greater than 2 which gives a remainder 2 when divided by 16, 18 and 24.

33. Find the smallest number which when added by 6 is exactly divisible by 9 and 33.

34. Find the greatest 3-digit number which is a common multiple of 6, 15, and 21.

35. A number P is divisible by 5, 4, 8 and 9. If P is a 3-digit number, then find all the possible values for P.

36. Find the HCF of 84 and 112 by division method.

37. Find the least common multiple of 8, 15 and 20 by prime factorization method.

Essay Type Questions

38. (i) Find the HCF of the following numbers by prime factorization method.
    (a) 24, 60 (b) 48, 64, 80
    (ii) Find the HCF of 72, 140, 256 by division method.

39. Rishitha and Lohitha are twins. They play a game, in which they open a page of a text book printed in English. From the first letter of the page, Rishitha strikes every 12th letter and Lohitha strikes every 18th letter. If they strike the same letter 17 times in the page, then find the minimum number of letters in the page selected.

40. The HCF and the LCM of two numbers are 2 and 12. Find the possible pairs of numbers.

PRACTICE QUESTIONS COMPETITION WING

Level 1: Apply Your Concepts

***Direction for questions from 1 to 5:* Fill in the blanks.**

1. The number of multiples of the least prime number is ______.
2. The HCF of any two primes is ______.
3. The greatest common factor of 9 and 15 is ______.
4. The number of prime factors of 48 is ______.
5. The greatest pair of twin primes of 2-digit numbers is ______.

***Direction for questions from 6 to 11:* Select the correct alternative from given choices.**

6. On her birthday, Jyothsna received three different cakes of weight 3 kg, 2.6 kg and 2 kg from her father, mother and sister respectively. She cut the three cakes into pieces of equal weights without any remainder. Find the minimum number of pieces that she can get from the three cakes.
   (a) 15 (b) 28
   (c) 38 (d) 40
7. Bhavagna celebrates her birthday every year. The number of chocolates that she distributes every year is the greatest 3-digit common multiple of all the prime factors of the number representing that year. How many chocolates should Bhavagna distribute in the year 2016?
   (a) 815 (b) 128
   (c) 388 (d) 966
8. There are three empty drums which can hold 384 litres, 576 litres and 288 litres of water. Each of them is to be filled by using a measuring jar, a whole number of times. What is the largest possible capacity of the measuring jar with which we can fill all the three drums?
   (a) 96 litres (b) 24 litres
   (c) 72 litres (d) 36 litres
9. The dimensions of a hall are 6048 cm × 2440 cm. What is the minimum number of identical square shaped tiles that is required to furnish the hall?
   (a) 2320 (b) 1061
   (c) 1240 (d) 2320
10. Which of the following is a factor of 143?
    (a) 11 (b) 13
    (c) Both (a) and (b) (d) None of these
11. Which of the following are coprime?
    (a) (21, 23) (b) (25, 27)
    (c) (23, 29) (d) All of these

Level 2: Review Your Concepts

12. A father gave equal amount of money to his three daughters Simron, Cinderella and Sreya to purchase some items for his birthday party. Simron brought puffs which costs ₹18 each, Cinderella bought cakes which costs ₹24 each and Sreya bought cool drinks which costs ₹30 each. If they spent their money completely on these items, then find the minimum number of cakes that Cinderella bought.
    (a) 12 (b) 16
    (c) 24 (d) 15
13. There are 72 green colour, 144 red colour and 234 orange colour chairs in an auditorium. A boy want to put the chairs in rows such that each row is of the same coloured chairs and the number of chairs is equal in each row. Find the minimum number of rows of chairs in the auditorium.
    (a) 30 (b) 25
    (c) 15 (d) 45
14. The HCF of two numbers is 4. Find the numbers.
15. Find the LCM of all the factors (except 1 and the number itself) of the least three-digit number formed by a single digit.

Level 3: Assess Your Concepts

16. A small-scale industry made different kinds of bulbs. The details are as follows:

Type of Bulbs (in watts)	60 w	90 w	120 w
No. of Bulbs	240	180	120

These bulbs are packed in cartons. Each carton contains same number of bulbs and only one variety. Find the minimum number of bulbs required to pack these bulbs.

(a) 6 (b) 7
(c) 8 (d) 9

17. Find the greatest 4-digit number which is common multiple of 12, 16, and 24.

(a) 9984 (b) 9980
(c) 9999 (d) 9890

18. Ranga and Pranav are good friends from their childhood. They play a game in which they select a number from 1 to 1000. Ranga selects every 12th number and Pranav selects every 27th number. What are the numbers selected by the friends in common?

(a) 8 (b) 9
(c) 10 (d) 11

AT

ANSWER KEYS

Crossword

Across

2. HCF 5. Composite 6. Twin primes 8. LCM 11. Cryptography
12. Odd 13. Even

Down

1. Sphenic 3. Prime 4. Divisibility 7. Multiple 9. Coprimes
10. Factor

Classroom Wing

Very Short Answer Type Questions

1. (d) 2. (c) 3. (c) 4. (d) 5. (d)
6. (a) → (s), (b) → (p), (c) → (r), (d) → (q) 7. 3 8. 2
9. $a \times b$ 10. 999 11. 1001 12. (c) 13. (d) 14. (d)
15. (d) 16. (c) 17. (c) 18. (a) → (s), (b) → (p), (c) → (q), (d) → (r)
19. 55 20. Yes 21. All

Short Answer Type Questions

22. (i) 1, 2, 4, 5, 8, 10, 20, 40 (ii) 1, 2, 4 23. 53, 59, 61, 67, 71, 73, 79, 83, 89 and 97
24. (i) $2^2 \times 3^2$ (ii) 3×5^2 25. 1, 3, 5, 7, 9, 11, 13, and 15 26. 1, 2 or 4 27. 36
28. 600 29. 1680 30. 4 31. 864 32. 146 33. 93
34. 840 35. 360 and 720 36. 28 37. 120

Essay Type Questions

38. **(i)** (a) 12 (b) 16 **(ii)** 4 39. 612 40. 2, 12 (or) 4, 6

Competition Wing

Level 1: Apply Your Concepts

1. infinite 2. 1 3. 3 4. 2 5. (71, 73) 6. (c)
7. (d) 8. (a) 9. (b) 10. (c) 11. (d)

Level 2: Review Your Concepts

12. (d) 13. (b) 14. infinte 15. 111

Level 3: Assess Your Concepts

16. (d) 17. (a) 18. (5, 6)

Hints and Explanations

CLASSROOM WING

Very Short Answer Type Questions

1. All the given numbers 1434, 792, and 924 are divisible by 6.
   Hence, the correct option is (d).
2. Pairs of primes whose difference is 2 are called twin primes.
   33, 35, 39 are not prime.
   Hence, (41, 43) are twin primes.
   Hence, the correct option is (c).
3. 57 is divisible by 3.
   Hence, the correct option is (c).
4. HCF (12, 18) = 6
   HCF (24, 30) = 6
   HCF (18, 30) = 6
   HCF (18, 45) = 9
   Hence, the correct option is (d).
5. Given: 68, 102, 119
   $68 = 17 \times 4$; $102 = 17 \times 6$; $119 = 17 \times 7$
   Hence, the correct option is (d).
6. (a) Prime number has only 2 factors → (s)
   (b) Sphenic number should have only 3 prime factors → (p)
   (c) Composite number should have at least 3 factors → (r)
   (d) '2' must be a factor of an even number → (q)
   The correct match is as follows:
   (a) → (s), (b) → (p), (c) → (r), (d) → (q)
7. The least composite number is 4. The factors of 4 are 1, 2, and 4.
   Hence, the number of factors of the least composite number is **3**.
8. HCF (2, 4) = HCF (4, 6) = HCF (6, 8) = … = 2.
   The HCF of any two consecutive even numbers is **2**.
9. $a \times b$
10. 999
11. When 1000 is divided by 11, the reminder is 10.
   ∴ 1001 is the smallest 4-digit number divisible by 11.
12. The HCF must be a factor of LCM.
   Hence, the correct option is (c).
13. Here, 9 and 16 are co-primes.
   Hence, the LCM = $9 \times 16 = 144$
   Hence, the correct option is (d).
14. The HCF is the factor of LCM.
   12 is a factor of 96.
   Hence, the correct option is (d).
15. LCM of 8, 15, 6:

2	8, 15, 6
3	4, 15, 3
	4, 5, 1

   ∴ LCM = 120
   All the multiples of 120 are divisible by 8, 15 and 6.
   Hence, the correct option is (d).
16. Going by options: 46938
   $4 + 6 + 9 + 2 + 8 = 30$ is not divisible by 9.
   Hence, the correct option is (c).
17. 92304, the number formed by the last 3 digits (304) is divisible by 8.
   Hence, the correct option is (c).
18. (a) 6, 8, 12
   $6 = 2 \times 3$; $8 = 2^3$; $12 = 2^2 \times 3$;
   LCM = $2^3 \times 3 = 24$ → (s)
   (b) 8, 12, 18
   $8 = 2^3$; $12 = 2^2 \times 3$; $18 = 3^2 \times 2$
   LCM = $2^3 \times 3^2 = 72$ → (p)

(c) 12, 18, 30

$12 = 2^2 \times 3$; $18 = 2 \times 3^2$; $30 = 2 \times 3 \times 5$

LCM = $2^2 \times 3^2 \times 5 = 180 \rightarrow$ (q)

(d) 18, 24, 32

$18 = 3^2 \times 2$; $24 = 3 \times 2^3$; $32 = 2^5$

LCM = $2^5 \times 3^2 = 288 \rightarrow$ (r)

The correct match is as follows:

(a) → (s), (b) → (p), (c) → (q), (d) → (r)

19. For a number to be divisible by 5, the digit at the units place should be either 0 or 5.

Out of the given numbers, only 55 is divisible by 5.

20. 199 would be a prime number if it is not divisible by any prime number other than itself.

It can be obtained that 199 is not divisible by 2, 3, 5, 7, 11, 13. Hence, it is a prime number.

21. All of the pairs are co-primes.

Short Answer Type Questions

22. (a)

120 = 1 × 120	160 = 1 × 160
= 2 × 60	= 2 × 80
= 3 × 40	= 4 × 40
= 4 × 30	= 5 × 32
= 5 × 24	= 8 × 20
= 6 × 20	= 10 × 16
= 8 × 15	
= 10 × 12	

The common factors of 120 and 160 are {1, 2, 4, 5, 8, 10, 20, 40}.

(b)

52 = 1 × 52	32 = 1 × 32
= 2 × 26	= 2 × 16
= 4 × 13	= 4 × 8

The common factors of 52, 32 are {1, 2, 4}.

23. The 2-digit prime numbers greater than 50 are 53, 59, 61, 67, 71, 73, 79, 83, 89 and 97.

24. (a) $36 = 2^2 \times 3^2$

(b) $75 = 3 \times 5^2$

25. Numbers which are having only 1 as common factor are called coprime.

1 and 16 are coprime.

3 and 16 are coprime.

5 and 16 are coprime.

7 and 16 are coprime.

9 and 16 are coprime.

11 and 16 are coprime.

13 and 16 are coprime.

15 and 16 are coprime.

Hence, **1, 3, 5, 7, 9, 11, 13, and 15** are coprime to 16.

26. Given that the LCM of two numbers is 4.

The numbers can be (1, 4), (2, 2), or (4, 4).

The HCF (1, 4) = 1.

The HCF (2, 2) = 2.

The HCF (4, 4) = 4

The HCF of the two numbers can be **1, 2 or 4**.

27. The required number is the HCF of (80 – 8) and (115 – 7), i.e., HCF (72, 108)

```
72) 108 (1
    -72
    36) 72 (2
        -72
          0
```

∴ The required number is 36.

28. LCM of 30, 75, 120:

$30 = 2 \times 3 \times 5$; $75 = 3 \times 5^2$

$120 = 2 \times 2 \times 2 \times 3 \times 5 = 2^3 \times 3 \times 5$

LCM = $2^3 \times 3 \times 5^2 = 600$

29. LCM of 48, 60, 280:

48, 60, 280

```
2 | 48, 60, 280
2 | 24, 30, 140
2 | 12, 15, 70
3 | 6, 15, 35
5 | 2, 5, 35
  | 2, 1, 7
```

LCM = $2 \times 2 \times 2 \times 3 \times 5 \times 2 \times 7 = 1680$

30. Let the two numbers be a and b.

We know that:

LCM × HCF = $a \times b$

420 × HCF = 1680

$$\text{HCF} = \frac{1680}{420} = 4$$

31. Let us find the LCM of 16, 18 and 24.

2	16, 18, 24
2	8, 9, 12
2	4, 9, 6
3	2, 9, 3
	2, 3, 1

LCM = $2 \times 2 \times 2 \times 3 \times 2 \times 3 = 144$

All multiples of 144 are also divisible by 16, 18 and 24.

$\therefore$ $144 \times 6 = 864$ is the required 3-digit number.

32. The required number is the least common multiple of (16, 18, 24) + 2.

2	16, 18, 24
2	8, 9, 12
2	4, 9, 6
3	2, 9, 3
	2, 3, 1

LCM = $2 \times 2 \times 2 \times 3 \times 2 \times 3 = 144$

$\therefore$ The required number is $144 + 2 = 146$

33. The required number is LCM of (9, 33) – 6.

3	9, 33
	3, 11

LCM = $3 \times 3 \times 11 = 99$

$\therefore$ The required number is $99 - 6 = 93$

34. LCM 6, 15, 21:

3	6, 15, 21
	2, 5, 7

LCM = $3 \times 2 \times 5 \times 7 = 210$

$\therefore$ The required number is $210 \times 4 = 840$

35. P is the common multiple of 5, 4, 8, 9.

2	5, 4, 8, 9
2	5, 2, 4, 9
	5, 1, 2, 9

LCM = $2 \times 2 \times 5 \times 2 \times 9 = 360$

$360 \times 1 = 360$

$360 \times 2 = 720$

$360 \times 3 = 1080$ is a 4 digit number

$\therefore$ *P* can be 360 and 720.

36. Division method:

```
84 )112 (1
     84
    28) 84 (3
        84
         0
```

$\therefore$ HCF of 84, 112 is 28.

37. LCM of 8, 15, 20 by prime factorization method:

$8 = 2^3$; $15 = 3 \times 5$; $20 = 2^2 \times 5$

LCM = $2^3 \times 3 \times 5 = 120$

Essay Type Questions

38. **(a)** (i) $24 = 2^3 \times 3$; $60 = 2^2 \times 3^1 \times 5^1$

HCF = $2^2 \times 3 = 12$

(ii) 48, 64, 80

$48 = 2^4 \times 3$; $64 = 2^6$; $80 = 2^4 \times 5$

HCF = $2^4 = 16$

(b) The HCF of 72, 140, 256:

```
72) 140 (1
     72
    68) 72 (1
        68
         4) 68 (17
            68
             0
```

$\therefore$ The HCF of 72 and 140 is 4.

```
4) 256 (64
   24
    16
    16
     0
```

$\therefore$ The HCF of 72, 140, 256 is 4.

39. LCM of 12, 18:

2	12, 18
3	6, 9
	2, 3

LCM = $2 \times 3 \times 2 \times 3 = 36$

$\therefore$ Both of them strike every 36th letter of the page.

Since both of them strike 17 times, the page should contain at least $36 \times 17 = 612$ letters.

40. Given that HCF = 2 and LCM = 12.

We know that the product of two numbers is equal to the product of their HCF and their LCM.

The product of two numbers = 2(12) = 24.

But 24 can be expressed as 1(24), 2(12), 3(8) or 4(6).

As HCF = 2 and LCM = 12, only (2, 12) and (4, 6) satisfies the given conditions.

The two numbers are 2, 12 (or) 4, 6.

COMPETITION WING

Level 1: Apply Your Concepts

1. The least prime number is 2.
   The multiples of 2 are 2, 4, 6, 8, 10, …
   The number of multiples of any number is **infinite**.

2. As any two primes do not have common factor other than 1, the HCF of any two primes is **1**.

3. $3 \times 3 = 9$, $3 \times 5 = 15$

   3 is the greatest common factor of 9 and 15.

4. $48 = 2 \times 2 \times 2 \times 2 \times 3$

   2 and 3 are the prime factors of 48.

   ∴ The number of prime factors = 2

5. (71, 73) is the greatest pair of twin primes of the two-digit primes.

6. Converting kg into gm:

   3 kg = 3000 gm

   2.6 kg = 2600 gm

   2 kg = 2000 gm

   HCF of 3000, 2600, 2000 is

   $3000 = 3 \times 2^3 \times 5^3$

   $2600 = 2^3 \times 5^2 \times 13$

   $2000 = 2^4 \times 5^3$

   HCF $= 2^3 \times 5^2 = 8 \times 25 = 200$ gm

   ∴ The minimum number of pieces that Jyothsna get from the three cakes

   $$= \frac{3000}{200} + \frac{2600}{200} + \frac{2000}{200} = 15 + 13 + 10 = 38$$

7. LCM of 2016:

2	2016
2	1008
2	504
2	252
2	126
3	63
3	21
	7

   ∴ The prime factors of 2016 are 2, 3, 7.

   LCM of 2, 3, 7 is = 42

   $42 \times 10 = 420$

   $42 \times 20 = 840$

   $42 \times 23 = 966$

   ∴ The number of chocolates that Bhavagna distributed in the year 2016 is 966.

8. The HCF of 384, 576 and 288 is 96.

   Hence, the greatest possible size of the measuring vessel is 96 litres.

   Hence, the correct option is (a).

9. The HCF of 6048 and 2440 is 8.
   Therefore the number of tiles required

   $$= \frac{(6048 + 2440)}{8}$$

   $$= \frac{8488}{8} = 1061$$

   Hence, the correct option is (b).

10. $143 = 11 \times 13$.

    Both 11 and 13 are factors 143.

    Hence, the correct option is (c).

11. Numbers which are having only 1 as common factor are called coprime.

    21, and 23 are coprime.

    25, and 27 are coprime.

    23, and 29 are coprime.

    Hence, the correct option is (d).

Level 2: Review Your Concepts

12. The LCM of 18, 24, 30 is 360.

    Hence, the minimum amount given to each daughter is ₹360

    Therefore, the number of cakes bought by cinderella

    $$= \frac{360}{24} = 15$$

    Hence, the correct option is (d).

13. The HCF of 72, 144, 234 is 18.

The total number of rows

$$= \frac{(72+144+234)}{18} = \frac{450}{18} = 25$$

Hence, the correct option is (b).

14. Given that the HCF of two numbers is 4.

The numbers can be (4, 4), (4, 8), (4, 12), (4, 16) …

There exists **infinite** pairs of numbers whose HCF is 4.

15. The least three-digit number formed by a single digit 111.

$111 = 1 \times 111$

$= 3 \times 37$

The factors of 111 are 1, 3, 37, and 111.

The LCM (3, 37) = 3 × 37 = **111**.

Level 3: Assess Your Concepts

16. The details are as follows:

Type of Bulbs (in watts)	60 w	90 w	120 w
No. of Bulbs	240	180	120

For the minimum number of cartons, the number of bulbs in each carton must be maximum.

As each carton should consists of same number of bulbs and only one variety, the maximum number of bulbs in each carton is the HCF of 120, 180 and 240.

The required HCF = 60.

The total number of cartons required

$$= \frac{240}{60} + \frac{180}{60} + \frac{120}{60}$$

$= 4 + 3 + 2$

$= 9.$

17. Given numbers: 12, 16, and 24.

The least common multiple (LCM) of 12, 16, and 24 = 48.

The largest four-digit number which is a multiple of 12, 16, and 24 = 48(k), where k is some positive integer.

Also 48(k) is less than or equal to 9999.

The required number = 48(208) = 9984.

18. Given numbers, 1 to 1000.

Ranga selects every 12th number and Pranav selects every 27th number.

The least common number selected = LCM (12 and 27) = 108.

The common numbers are: 108, 108(2) = 216, 108(3) = 324, 108(4) = 432, 108(5) = 540, 108(6) = 648, 108(7) = 756, 108(8) = 864 and 108(9) = 972.

CHAPTER

3

Fractions and Decimals

Remember

Before beginning this chapter, you should be able to:

- Recall representation of fractions
- Perform multiplication and division of numbers

Key Ideas

After completing this chapter, you should be able to:

- Know types of fractions
- Understand comparison of fractions
- Perform operations on fractions
- Describe decimal numbers
- Understand comparison of decimals and work on decimals operations

Scientific Crypt

A Tribute to Leonhard Euler (1707-1783)

Leonhard Euler (1707–1783) was a Swiss mathematician, physicist, and polymath who made pioneering contributions across a wide range of fields. He is renowned for introducing mathematical symbols and notations that are widely used today. His impact extended to mechanics, fluid dynamics, optics, astronomy, and music theory, leaving an indelible mark on multiple disciplines.

Born in 1707, in Basel, Switzerland, Leonhard Euler demonstrated remarkable mathematical talent from a young age. He received early education in mathematics and physics from his father, a pastor and mathematician. He enrolled at the University of Basel at 13, initially studying theology but gravitated toward mathematics under Johann and Daniel Bernoulli. Despite a temporary blindness due to fever, he excelled in mental calculations and earned a master's degree in philosophy in 1723.

Euler's introduced mathematical functions and modern trigonometric notation, formulated Euler's equations of motion, and made strides in understanding light, colour, and celestial mechanics. He popularized the use of π for the circle's ratio, $f(x)$ for functions, Σ for summations, Δ for finite differences, and more. He defined the constant e, known as Euler's number.

Beyond academia, he played a pivotal role in establishing the St. Petersburg Academy of Sciences. With over 800 publications, his impact spanned mathematics, philosophy, and graph theory, where he pioneered concepts like Eulerian paths and circuits, founding modern graph theory.

FUN TIME

CROSSWORD

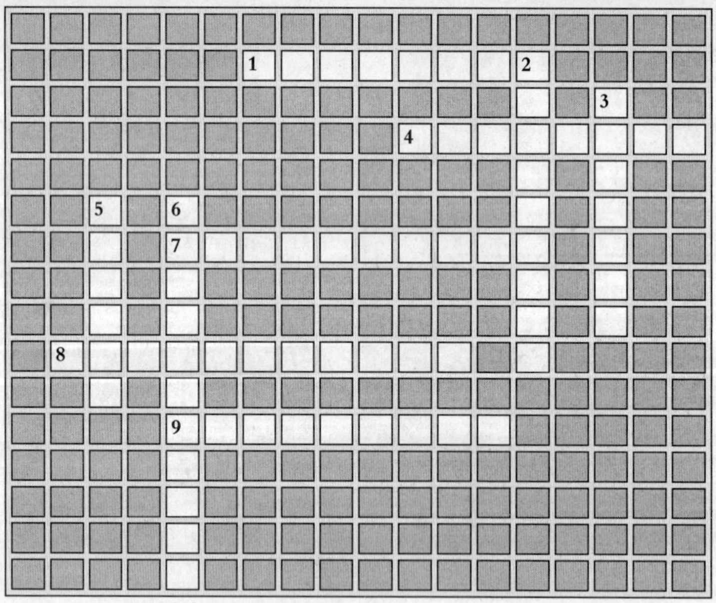

Across

1. ________ fraction is a fraction where the numerator exceeds the denominator.
4. ________ form is fraction that has only 1 as a common factor between its numerator and denominator.
7. ________ fraction is a fraction that represents the same value but with different numbers.
8. ________ decimal is a decimal that has a definitive end.
9. The number above the line in a fraction, representing the parts being considered.

Down

2. ________ decimals is a decimal with one or more digits that recur indefinitely.
3. ________ point separates whole numbers from fractional parts in a decimal.
5. ________ fraction is a fraction with a numerator less than its denominator and greater than zero.
6. The number below the line in a fraction, indicating into how many parts the whole is divided.

INTRODUCTION

In previous classes, we have studied the concept of 'fraction'. In this chapter, we will discuss the types of fractions, ordering of fractions and the basic arithmetic operations in fractions, etc.

Fractions

A number of the form a/b, where a, b are whole numbers and $b \neq 0$ is a **fraction**. The number a is the numerator and b is the denominator. There are three types of fractions.

Info Bytes!

Fractions with same denominators are called **like fractions.**

Example: Rahul have invited four friends to his birthday party. He has cut the cake into six equal pieces. Each person gets one piece out of a total of six pieces. In other words, each person gets one-sixth of the cake. Here, cake is considered as whole and a piece is a part. We know that $\frac{1}{6}$ is a fraction. $\frac{3}{4}, \frac{4}{5}, \frac{4}{9}$ and $\frac{21}{2}$ are some examples of fractions.

Types of Fraction

There are three type of fractions

1. **Proper fraction:** A fraction that represents a part of whole is a **proper fraction**. The numbers $\frac{1}{2}, \frac{3}{4}, \frac{5}{6}, \frac{0}{7}$ are some examples of proper fractions. In a proper fraction, the numerator is less than the denominator. The whole number 0 can be expressed as a proper fraction.
2. **Improper fraction:** A fraction that represents a combination of a whole and a part of the whole is an **improper fraction**. The numbers $\frac{5}{4}, \frac{8}{3}, \frac{20}{9}, \frac{7}{7}$ are some examples of improper fractions. In an improper fraction, the numerator is greater or equal to its denominator. All natural numbers can be expressed as improper fractions.
3. **Mixed fraction:** When an improper fraction is written as an integer followed by a proper fraction, it is a **mixed fraction**.

   Example: The fraction $\frac{5}{4}$ can be written as $1 + \frac{1}{4}$. Here, 1 is a whole and $\frac{1}{4}$ is a part. $\left(1\frac{1}{4}\right)$

EXAMPLE 3.1

(a) Convert $\frac{29}{11}$ into a mixed fraction.

(b) Convert $3\frac{5}{7}$ into a improper fraction.

SOLUTION

(a) Here, 29 is divided by 11, the quotient is 2 and the remainder is 7.

$$\therefore \frac{29}{11} = 2\frac{7}{11}$$

(b) $3\frac{5}{7} = \frac{(3\times7)+5}{7} = \frac{21+5}{7} = \frac{26}{7}$.

Comparison of Fractions

A set of fractions can be compared by using the following steps.

1. First, convert the given fractions into like fractions.
2. Second, the fraction which has the greater numerator will be the greater fraction.

Let us learn this with the help of examples.

Konnect

If there is a set of two unlike fractions with same numerators, then the fraction with the smaller denominator will be the greater fraction.

Example: Between $\frac{4}{9}$ and $\frac{4}{6}$, $\frac{4}{6}$ will be greater.

EXAMPLE 3.2 Compare $\frac{5}{7}$ and $\frac{11}{49}$ into a improper fraction.

SOLUTION

$\frac{5}{7}$ can be written as $\frac{5\times7}{7\times7}=\frac{35}{49}$. Now, $\frac{35}{49}>\frac{11}{49}\Rightarrow\frac{5}{7}>\frac{11}{49}$

Addition of Fractions

Let us understand the addition of fractions with the help of following points.

1. **A fraction and an integer:** The integer is expressed as a fraction with the same denominator as the fraction and the numerators are added.

   Example: $\frac{3}{8}+2=\frac{3}{8}+\frac{16}{8}=\frac{19}{8}$

2. **Two or more fractions:** All the fractions in the expression are expressed with a common denominator and the numerators are added.

   Example: $\frac{2}{3}+\frac{3}{5}=\frac{2(5)}{3(5)}+\frac{3(3)}{5(3)}=\frac{10}{15}+\frac{9}{15}=\frac{19}{15}$

Multiplication of Fractions

We shall now learn how to multiply fractions.

1. **A fraction and an integer:** First let us consider the multiplication of a proper fraction with a whole number.

   Example: $2\left(\frac{1}{2}\right)=\frac{2(1)}{2}=1$

2. **Multiplication of a mixed fraction by a whole number:**

   Example: $2\left(5\frac{1}{3}\right)=2\left(\frac{16}{3}\right)=\frac{32}{3}$

Info Bytes!

Product of a fraction and its reciprocal is 1.

3. **Multiplication of a fraction by a fraction:**

   $$\text{The product of two fractions} = \frac{\text{The product of their numerators}}{\text{The product of their denominators}}$$

   Example: $\frac{3}{5}\left(\frac{3}{4}\right)=\frac{9}{20}$

Division of Fractions

We shall now learn how to divide fractions with the help of following points.

1. **Whole number by a fraction:** We find that the division sign is replaced by a multiplication sign and the fraction a/b is replaced by the fraction b/a.

   Example: $5 \div \frac{1}{2} = 5\left(\frac{2}{1}\right) = 10.$

2. **Division of a fraction by a whole number:** We multiply the fraction by the multiplicative inverse of the whole number.

   Example: $\frac{1}{4} \div 3$ can be written as $\frac{1}{4} \div \frac{3}{1} = \frac{1}{4}\left(\frac{1}{3}\right) = \frac{1}{12}.$

3. **Division of a fraction by another fraction:** We multiply the first fraction by the multiplicative inverse of the second.

   Example: $\frac{3}{2} \div \frac{6}{8} = \frac{3}{2} \times \frac{8}{6} = 2.$

Konnect

The multiplicative inverse of $\frac{1}{5}$ is 5 and that of $\frac{1}{4}$ is 4. The multiplicative inverse of a number is also known as **its reciprocal**. The product of a number and its reciprocal is one. When the product of two non-zero numbers is one, each of them is the reciprocal of the other.

EXAMPLE 3.3

Simplify: $\frac{7}{12} + \frac{4}{9} - \frac{5}{18}$

SOLUTION

$$\frac{7}{12} + \frac{4}{9} - \frac{5}{18} = \frac{(7\times3)+(4\times4)-(5\times2)}{36} = \frac{(21+16-10)}{36} = \frac{27}{36} = \frac{3}{4}$$

EXAMPLE 3.4

Simplify: $\frac{9}{25} - \frac{2}{5} + \frac{8}{15} - \frac{7}{20}$

SOLUTION

$$\frac{9}{25} - \frac{2}{5} + \frac{8}{15} - \frac{7}{20}$$

$$= \frac{(9\times12)-(2\times60)+(8\times20)-(7\times15)}{300}$$

$$= \frac{108-120+160-105}{300} = \frac{43}{300}$$

EXAMPLE 3.5

Simplify: $2\frac{1}{9} \times 3\frac{5}{9} \div 5\frac{7}{9}$

SOLUTION

$$2\frac{1}{9} \times 3\frac{5}{9} \div 5\frac{7}{9} = \frac{19}{9} \times \frac{32}{9} \div \frac{42}{9} = \frac{19}{9} \times \frac{32}{9} \times \frac{9}{42} = \frac{19}{9} \times \frac{32}{42} = \frac{19}{9} \times \frac{16}{21} = \frac{304}{189} = 1\frac{115}{189}$$

Decimal Numbers

Consider the fractions 1/2, 1/4 and 1/8.

$\frac{1}{2}$ can be written as $\frac{1(5)}{2(5)} = \frac{5}{10}$ and 5/10 can be written as 0.5.

Similarly, $\frac{1}{4} = \frac{1(25)}{4(25)} = \frac{25}{100}$. This can be written as 0.25.

5/100 can be written as 0.05 and 32/10 can be written as 3.2.

A fraction in which the denominator is 10, 100, 1000, ...(i.e., a power of 10) is called a **decimal fraction**. When the denominator is indicated by placing a point in the numerator, the expression is called a **decimal**.

> ***Info Bytes!***
>
> Decimal comes from the Latin word 'decimus,' which means 'tenth.' The decimal system is based on powers of ten. This system was highly influenced by the fact that humans have 10 fingers, which early civilizations used for counting.

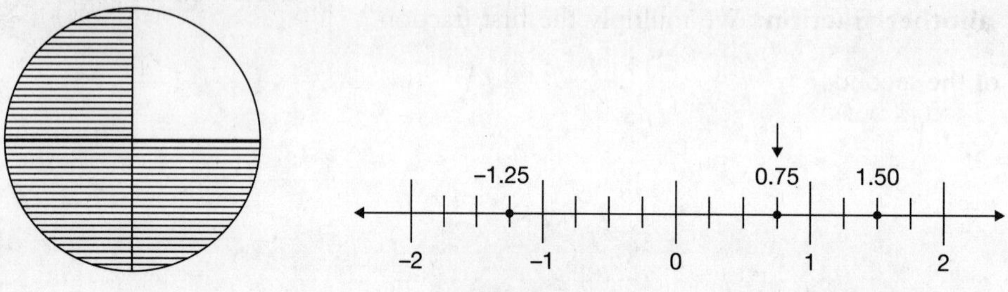

Figure 3.1 Three-fourth of a portion

0.5, 0.25, 0.03 and 3.5 are some examples of decimal numbers. In lower classes, we learnt about place value, units, tens, hundreds, etc. The place value of the first digit after the decimal point is 1/10 (called **tenths**), that of the second digit is 1/100 (called **hundredths**) and so on.

Example: 357.26 can be written in the expanded form as 3(100) + 5(10) + 7(1) + 2(1/10) + 6(1/100).

Comparison of Decimal Numbers

Consider the decimal numbers 32.24 and 32.41. Which of the two is greater?

Initially, we have to compare the digits on the left hand side of the decimal point, starting from the left most digits. In the given two numbers, 32 is common. Now the first digit after the decimal has to be considered. In 32.41, 4 is the first digit to the right of the decimal (the digit in the tenths place) and in 32.24, 2 is the first digit to the right of the decimal (the digit in the tenth place). As in this case, 4 > 2, 32.41 > 32.24.

Table 3.1 Common fractions and their decimal numbers

Fractions	Decimals
1/100	0.01
1/20	0.05
1/10	0.1
1/5	0.2
1/4	0.25
1/3	0.33
1/2	0.5
3/4	0.75

> ***Konnect***
>
> The decimal system is also known as the 'base 10' system because it's based on 10 symbols: 0, 1, 2, 3, 4, 5, 6, 7, 8, and 9.

Addition and Subtraction of Decimals

Decimal numbers are added and subtracted one from the other in the following way.

(i)
$$\begin{array}{r} 23.43 \\ +34.25 \\ \hline 57.68 \\ \hline \end{array}$$

(ii)
$$\begin{array}{r} 24.56 \\ -12.23 \\ \hline 12.33 \\ \hline \end{array}$$

Konnect

When we add two decimal numbers or subtract one decimal number from the other, we have to ensure that the digit in the units place of the second number is written exactly below the digit in the units place of the first number. Same is the case with digits in the 100's place, 1000's place, $\frac{1}{10}$th place, $\frac{1}{100}$th place and so on.

EXAMPLE 3.6 Find the sum of 1.4 and 2.23.

SOLUTION

1.4 + 2.23 = 3.63

EXAMPLE 3.7 Find the difference of 47.16 and 39.17.

SOLUTION

47.16 – 39.17 = 7.99

Multiplication and Division of Decimal Numbers

We shall begin with simpler examples.

(i) $(0.3)\ (0.7) = \left(\frac{3}{10}\right)\left(\frac{7}{10}\right) = \frac{21}{100} = 0.21$

(ii) Divide 12.4 by 0.4. 12.4 ÷ 0.4 can be written as $\left(\frac{124}{10}\right) \div \left(\frac{4}{10}\right)$

$$= \frac{124}{10} \times \frac{10}{4} = \frac{124}{4} = 31$$

EXAMPLE 3.8 Convert $\frac{24}{25}$ into a decimal fraction.

SOLUTION

$$\frac{24}{25} \times \frac{4}{4} = \frac{96}{100} = 0.96$$

EXAMPLE 3.9 Simplify: 27.47 × 10

SOLUTION

27.47 × 10 = 274.7

EXAMPLE 3.10 Divide 8.4 by 6.

SOLUTION

$$8.4 \div 6 = (84/10) \div 6 = (84/10)(1/6) = \frac{84}{6}\left(\frac{1}{10}\right) = \frac{14}{10} = 1.4$$

POINTS TO REMEMBER

- ✔ A fraction that represents a part of whole is a proper fraction.
- ✔ A fraction that represents a combination of a whole and a part of the whole is an improper fraction.
- ✔ When an improper fraction is written as an integer followed by a proper fraction, it is a mixed fraction.
- ✔ When the denominator is indicated by placing a point in the numerator, the expression is called a decimal.

DW

PRACTICE QUESTIONS CLASSROOM WING

Very Short Answer Type Questions

Direction for questions from 1 to 5: **Select the correct alternative from given choices.**

1. The improper fraction which equivalents $2\frac{3}{7}$ is ______.

(a) $\frac{15}{7}$ (b) $\frac{17}{7}$

(c) $\frac{34}{14}$ (d) Both (b) and (c)

2. $\left(\frac{1}{4}+\frac{1}{5}\right)$ of 20 is ____.

(a) $\frac{40}{9}$ (b) $\frac{20}{9}$ (c) 9 (d) 2

3. $13\frac{4}{5}$ = ______________.

(a) 65/5 (b) 72/5

(c) 69/5 (d) 17/5

4. What part of the given figure is shaded?

(a) 2/3 (b) 1/3 (c) 1/2 (d) 2/5

5. Which of the following is the largest?

(a) 2/3 (b) 4/7 (c) 3/5 (d) 7/15

Direction for question 6: **Match Column A with Column B.**

6.

	Column A (Fraction of shaded part)		Column B
(a)	$\frac{1}{2}$	(p)	
(b)	$\frac{1}{3}$	(q)	
(c)	$\frac{1}{4}$	(r)	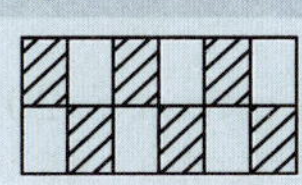
(d)	$\frac{3}{4}$	(s)	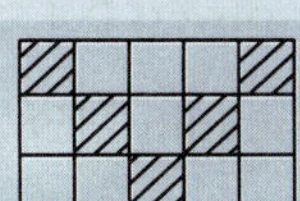

Direction for questions from 7 to 11: **Fill in the blanks.**

7. If $\frac{2p}{5}=\frac{4}{10}$, then the value of p is _____.

8. The value of $\frac{3}{4}-\frac{7}{2}=$ _____.

9. $\frac{2}{5}$ of $3\frac{4}{7}$ = _________.

10. $\left[\frac{2}{7}+\frac{4}{7}\right]\times\left[4\frac{2}{3}\right]=$ _________.

11. $\left(2\frac{2}{5}\right)\left(1\frac{2}{3}\right)=$ _________.

Direction for questions from 12 to 15: **Select the correct alternative from given choices.**

12. Sujith travels one-third of a distance. If the distance is 12 km, then find the remaining distance that he would have travelled (in km).

(a) 2 (b) 4

(c) 6 (d) 8

13. The total strength of a class is 36 students. If three-fourth of the students is taking an examination from the class, then how many students are not taking the examination?

(a) 9 (b) 12

(c) 24 (d) 27

14. $\frac{1}{2}+\frac{3}{4}+\frac{1}{8}=$ ______________.

(a) 1/2 (b) 5/4

(c) 9/8 (d) 11/8

15. $\frac{2}{3}\div\frac{4}{3}\times\frac{2}{3}+1=$ ______________.

(a) 7/3 (b) 4/3

(c) 3/10 (d) 6/17

Direction for questions from 16 to 20: **Fill in the blanks.**

16. 23.143 + 17.159 = ______.

17. 36.121 – 33.429 = ______.

18. 0.00125 × 200 = ______.

19. 50.2 ÷ 1.255 = ______.

20. 2.3 + 4.4 + 6.9 = ______.

Direction for questions from 21 to 25: **Select the correct alternative from the given choices.**

21. $\frac{120}{25}$ = ______.

(a) 0.048 (b) 4.8

(c) 48 (d) 4.08

22. 1.36 = ______.

(a) $\frac{24}{25}$ (b) $\frac{14}{25}$

(c) $\frac{32}{25}$ (d) $\frac{34}{25}$

23. 18 – 13.169 = ______.

(a) 3.831 (b) 4.831

(c) 5.831 (d) 2.831

24. 37.23 ÷ 10 = ______.

(a) 372.3 (b) 3.723

(c) 37.23 (d) 0.3723

25. 1.608 ÷ 1.34 = ______.

(a) 3.2 (b) 2.2

(c) 1.2 (d) 4.2

Direction for question 26: **Match Column A with Column B.**

26.

	Column A		Column B
(a)	0.456 × 0.3	(p)	0.1468
(b)	0.734 × 0.2	(q)	0.1368
(c)	0.0739 × 2	(r)	0.1478
(d)	0.0689 × 2	(s)	0.1378

Short Answer Type Questions

27. List out the proper and improper fractions from the following.

(a) 7/2 (b) 3/4 (c) 5/2

(d) 11/13 (e) 7/15 (f) 17/13

(g) 72/21 (h) 81/87 (i) 16/15

(j) 20/29

28. Compare:

(i) 27/40 and 31/50

(ii) 4/5 and 7/8

29. Arrange the following fractions in ascending order and descending order.

(i) $\frac{7}{9}, \frac{13}{15}, \frac{23}{27}, \frac{20}{21}$

(ii) $\frac{4}{5}, \frac{11}{20}, \frac{11}{15}, \frac{22}{25}$

30. Simplify: 123.01 + 23.2 – 12.24 – 9.256.

31. Simplify: $1\frac{7}{15}+2\frac{7}{15}-\frac{7}{2}+3\frac{7}{15}+4\frac{7}{15}+5\frac{7}{15}$.

32. Reduce 1562/1846 and 924/1188 in lowest terms.

33. What should be added to the sum of 1/8 and 1/7 so that the sum is 5/14?

34. What should be subtracted from the sum of $\frac{1}{12}$ and $\frac{1}{8}$ so that the difference is $\frac{1}{18}$?

35. Simplify: $\frac{1}{2} \div \frac{4}{3} \times \frac{2}{3} \div \frac{1}{2} + \frac{3}{4} - \frac{5}{2} + \frac{2}{3} \times \frac{9}{4} \div \frac{2}{3}$

36. Simplify:

$$3\frac{1}{2}-\left[9\div\left\{\frac{1}{6}\left[\frac{1}{2}+\frac{1}{2}+\frac{1}{2}\right]+\frac{1}{2}\right\}\times 3\right]\div 2\frac{1}{3}\times\frac{3}{4}$$

37. Simplify: $1\frac{2}{15}+2\frac{2}{15}+3\frac{2}{15}+\ldots+100\frac{2}{15}$

38. Simplify: $1\frac{1}{11}+2\frac{2}{11}+3\frac{3}{11}+\frac{4}{11}+\frac{5}{11}+\frac{6}{11}$

39. Convert 7/20 into a decimal fraction.

40. Convert 0.425 into a fraction.

41. Simplify: 128.364 + 10.08 – 132.16 + 9.8

42. Simplify:

$0.7 + 0.7 \times 0.7 \div 0.7 - 0.7 + 0.7 \div 0.7 \times 0.7$

43. What should be added to 1.834 so that the sum is 5?

44. What should be subtracted from the sum of 2.58 and 1.471 so that the difference 2?

45. By how much is the sum of 44.44 and 32.03 greater than their difference?

46. How many glasses of water is required to fill one litre water bottle, if one glass of water is 25 mL?

47. Arrange the following fractions in ascending order.

2/5, 3/5, 4/5, 5/5, 6/5

48. Arrange the following in descending order.

5/2, 5/3, 5/4, 5/5, 5/6

49. By how much is the difference of 18.89 and 11.21 less than that of their sum?

50. What should be added to 6.77 to get 7?

51. What should be added to the difference of 6.88 and 4.25 to get 5?

Essay Type Questions

52. Arrange the following fractions in ascending order and descending order?

(i) $\frac{15}{32}, \frac{13}{16}, \frac{9}{4}, \frac{11}{8}$

(ii) $\frac{4}{3}, \frac{3}{5}, \frac{3}{2}, \frac{5}{6}$

53. Joshna and Vijay have some chocolates. The number of chocolates with Joshna is two-third of the number of chocolates with Vijay. If Vijay gives five chocolates to Joshna, then both will have equal number of chocolates.

How many chocolates does Joshna have?

PRACTICE QUESTIONS COMPETITION WING

Level 1: Apply Your Concepts

Direction for questions from 1 to 5: **Fill in the blanks.**

1. $\frac{7}{16} \div \frac{7}{8} =$ ______.
2. $\frac{7}{7}$ is a/ an ______(proper/improper) fraction.
3. 6/7 is a/an ______ (proper/improper) fraction.
4. Convert 9/2 as a mixed fraction, the answer is ______.
5. The fraction 744/496 in its lowest terms is ______.
6. Anil travels from place *A* to place *B* and Akhil travels from place *B* to place *A*. Anil travels one-third of the distance and Akhil travels one-fourth of the distance. The distance travelled by Anil is one kilometre more than the distance travelled by Akhil. What is the distance between place *A* and place *B*? (In km)
   (a) 9 (b) 10
   (c) 12 (d) 18

Direction for question 7: **Match Column A with Column B.**

7.

	Column A		Column B
(a)	$\left(\frac{1}{2}+\frac{1}{3}\right)$ of 6	(p)	$\left(\frac{3}{4}-\frac{1}{3}\right)$ of 12
(b)	$\left(\frac{1}{3}+\frac{1}{6}\right)$ of 18	(q)	$\left(\frac{5}{2}-\frac{2}{3}\right)$ of 6
(c)	$\left(\frac{1}{4}+\frac{1}{3}\right)$ of 12	(r)	$\left(\frac{5}{4}-\frac{1}{2}\right)$ of 12
(d)	$\left(\frac{1}{5}+\frac{1}{6}\right)$ of 30	(s)	$\left(\frac{3}{4}-\frac{1}{6}\right)$ of 12

8. There are 125 balls in a basket. Out of which, 15 are white, 25 are brown, 35 are green, and the remaining are pink in colour. Find the share of the balls for each colour in the basket.
9. A rope of length $21\frac{1}{2}$ m is cut into equal pieces of $2\frac{3}{20}$ m each. Find the number of pieces.
10. Mr Perfect earns ₹54000 per month. He spends $\frac{2}{15}$ of his earnings on house rent, $\frac{4}{9}$ of his earnings on other household items and saves the remaining. What fraction of amount is the savings in his earnings?
    (a) $\frac{19}{45}$ (b) $\frac{17}{45}$
    (c) $\frac{13}{24}$ (d) $\frac{11}{25}$
11. Which of the following is the largest?
    (a) $\frac{4}{5}$ (b) $\frac{1}{2}$
    (c) $\frac{5}{6}$ (d) $\frac{7}{20}$
12. $\frac{221}{34}$ is equivalent to ______.
    (a) $\frac{13}{4}$ (b) $\frac{17}{2}$
    (c) $\frac{26}{4}$ (d) None of these

Level 2: Review Your Concepts

13. Three friends *A*, *B* and *C* have some money. If *A* has 3/10 of the total money, *B* has 7/15 of the total money and *C* has 7/30 of the total money. Who has the biggest share of the money? If the total money is ₹1500, then how much money does *A* have?
14. Priyanka spends 2/15 of her income on clothes, 1/9 of her income on entertainment, 4/15 of her income on rent, 1/3 of the income on food and she saves the remaining amount of ₹10,500. What is the income of Priyanka?

15. A 182 m long string is cut into pieces, each of length $6\frac{1}{15}$ m. How many pieces are obtained?

(a) 40 (b) 45

(c) 30 (d) 35

16. What should be subtracted from the sum of −3.482 and −4.368 so that the difference is 7.234?

(a) −15.084 (b) −15.840

(c) −14.085 (d) 15.084

Level 3: Assess Your Concepts

17. What is the number exactly halfway between $\frac{1}{10}$ and $\frac{1}{8}$?

(a) 9/80 (b) 9/40

(c) 1/90 (d) 2/45

18. Express $2.\overline{3}$ as a fraction.

19. Three–fifth of my pocket money is spent on buying a T-Shirt, one fifth of my pocket money spent on buying movie tickets. If ₹220 is still left with me.

Find the pocket money I had initially.

AT

ANSWER KEYS

Crossword

Across

1. Improper 4. Simplest 7. Equivalent 8. Terminating 9. Numerator

Down

2. Repeating 3. Decimal 5. Proper 6. Denominator

Classroom Wing

Very Short Answer Type Questions

1. (d) 2. (c) 3. (c) 4. (b) 5. (a)

6. (a) → (r); (b) → (s); (c) → (p); (d) → (q) 7. 1 8. $-\frac{11}{4}$ 9. $1\frac{3}{7}$ 10. 4 11. 4 12. (d)

13. (a) 14. (d) 15. (b) 16. 40.302 17. 2.692 18. 0.25 19. 40 20. 13.6

21. (b) 22. (d) 23. (b) 24. (b) 25. (c) 26. (a) → (q); (b) → (p); (c) → (r); (d) → (s)

Short Answer Type Questions

28. (i) $\frac{27}{40} > \frac{31}{50}$; (ii) $\frac{4}{5} < \frac{7}{8}$

29. (i) $\frac{7}{9} < \frac{23}{27} < \frac{13}{15} < \frac{20}{21}$; $\frac{20}{21} > \frac{13}{15} > \frac{23}{27} > \frac{7}{9}$; (ii) $\frac{11}{20} < \frac{11}{15} < \frac{4}{5} < \frac{22}{25}$; $\frac{22}{25} > \frac{4}{5} > \frac{11}{15} > \frac{11}{20}$

30. 124.714 31. $\frac{83}{6}$ 32. (i) $\frac{11}{13}$; (ii) $\frac{7}{9}$ 33. $\frac{5}{56}$

34. $\frac{11}{72}$ 35. 1 36. 31/14 37. $5063\frac{1}{3}$ 38. $7\frac{10}{11}$ 39. 0.35

40. $\frac{17}{40}$ 41. 16.084 42. 1.4 43. 3.166 44. 2.051 45. 64.06

46. 40 47. 2/5 < 3/5 < 4/5 < 5/5 < 6/5 48. 5/6 < 5/5 < 5/4 < 5/3 < 5/2

49. 22.42 50. 0.23 51. 2.37 52. (i) $\frac{1}{6}, \frac{2}{3}, \frac{7}{10}, \frac{4}{5}$ (ii) $\frac{7}{6}, \frac{11}{12}, \frac{3}{4}, \frac{5}{18}$

Competition Wing

Level 1: Apply Your Concepts

1. $\frac{1}{2}$ 2. Improper 3. Proper 4. $4\frac{1}{2}$ 5. $\frac{3}{2}$ 6. (c)

7. (a) → (p); (b) → (r); (c) → (s); (d) → (q) 8. $\frac{3}{25}, \frac{1}{5}, \frac{7}{25}, \frac{2}{5}$ 9. 10 10. (a) 11. (c) 12. (c)

Level 2: Review Your Concepts

13. *B*; ₹450 14. ₹67, 500 15. (c) 16. (b)

Level 3: Assess Your Concepts

17. (a) 18. $\frac{7}{3}$ 19. ₹1100

Hints and Explanations

CLASSROOM WING

Very Short Answer Type Questions

1. $2\frac{3}{7} = \frac{2\times 7+3}{7} = \frac{17}{7}$

$\frac{17}{7} = \frac{17}{7}\times\frac{2}{2} = \frac{34}{14}$

The required answers are $\frac{17}{7}$ and $\frac{34}{14}$.

Hence, the correct option is (d).

2. $\left(\frac{1}{4}+\frac{1}{5}\right)$ of $20 = \frac{20}{4}+\frac{20}{5}$

$= 5+4 = 9.$

Hence, the correct option is (c).

3. $13\frac{4}{5} = \frac{(13\times 5)+4}{5} = \frac{65+4}{5} = \frac{69}{5}$

Hence, the correct option is (c).

4. $\frac{2}{6} = \frac{1}{3}$

Hence, the correct option is (b).

5. Given that: $\frac{2}{3}, \frac{4}{7}, \frac{3}{5}, \frac{7}{15}$

LCM of 3, 7, 5 is 105.

$\frac{2}{3}\times\frac{35}{35} = \frac{70}{105}$; $\frac{4}{7}\times\frac{15}{15} = \frac{60}{105}$

$\frac{3}{5}\times\frac{21}{21} = \frac{63}{105}$; $\frac{7}{15}\times\frac{7}{7} = \frac{49}{105}$

$\therefore \frac{70}{105}$, i.e., $\frac{2}{3}$ is the largest fraction.

Hence, the correct option is (a).

6. (a) $\frac{1}{2} = \frac{6}{12} \rightarrow$ (r)

(b) $\frac{1}{3} = \frac{5}{15} \rightarrow$ (s)

(c) $\frac{1}{4} \rightarrow$ (p)

(d) $\frac{3}{4} \rightarrow$ (q)

Therefore, the correct match is:

$\therefore$ (a) $\rightarrow$ (r); (b) $\rightarrow$ (s); (c) $\rightarrow$ (p); (d) $\rightarrow$ (q)

7. Given that $\frac{2p}{5} = \frac{4}{10}$

$\Rightarrow 20p = 20$

$\Rightarrow p = \frac{20}{20} = 1.$

8. $\frac{3}{4}-\frac{7}{2} = \frac{3}{4}\times\frac{1}{1}-\frac{7}{2}\times\frac{2}{2}$ $[\because$ LCM of 4 and 2 is 4$]$

$= \frac{3}{4}-\frac{14}{4} = -\frac{11}{4}.$

9. $\frac{2}{5}$ of $3\frac{4}{7} = \frac{2}{5}\times\frac{25}{7} = \frac{10}{7} = 1\frac{3}{7}$

10. $\left[\frac{2}{7}+\frac{4}{7}\right]\times\left[4\frac{2}{3}\right] = \frac{6}{7}\times\left[\frac{14}{3}\right] = 4$

11. $\left(2\frac{2}{5}\right)\left(1\frac{2}{3}\right) = \left(\frac{12}{5}\right)\left(\frac{5}{3}\right) = 4$

12. Required distance $= \left(\frac{2}{3}\right)$ of 12 km $= \frac{2}{3}\times 12 = 8$ km.

Hence, the correct option is (d).

13. Required number of students $= \left(\frac{1}{4}\right)(36) = 9$

Hence, the correct option is (a).

14. $\frac{1}{2}+\frac{3}{4}+\frac{1}{8} = \frac{(1\times 4)+(3\times 2)+(1\times 1)}{8}$

$= \frac{4+6+1}{8} = \frac{11}{8}$

Hence, the correct option is (d).

15. $\frac{2}{3}\div\frac{4}{3}\times\frac{2}{3}+1 = \frac{\left(\frac{2}{3}\right)}{\left(\frac{4}{3}\right)}\times\frac{2}{3}+1$ (BODMAS)

$= \frac{1}{2}\times\frac{2}{3}+1 = \frac{1}{3}+1 = \frac{4}{3}$

Hence, the correct option is (b).

16. 23.143 + 17.159 = 40.302

17. 36.121 – 33.429 = 2.692

18. 0.00125 × 200 = 0.25

19. $\dfrac{50.2}{1.255} = \dfrac{50200}{1255} = 40$

20. 2.3 + 4.4 + 6.9 = 13.6

21. $\dfrac{120}{25} = \dfrac{120}{25} \times \dfrac{4}{4} = \dfrac{480}{100} = 4.8$

Hence, the correct option is (b).

22. $1.36 = \dfrac{136}{100} = \dfrac{34}{25}$

Hence, the correct option is (d).

23. 18 – 13.169 = 4.831

Hence, the correct option is (b).

24. $37.23 \div 10 = \dfrac{37.23}{10} = 3.723$

Hence, the correct option is (b).

25. $\dfrac{1.608}{1.34} = 1.2$

Hence, the correct option is (c).

26. (a) 0.456 × 0.3 = 0.1368 → (q)

(b) 0.734 × 0.2 = 0.1468 → (p)

(c) 0.0739 × 2 = 0.1478 → (r)

(d) 0.0689 × 2 = 0.1378 → (s)

Therefore, the correct match is:

(a) → (q); (b) → (p); (c) → (r); (d) → (s)

Short Answer Type Questions

27. Proper fractions

$\dfrac{3}{4}, \dfrac{11}{13}, \dfrac{7}{15}, \dfrac{81}{87}, \dfrac{20}{29}$

Improper fractions

$\dfrac{7}{2}, \dfrac{5}{2}, \dfrac{17}{13}, \dfrac{72}{21}, \dfrac{16}{15}$

28. (i) Given $\dfrac{27}{40}$ and $\dfrac{31}{50}$.

LCM of 40 and 50 is 200.

$\dfrac{27}{40} = \dfrac{27}{40} \times \dfrac{5}{5} = \dfrac{135}{200}; \dfrac{31}{50} = \dfrac{31}{50} \times \dfrac{4}{4} = \dfrac{124}{200}$

$\dfrac{135}{200} > \dfrac{124}{200}; \Rightarrow \dfrac{27}{40} > \dfrac{31}{50}$

(ii) Given $\dfrac{4}{5}$ and $\dfrac{7}{8}$.

LCM of 5, and 8 are 40.

$\dfrac{4}{5} = \dfrac{4}{5} \times \dfrac{8}{8} = \dfrac{32}{40}; \dfrac{7}{8} = \dfrac{7}{8} \times \dfrac{5}{5} = \dfrac{35}{40}$

$\dfrac{32}{40} < \dfrac{35}{40} \Rightarrow \dfrac{4}{5} < \dfrac{7}{8}$

29. (i) Given, $\dfrac{7}{9}, \dfrac{13}{15}, \dfrac{23}{27}, \dfrac{20}{21}$.

LCM of 9, 15, 27 and 21 is 945.

$\dfrac{7}{9} = \dfrac{7}{9} \times \dfrac{105}{105} = \dfrac{735}{945}; \dfrac{13}{15} = \dfrac{13}{15} \times \dfrac{63}{63} = \dfrac{819}{945}$

$\dfrac{23}{27} = \dfrac{23}{27} \times \dfrac{35}{35} = \dfrac{805}{945}; \dfrac{20}{21} = \dfrac{20}{21} \times \dfrac{45}{45} = \dfrac{900}{945}$

$\dfrac{735}{945} < \dfrac{805}{945} < \dfrac{819}{945} < \dfrac{900}{945} \Rightarrow \dfrac{7}{9} < \dfrac{23}{27} < \dfrac{13}{15} < \dfrac{20}{21}$

Descending Order: $\dfrac{20}{21} > \dfrac{13}{15} > \dfrac{23}{27} > \dfrac{7}{9}$

(ii) $\dfrac{4}{5}, \dfrac{11}{20}, \dfrac{11}{15}, \dfrac{22}{25}$.

LCM of 5, 20, 15 and 25 is 300.

$\dfrac{4}{5} = \dfrac{4}{5} \times \dfrac{60}{60} = \dfrac{240}{300}; \dfrac{11}{20} = \dfrac{11}{20} \times \dfrac{15}{15} = \dfrac{165}{300}$

$\dfrac{11}{15} = \dfrac{11}{15} \times \dfrac{20}{20} = \dfrac{220}{300}; \dfrac{22}{25} = \dfrac{22}{25} \times \dfrac{12}{12} = \dfrac{264}{300}$

$\dfrac{165}{300} < \dfrac{220}{300} < \dfrac{240}{300} < \dfrac{264}{300} \Rightarrow \dfrac{11}{20} < \dfrac{11}{15} < \dfrac{4}{5} < \dfrac{22}{25}$

Descending Order: $\dfrac{22}{25} > \dfrac{4}{5} > \dfrac{11}{15} > \dfrac{11}{2}$

30. 123.01 + 23.2 – 12.24 – 9.256

Consider

123.01 + 23.2 = 146.21

146.21 – 12.24 = 133.97

133.97 – 9.256 = **124.714**.

31. $1\dfrac{7}{15} + 2\dfrac{7}{15} - \dfrac{7}{2} + 3\dfrac{7}{15} + 4\dfrac{7}{15} + 5\dfrac{7}{15}$

$= 1\dfrac{7}{15} + 2\dfrac{7}{15} + 3\dfrac{7}{15} + 4\dfrac{7}{15} + 5\dfrac{7}{15} - \dfrac{7}{2}$

$= 1 + \dfrac{7}{15} + 2 + \dfrac{7}{15} + 3 + \dfrac{7}{15} + 4 + \dfrac{7}{15} + 5 + \dfrac{7}{15} - \dfrac{7}{2}$

$= (1+2+3+4+5) + 5 \times \dfrac{7}{15} - \dfrac{7}{2}$

$= 15 + \frac{7}{3} - \frac{7}{2}$

$= 15 + \frac{7}{3} \times \frac{2}{2} - \frac{7}{2} \times \frac{3}{3}$

$= 15 + \frac{14}{6} - \frac{21}{6}$

$= 15 - \frac{7}{6}$

$= \frac{15}{1} \times \frac{6}{6} - \frac{7}{6}$

$= \frac{90}{6} - \frac{7}{6}$

$= \frac{83}{6}.$

32. (i) $\frac{1562}{1846} = \frac{11 \times 142}{13 \times 142} = \frac{11}{13}$

(ii) $\frac{924}{1188} = \frac{7 \times 132}{9 \times 132} = \frac{7}{9}$

33. $\frac{1}{8} + \frac{1}{7} = \frac{7+8}{56} = \frac{15}{56}$

The required fraction $= \frac{5}{14} - \frac{15}{56} = \frac{20-15}{56} = \frac{5}{56}$

$\therefore \frac{5}{56}$ should be added to the sum of $\frac{1}{8}$ and $\frac{1}{7}$ to get $\frac{5}{14}$.

34. $\frac{1}{12} + \frac{1}{8} = \frac{2+3}{24} = \frac{5}{24}$

The required fraction $= \frac{5}{24} - \frac{1}{18}$

$= \frac{3 \times 5 - 4 \times 1}{72} = \frac{15-4}{72} = \frac{11}{72}$

$\therefore \frac{11}{72}$ should be subtracted from the sum of $\frac{1}{12}$ and $\frac{1}{8}$ to get $\frac{1}{18}$.

35. $\frac{1}{2} \div \frac{4}{3} \times \frac{2}{3} \div \frac{1}{2} + \frac{3}{4} - \frac{5}{2} + \frac{2}{3} \times \frac{9}{4} \div \frac{2}{3}$

$= \frac{1}{2} \times \frac{3}{4} \times \frac{2}{3} \times 2 + \frac{3}{4} - \frac{5}{2} + \frac{2}{3} \times \frac{9}{4} \times \frac{3}{2}$

$= \frac{1}{2} + \frac{3}{4} - \frac{5}{2} + \frac{9}{4} = \frac{12}{4} - \frac{4}{2} = 1$

36. $= \frac{7}{2} - \left[9 \div \left\{\frac{1}{6}\left[\frac{3}{2}\right] + \frac{1}{2}\right\} \times 3\right] \div \frac{7}{3} \times \frac{3}{4}$

$= \frac{7}{2} - \left[9 \div \left\{\frac{1}{4} + \frac{1}{2}\right\} \times 3\right] \div \frac{7}{3} \times \frac{3}{4}$

$= \frac{7}{2} - \left[9 \div \frac{3}{4} \times 3\right] \div \frac{7}{3} \times \frac{3}{4}$

$= \frac{7}{2} - \left[9 \div \frac{9}{4}\right] \div \frac{7}{3} \times \frac{3}{4}$

$= \frac{7}{2} - 4 \div \frac{7}{3} \times \frac{3}{4}$

$= \frac{7}{2} - \frac{12}{7} \times \frac{3}{4}$

$= \frac{7}{2} - \frac{9}{7}$

$= \frac{31}{14}$

37. $1\frac{2}{15} + 2\frac{2}{15} + 3\frac{2}{15} + \ldots\ldots + 100\frac{2}{15}$

$= (1+2+3+\ldots.+100) + \left(\frac{2}{15} + \frac{2}{15} + \ldots.. + \frac{2}{15} (100 \text{ terms})\right)$

$= ((100 + 1) + (99 + 2) + \ldots\ldots + (50 + 51)) + \left(\frac{2}{15} \times 100\right)$

$= (101 + 101 + \ldots\ldots + 101)(50 \text{ terms}) + \left(\frac{200}{15}\right)$

$= (50 \times 101) + \left(\frac{40}{3}\right) = 5050 + 13\frac{1}{3} = 5063\frac{1}{3}$

38. $1\frac{1}{11} + 2\frac{2}{11} + 3\frac{3}{11} + \frac{4}{11} + \frac{5}{11} + \frac{6}{11}$

$= (1 + 2 + 3) + \frac{1}{11} + \frac{2}{11} + \frac{3}{11} + \frac{4}{11} + \frac{5}{11} + \frac{6}{11}$

$= 6 + \left(\frac{1}{11} + \frac{2}{11} + \frac{3}{11} + \frac{4}{11} + \frac{5}{11} + \frac{6}{11}\right)$

$= 6 + \left(\frac{1+2+3+4+5+6}{11}\right) = 6 + \frac{21}{11}$

$= 6 + 1\frac{10}{11} = 7\frac{10}{11}$

39. $\frac{7}{20} = \frac{7}{20} \times \frac{5}{5} = \frac{35}{100} = 0.35$

40. $0.425 = \frac{425}{1000} = \frac{17}{40}$

41. 128.364 + 10.08 – 132.16 + 9.8

$$\begin{array}{r} 128.364 \\ +10.080 \\ +9.800 \\ \hline 148.244 \end{array}$$

Now, $\begin{array}{r} 148.244 \\ -132.160 \\ \hline 16.084 \end{array}$

∴ 128.364 + 10.8 – 132.16 + 9.8 = 16.084

42. 0.7 + 0.7 × 0.7 ÷ 0.7 – 0.7 + 0.7 ÷ 0.7 × 0.7

$= \frac{7}{10} + \frac{7}{10} \times \frac{7}{10} \div \frac{7}{10} - \frac{7}{10} + \frac{7}{10} \div \frac{7}{10} \times \frac{7}{10}$

$= \frac{7}{10} + \frac{7}{10} \times 1 - \frac{7}{10} + 1 \times \frac{7}{10}$

$= \frac{7}{10} + \frac{7}{10} - \frac{7}{10} + \frac{7}{10}$

$= \frac{4}{10} = 1.4$

43. $\begin{array}{r} 5.000 \\ -1.834 \\ \hline 3.166 \end{array}$

3.166 should be added to 1.834 to get 5.

44. Sum:

$\begin{array}{r} 2.580 \\ 1.471 \\ \hline 4.051 \end{array}$

Now, 4.051 – 2.000 = 2.051

2.051 should be subtracted from the sum of 2.58 and 1.471 to get 2.

45. Sum: Difference:

$\begin{array}{r} 44.44 \\ +32.03 \\ \hline 76.47 \end{array} \qquad \begin{array}{r} 44.44 \\ -32.03 \\ \hline 12.41 \end{array}$

∴ Required quantity:

$$\begin{array}{r} 76.47 \\ -12.41 \\ \hline 64.06 \end{array}$$

46. Quantity of water in one glass = 25 mL

Required number of glasses $= \frac{1000}{25} = 40$

47. 2/5 < 3/5 < 4/5 < 5/5 < 6/5

48. 5/6 < 5/5 < 5/4 < 5/3 < 5/2

49. Difference is 7.68. Sum is 30.10

Sum – Difference = 22.42

50. 7.00 – 6.77 = 0.23

51. 6.88 – 4.25 = 2.63

To get 5, we need to add (5 – 2.63) = 2.37

Essay Type Questions

52. (i) $\frac{15}{32}, \frac{13}{16}, \frac{9}{4}, \frac{11}{8}$

⇒ L.C.M of 32, 16, 4, 8 is 32.

$\frac{15}{32} = \frac{15}{32} \times \frac{1}{1} = \frac{15}{32}$

$\frac{13}{16} = \frac{13}{16} \times \frac{2}{2} = \frac{26}{32}$

$\frac{9}{4} = \frac{9}{4} \times \frac{8}{8} = \frac{72}{32}$

$\frac{11}{8} = \frac{11}{8} \times \frac{4}{4} = \frac{44}{32}$

A.O: $\frac{15}{32}, \frac{26}{32}, \frac{44}{32}$ and $\frac{72}{32}$

⇒ $\frac{15}{32}, \frac{13}{16}, \frac{11}{8}$ and $\frac{9}{4}$.

D.O: $\frac{9}{4}, \frac{11}{8}, \frac{13}{16}$ and $\frac{15}{32}$

(ii) $\frac{4}{3}, \frac{3}{5}, \frac{3}{2}, \frac{5}{6}$

⇒ L.C.M of 3, 5, 2 and 6 is 30.

$\frac{4}{3} = \frac{4}{3} \times \frac{10}{10} = \frac{40}{30}$

$\frac{3}{5} = \frac{3}{5} \times \frac{6}{6} = \frac{18}{30}$

$\frac{3}{2} = \frac{3}{2} \times \frac{15}{15} = \frac{45}{30}$

$\frac{5}{6} = \frac{5}{6} \times \frac{5}{5} = \frac{25}{30}$

A.O: $\frac{18}{30}, \frac{25}{30}, \frac{40}{30}$ and $\frac{45}{30}$

$\Rightarrow \frac{3}{5}, \frac{5}{6}, \frac{4}{3}$ and $\frac{3}{2}$.

D.O: $\frac{3}{2}, \frac{4}{3}, \frac{5}{6}$ and $\frac{3}{5}$.

53. Let the number of chocolates with Vijay be x.

Number of chocolates with Joshna $= \frac{2}{3}x$

Given, $x - 5 = \frac{2}{3}x + 5 \Rightarrow x = 30$

Number of chocolates with Joshna $= \frac{2}{3} \times 30 = 20$.

COMPETITION WING

Level 1: Apply Your Concepts

1. $\frac{7}{16} \div \frac{7}{8} = \frac{7}{16} \times \frac{8}{7} = \frac{1}{2}$ $\left[\because \frac{A}{B} \div \frac{C}{D} = \frac{A}{B} \times \frac{D}{C}\right]$

2. $\frac{7}{7} = 1$ is an **improper** fraction.

3. A proper fraction (Numerator < Denominator)

4. $\frac{9}{2} = 4\frac{1}{2}$

5. $\frac{744}{496} = \frac{3}{2}$

6. Let the distance between place A and place B be 'd'.

$\frac{d}{3} = \frac{d}{4} + 1$

$\frac{d}{3} = \frac{d+4}{4}$

$4d = 3d + 12 \Rightarrow d = 12$

The distance between the place A and place B is 12 km.

Hence, the correct option is (c).

7. (a) $\left(\frac{1}{2} + \frac{1}{3}\right)$ of $6 = \left(\frac{3+2}{6}\right) \times 6 = \frac{5}{6} \times 6 = 5$

(b) $\left(\frac{1}{3} + \frac{1}{6}\right)\frac{7}{9}$ of $18 = \left(\frac{2+1}{6}\right) \times 18 = 9$

(c) $\left(\frac{1}{4} + \frac{1}{3}\right)$ of $12 = \left(\frac{3+4}{12}\right) \times 12 = 7$

(d) $\left(\frac{1}{5} + \frac{1}{6}\right)$ of $30 = \left(\frac{6+5}{30}\right) \times 30 = 11$

(p) $\left(\frac{3}{4} - \frac{1}{3}\right)$ of $12 = \left(\frac{9-4}{12}\right) \times 12 = 5$

(q) $\left(\frac{5}{2} - \frac{2}{3}\right)$ of $6 = \left(\frac{15-4}{6}\right) \times 6 = 11$

(r) $\left(\frac{5}{4} - \frac{1}{2}\right)$ of $12 = \left(\frac{5-2}{4}\right) \times 12 = 9$

(s) $\left(\frac{3}{4} - \frac{1}{6}\right)$ of $12 = \left(\frac{9-2}{12}\right) \times 12 = 7$

Therefore, the correct match is:

(a) → (p); (b) → (r); (c) → (s); (d) → (q)

8. The number of pink balls = 125 – (15 + 25 + 35)

= 125 – 75 = 50

Share of the different coloured balls in the total number of balls			
White	Brown	Green	Pink
$\frac{15}{125} = \frac{3}{25}$	$\frac{25}{125} = \frac{1}{5}$	$\frac{35}{125} = \frac{7}{25}$	$\frac{50}{125} = \frac{2}{5}$

9. Required number of pieces $= \frac{\left(21\frac{1}{2}\right)}{\left(2\frac{3}{20}\right)}$

$= \frac{\left(\frac{43}{2}\right)}{\left(\frac{43}{20}\right)} = 10$

10. Savings $= 54000 - \left(\frac{2}{15} + \frac{4}{9}\right) = 54000\left(\frac{19}{45}\right)$

Hence, the correct option is (a).

11. $\frac{4}{5}, \frac{1}{2}, \frac{5}{6}, \frac{7}{20}$

LCM of 5, 2, 6, and 20 is 60.

$\frac{4}{5} = \frac{4}{5} \times \frac{12}{12} = \frac{48}{60}$

$\frac{1}{2} = \frac{1}{2} \times \frac{30}{30} = \frac{30}{60}$

$\frac{5}{6} = \frac{5}{6} \times \frac{10}{10} = \frac{50}{60}$

$\frac{7}{20} = \frac{7}{20} \times \frac{3}{3} = \frac{21}{60}$.

∴ The largest fraction is $\frac{50}{60} = \frac{5}{6}$

Hence, the correct option is (c).

12. $\frac{221}{34} = \frac{13 \times 17}{17 \times 2} = \frac{13}{2}$.

$= \frac{13 \times 2}{2 \times 2} = \frac{26}{4}$.

Hence, the correct option is (c).

Level 2: Review Your Concepts

13. Given that:

A has $\frac{3}{10}$, B has $\frac{7}{15}$ and C has $\frac{7}{30}$ of the total money.

LCM of 10, 15, and 30 is 30.

$$\frac{3}{10}=\frac{3}{10}\times\frac{3}{3}=\frac{9}{30};\frac{7}{15}=\frac{7}{15}\times\frac{2}{2}=\frac{14}{30};\frac{7}{30}=\frac{7}{30}$$

$\therefore$ B has the biggest share among the three.

If the total money is ₹1500, then A has $\frac{9}{30}\times$ ₹1500 = ₹450.

Hence, the correct option is (a).

14. Let I be the income of Priyanka.

Expenditure of Priyanka

$$=\left(\frac{2}{15}+\frac{1}{9}+\frac{4}{15}+\frac{1}{3}\right) \text{ of } I$$

$$=\left(\frac{6+5+12+15}{45}\right)I=\left(\frac{38}{45}\right)I$$

$$\text{Savings}=\left(1-\frac{38}{45}\right)I=₹10{,}500$$

$$\left(\frac{45-38}{45}\right)I=10500$$

$$\left(\frac{7}{45}\right)I=10500$$

$$\text{Income}=10500\times\frac{45}{7}$$

The income of Priyanka is ₹67,500.

15. Length of the string = 182 m

Length of each piece of the string $=6\frac{1}{15}=\frac{91}{15}$

Number of pieces obtained $=182\div\frac{91}{15}=182\times\frac{15}{91}=30.$

Hence, the correct option is (c).

16. The sum of -3.482 and -4.368

$=(-3.482)+(-4.368)$

$=-7.85$

As per the data

$=-7.85-7.234$

$=-15.084$

Hence, the correct option is (b).

Level 3: Assess Your Concepts

17. To find the number exactly in the middle (halfway), find the arithmetic mean as shown below:

$$\frac{\left(\frac{1}{10}+\frac{1}{8}\right)}{2}=\frac{\left(\frac{9}{40}\right)}{2}=\frac{9}{80}$$

18. Let $x=2.\overline{3}$

$\Rightarrow x=2.333333\ldots$ (1)

Multiply the equation by 10, we get.

$\Rightarrow 10x=23.3333\ldots.$ (2)

Subtract equation (1) from (2)

$10x-x=23.333\ldots-2.333\ldots..$

$9x=21.0$

$x=\frac{21}{9}=\frac{7}{3}.$

19. Let the total pocket money be ₹x.

The amount of pocket money spent for T – shirt = ₹$\frac{3}{5}x$

The amount of pocket money spent to buy movie ticket = ₹$\frac{1}{5}x$.

The amount of pocket money left with me = ₹220.

As per the data

$$\frac{3}{5}x+\frac{1}{5}x+220=x$$

$$\Rightarrow\frac{4}{5}x+220=x$$

$$\Rightarrow 220=x-\frac{4x}{5}$$

$$\Rightarrow 220=\frac{x}{1}\times\frac{5}{5}-\frac{4x}{5}$$

$$\Rightarrow 220=\frac{5x-4x}{5}$$

$$\Rightarrow 220=\frac{x}{5}$$

$\Rightarrow x=220\times5=1100$

The total pocket money = ₹1100.

CHAPTER

4

Powers and Roots

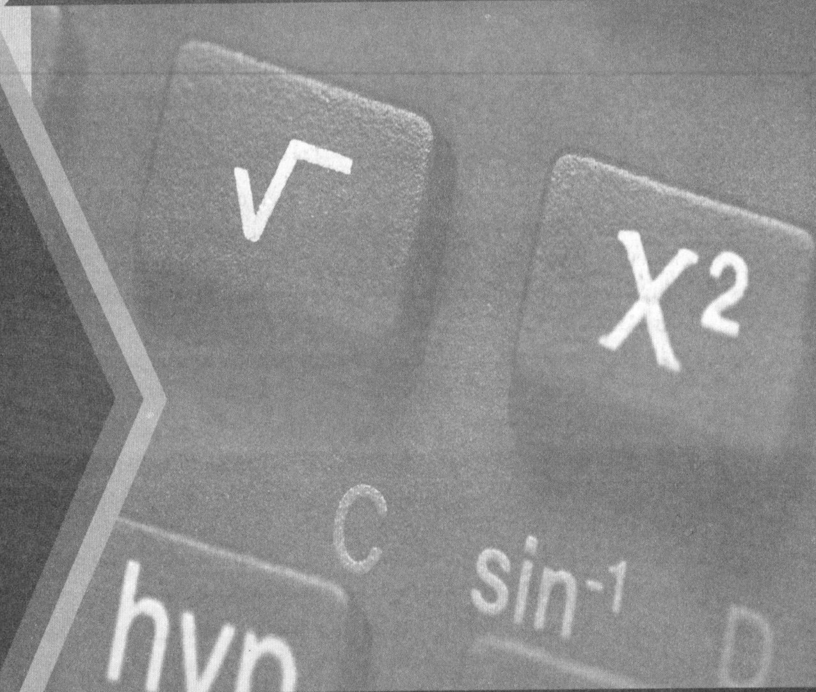

Remember

Before beginning this chapter, you should be able to:

- Perform addition of repeated numbers
- Calculate multiplication of repeated numbers

Key Ideas

After completing this chapter, you should be able to:

- Apply laws of exponents
- Understand squares and square roots applications
- Calculate cubes and cube roots

Scientific Crypt

A Tribute to Alan Mathison Turing (1912-1954)

In human history, certain individuals emerge as brilliant threads that weave innovation and progress into the very fabric of our existence. Alan Mathison Turing was unquestionably one such luminary—a polymath whose contributions have indelibly marked mathematics, computer science, cryptography, and the fight for human rights. Turing is widely acknowledged as one of the founding fathers of computer science and artificial intelligence.

Born in 1912, Turing's life was destined for exceptionalism from the outset. His early passion for mathematics thrived at Sherborne School and King's College, Cambridge, where he laid the foundations for concepts that would revolutionize the world. His ideas about computable numbers and universal machines provided the bedrock for the digital age.

After the war, Turing continued his pioneering work in computer science and artificial intelligence, including the development of the Automatic Computing Engine (ACE), one of the earliest stored-program computers. He introduced the "Turing test," a criterion for assessing a machine's ability to exhibit human-like intelligent behaviour, which remains a fundamental concept in AI.

Alan Turing received several awards and honours for his outstanding contributions, including being named a Fellow of the Royal Society and receiving the OBE (Officer of the Order of the British Empire) and CBE (Commander of the Order of the British Empire) for his code-breaking efforts during World War II. He was further honoured through the Turing Award, referred to as the "Nobel Prize of Computing," which was named in his honour, representing the pinnacle of achievements in computer science.

FUN TIME

CROSSWORD

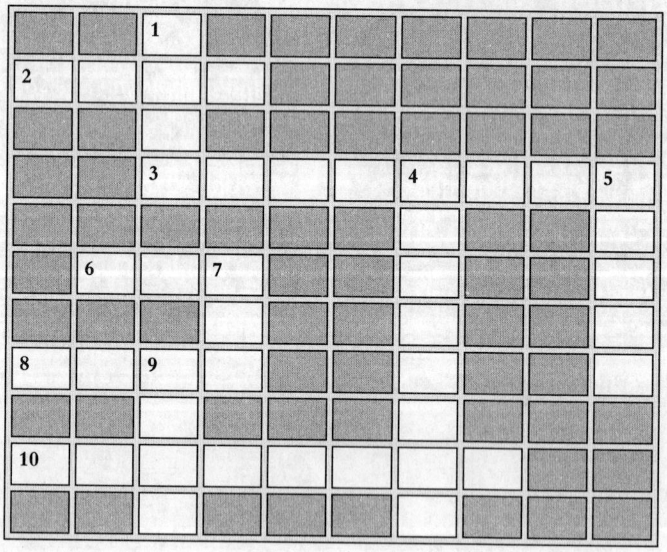

Across

2. The square root of the 'area of a square'
3. In 2^5, the position of 5
6. The least number to be multiplied to 18 so that the product is perfect square
8. The result, when a number is multiplied by the square of the number
10. The result, when a negative number is raised to the power of even integer

Down

1. The cube root of the 'volume of a cube'
4. The result, when a negative number is raised to the power of odd integer
5. The least number should 81 be divided so that the quotient is perfect cube
7. The result, when a rational number is raised to the power of non-negative and non-positive
9. In 2^5, the position of 2

INTRODUCTION

The sum of four instances of a number a is four times of a, **i.e**, $a + a + a + a = 4a$. Similarly, the sum of n instances of a number a is n times a, and is denoted as na, i.e., multiplication is nothing but repeated addition.

The product of n instances of a number a is denoted as a^n. This is an exponential expression. It can be read as a to the power of n or a raised to n. Exponentiation is nothing but repeated multiplication.

So, $a \times a \times a \times ...... \times a$ (n times) $= a^n$. In the exponential expression a^n, a is called the **base** and n is called the **exponent** or **index**.

Example: $5 \times 5 \times 5 \times 5 = 5^4$

Laws of Exponents

We shall look at some of the laws (properties) pertaining to these exponential expressions. The multiplication and the division of exponential expressions can be derived using the laws, which is simple and easier.

Law 1: $2^3 \times 2^2 = (2 \times 2 \times 2)(2 \times 2) = 2 \times 2 \times 2 \times 2 \times 2 = 2^5 = 2^{3+2}$

We can conclude that $a^m \times a^n = a^{m+n}$, where a, m and n are any three numbers.

Law 2: $2^5 \div 2^2 = (2 \times 2 \times 2 \times 2 \times 2) \div (2 \times 2) = 2 \times 2 \times 2 = 2^3 = 2^{5-2}$

We can conclude that $a^m \div a^n = a^{m-n}$, where $a \neq 0$, m and n are any three numbers and $m \geq n$.

Law 3: $a^0 = 1$, where a is any non-zero number.

Info Bytes!

Exponents have been used by mathematicians for centuries. Ancient Egyptians used a form of exponents in their hieroglyphics over 3,000 years ago, though they didn't use them quite the way we do today.

EXAMPLE 4.1 Prime factorize the following:

(I) 560 **(II)** 840 **(III)** 1008 **(IV)** 1176

SOLUTION

(I)	(II)	(III)	(IV)
$560 = 2 \times 280$ $= 2 \times 2 \times 140$ $= 2 \times 2 \times 2 \times 70$ $= 2 \times 2 \times 2 \times 2 \times 35$ $= 2 \times 2 \times 2 \times 2 \times 5 \times 7$	$840 = 2 \times 420$ $= 2 \times 2 \times 210$ $= 2 \times 2 \times 2 \times 105$ $= 2 \times 2 \times 2 \times 3 \times 35$ $= 2 \times 2 \times 2 \times 3 \times 5 \times 7$	$1008 = 2 \times 504$ $= 2 \times 2 \times 252$ $= 2 \times 2 \times 2 \times 126$ $= 2 \times 2 \times 2 \times 2 \times 63$ $= 2 \times 2 \times 2 \times 2 \times 3 \times 21$ $= 2 \times 2 \times 2 \times 2 \times 3 \times 3 \times 7$	$1176 = 2 \times 588$ $= 2 \times 2 \times 294$ $= 2 \times 2 \times 2 \times 147$ $= 2 \times 2 \times 2 \times 3 \times 49$ $= 2 \times 2 \times 2 \times 3 \times 7 \times 7$
$\therefore 560 = 2^4 \times 5^1 \times 7^1$	$\therefore 840 = 2^3 \times 3^1 \times 5^1 \times 7^1$	$\therefore 1008 = 2^4 \times 3^1 \times 3^1 \times 7^1$	$\therefore 1176 = 2^3 \times 3^1 \times 7^1 \times 7^1$

EXAMPLE 4.2 Write the bases and exponents of the following.

(I) 5^8 **(II)** 8^{40} **(III)** -28^{25} **(IV)** $(-25)^{28}$

SOLUTION

(I) Base = 5; Exponent = 8 **(II)** Base = 8; Exponent = 40

(III) Base = –28; Exponent = 25 **(IV)** Base = –25; Exponent = 28

EXAMPLE 4.3 Express the following into the exponential form.

(I) $2 \times 2 \times 3 \times 3 \times 3 \times 5 \times 5 \times 5 \times 7 \times 7$

(II) $5 \times 5 \times 5 \times 11 \times 11 \times 13 \times 13 \times 13 \times 13$

SOLUTION

(I) $2 \times 2 \times 3 \times 3 \times 3 \times 5 \times 5 \times 5 \times 7 \times 7 = 2^2 \times 3^3 \times 5^3 \times 7^2$

(II) $5 \times 5 \times 5 \times 11 \times 11 \times 13 \times 13 \times 13 \times 13 = 5^3 \times 11^2 \times 13^4$

EXAMPLE 4.4 Simplify the following using suitable laws of exponents.

(I) $5^6 \times 5^8$ (II) $11^2 \times 11^3 \times 11^6$ (III) $7^4 \times 7^8 \times 12^2 \times 12^5 \times 12^8$

SOLUTION

We have $a^m \times a^n = a^{m+n}$

(I) $5^6 \times 5^8 = 5^{(6+8)} = 5^{14}$

(II) $11^2 \times 11^3 \times 11^6 = 11^{(2+3+6)} = 11^{11}$

(III) $7^4 \times 7^8 \times 12^2 \times 12^5 \times 12^8 = 7^{(4+8)} \times 12^{(2+5+8)} = 7^{12} \times 12^{15}$

EXAMPLE 4.5 Simplify the following using suitable laws of exponents.

(I) $3^4 \div 3^2$ (II) $[5^7 \times 5^3] \div 5^6$

SOLUTION

We have $a^m \div a^n = a^{m-n}$

(I) $3^4 \div 3^2 = 3^{4-2} = 3^2$ (II) $[5^7 \times 5^3] \div 5^6 = [5^{7+3}] \div 5^6 = 5^{10} \div 5^6 = 5^{10-6} = 5^4$

Squares and Square Roots

If a number is multiplied by itself, then the product obtained is said to be the **square** of that number. A number which is the square of a natural number is called a **perfect square**.

Examples: (i) $1 \times 1 = 1$ ($= 1^2$), 1 is the square of 1.

(ii) $2 \times 2 = 4$ ($= 2^2$), 4 is the square of 2.

(iii) $3 \times 3 = 9$ ($= 3^2$), 9 is square of 3.

∴ 1, 4, 9, 16, 25, ... are the squares of 1, 2, 3, 4, 5, ... respectively.

Table 4.1 List of squares from 1 to 12

1^2	1×1	1
2^2	2×2	4
3^2	3×3	9
4^2	4×4	16
5^2	5×5	25
6^2	6×6	36
7^2	7×7	49
8^2	8×8	64
9^2	9×9	81
10^2	10×10	100
11^2	11×11	121
12^2	12×12	144

Info Bytes!

In art, squares and the idea of 'squaring' are everywhere. The ancient Greeks believed that squares represented order and perfection. Even in modern designs, we often see squared patterns and layouts.

Now, $a(a) = a^2$, a^2 is the square of a and a is the **square root** of a^2.

2 is the square root of 4.

3 is the square root of 9.

We write, $\sqrt{4} = 2$, $\sqrt{9} = 3$, $\sqrt{16} = 4$ and so on.

We use the symbol $\sqrt{\ }$ to denote a square root.

Methods for Finding the Square Root of a Number

Let us learn how to find the square root of a number by two methods described as follows.

Method 1

Step (i): Express the given perfect square number as a product of prime factors.
Step (ii): Pair the factors such that primes in each pair thus formed are equal.
Step (iii): Choose one prime from each pair and multiply all such primes.
Step (iv): The product of these primes is the square root of the given number.

EXAMPLE 4.6 Find the square root of **144.**

SOLUTION

Step (i): $144 = 2 \times 2 \times 2 \times 2 \times 3 \times 3$

Step (ii): $144 = (2 \times 2) \times (2 \times 2) \times (3 \times 3)$

Step (iii): Consider, $(2) \times (2) \times (3)$

Step (iv): The product $(2) \times (2) \times (3) = 12$

∴ 12 is the square root of 144.

Method 2

Step (i): Express the given perfect square as the product of prime factors.
Step (ii): Expand the expression in step (i), as an exponential expression.
Step (iii): The square root is the product obtained by taking half of the exponent with the same base.

EXAMPLE 4.7 Find the square root of **324.**

SOLUTION

Step (i): $324 = 2 \times 2 \times 3 \times 3 \times 3 \times 3$

Step (ii): $324 = 2^2 \times 3^4$

Step (iii): $\sqrt{324} = 2^1 \times 3^2 = 2 \times 9 = 18$

∴ 18 is the square root of 324.

EXAMPLE 4.8 Find the square root of **100.**

SOLUTION

$100 = 2 \times 2 \times 5 \times 5 = 2^2 \times 5^2$

$\sqrt{100} = 2 \times 5 = 10$

∴ 10 is the square root of 100.

Cubes and Cube Roots

If a number is multiplied by itself three times, then the product obtained is said to be the **cube** of that number. That means, when a number a is multiplied by itself three times (to obtain $a \times a \times a$), the product a^3 is said to be the cube of a. The cube of a natural number is called a **perfect cube**.

Examples: (i) $1 \times 1 \times 1 = 1$ $(= 1^3)$, 1 is cube of 1.
(ii) $2 \times 2 \times 2 = 8$ $(= 2^3)$, 8 is the cube of 2.
(iii) $3 \times 3 \times 3 = 27$ $(= 3^3)$, 27 is the cube of 3.

$\therefore$ 1, 8, 27, 64, 125 .... are the cubes of 1, 2, 3, 4, 5, ... respectively.

Now, $a(a)(a) = a^3$, a^3 is the cube of a and a is the **cube root** of a^3.

2 is the cube root of 8.

3 is the cube root of 27.

We write, $\sqrt[3]{8} = 2$, $\sqrt[3]{27} = 3$, $\sqrt[3]{64} = 4$ and .... so on.

We use the symbol $\sqrt[3]{\ }$ to denote cube root.

Konnect

- $\sqrt{x \times y} = \sqrt{x} \times \sqrt{y}$
- $\sqrt{\frac{x}{y}} = \frac{\sqrt{x}}{\sqrt{y}}$
- $\sqrt{x + y} \neq \sqrt{x} + \sqrt{y}$
- $\sqrt{x - y} \neq \sqrt{x} - \sqrt{y}$

Table 4.2 List of cubes from 1 to 12

1^3	$1 \times 1 \times 1$	1
2^3	$2 \times 2 \times 2$	8
3^3	$3 \times 3 \times 3$	27
4^3	$4 \times 4 \times 4$	64
5^3	$5 \times 5 \times 5$	125
6^3	$6 \times 6 \times 6$	216
7^3	$7 \times 7 \times 7$	343
8^3	$8 \times 8 \times 8$	512
9^3	$9 \times 9 \times 9$	729
10^3	$10 \times 10 \times 10$	1000
11^3	$11 \times 11 \times 11$	1331
12^3	$12 \times 12 \times 12$	1728

Info Bytes!

When cubing a number, we will multiply the number by itself twice. For instance, if you cube the number 7, you'd do $7 \times 7 \times 7$, which equals 343. When you're looking for the cube root of a number, you're trying to find which number, when cubed, gives that result. So, the cube root of 343 is 7.

Methods for Finding Cube Root of a Number

Let us learn how to find the cube root of a number by two methods described as follows.

Method 1

Step (i): Express the given perfect cube as the product of its prime factors.
Step (ii): Group the factors such that the primes in each group thus formed are three equal factors.
Step (iii): Choose one prime from each group and multiply all such primes.
Step (iv): The product of these primes is the cube root of the given number.

EXAMPLE 4.9 Find the cube root of 216.

SOLUTION

Step (i): $216 = 2 \times 2 \times 2 \times 3 \times 3 \times 3$

Step (ii): $216 = (2 \times 2 \times 2) \times (3 \times 3 \times 3)$

Step (iii): Consider, $(2) \times (3)$

Step (iv): The product $(2) \times (3) = 6$

∴ 6 is the cube root of 216.

Method 2

Step (i): Express the given perfect cube number as the product of prime factors.
Step (ii): Expand the expression in step (i), as exponential expression.
Step (iii): The cube root is the product obtained by taking one-third of the exponent with the same base.

EXAMPLE 4.10 Find the cube root of 1000.

SOLUTION

Step (i): $1000 = 2 \times 2 \times 2 \times 5 \times 5 \times 5$

Step (ii): $1000 = 2^3 \times 5^3$

Step (iii): $\sqrt[3]{1000} = 2^1 \times 5^1 = 10$

∴ 10 is the cube root of 1000.

Konnect

- $\sqrt[3]{\frac{x}{y}} = \frac{\sqrt[3]{x}}{\sqrt[3]{y}}$
- The cube root of a positive number is always positive.
- The cube root of a negative number is always negative.

POINTS TO REMEMBER

- ✔ If a number is multiplied by itself, then the product obtained is said to be the square of that number
- ✔ A number which is the square of a natural number is called a perfect square.
- ✔ If a number is multiplied by itself three times, then the product obtained is said to be the cube of that number.
- ✔ The cube of a natural number is called a perfect cube.

PRACTICE QUESTIONS CLASSROOM WING

Very Short Answer Type Questions

***Direction for questions from 1 to 5:* Select the correct alternative from the given choices.**

1. Which of the following is(are) perfect square(s)?

   (a) 729 (b) 784

   (c) 841 (d) All of these

2. What is the sum of the base and the exponent of -5^5?

   (a) 0 (b) 10

   (c) 5 (d) 1

3. Which of the following is/are true?

   (A) 2^6 (B) 3^4 (C) 3^3

   (D) 4^3 (E) 9^2

   (a) $A = D$ (b) $B = E$

   (c) $B = D$ (d) Both (a) and (b)

4. $3^6 - 3^4 \times 3^2 =$

   (a) 3^4 (b) 3^4 (c) 1 (d) 0

5. Which of the following is not equal to 4096?

   (a) 2^{12} (b) 4^6 (c) 8^5 (d) 16^3

***Direction for question 6:* Match Column A with Column B.**

6.

	Column A		Column B
(a)	$[2^9 \times 2^{12}] \div 2^5$	(p)	2^{10}
(b)	$[2^{19} \times 2^{14}] \div 2^{20}$	(q)	2^{13}
(c)	$[2^{17} \times 2^{18}] \div 2^{16}$	(r)	2^{16}
(d)	$[2^6 \times 2^{12}] \div 2^8$	(s)	2^{19}

***Direction for questions from 7 to 11:* Fill in the blanks**

7. The value of $\sqrt{9^2 + 12^2}$ is ______.

8. The square of the smallest two-digit natural number is ______.

9. The cube of the greatest single digit natural number is ______.

10. The sum of the square roots of all the 2-digit perfect squares is ______.

11. The sum of the cube roots of all the 2-digit perfect cubes is ______.

***Direction for questions from 12 to 15:* Select the correct alternative from the given choices.**

12. The square of a natural number and the cube of the number are same. The number(s) is/are

    (a) 0

    (b) 1

    (c) Both (a) and (b)

    (d) None of these

13. Which of the following is not a perfect square?

    (a) 16

    (b) 36

    (c) 64

    (d) 91

14. Which of the following is/are true?

    (a) $\sqrt{16 + 9} = 7$

    (b) $\sqrt{9 + 7} = 4$

    (c) $\sqrt{64 + 36} = 14$

    (d) Both (a) and (c)

15. $\sqrt[3]{829 - 486} =$

    (a) 9 (b) 8 (c) 7 (d) 6

***Direction for question 16:* Match Column A with Column B.**

16.

	Column A		Column B
(a)	$\sqrt[3]{2^9 \times 3^{12}}$	(p)	$2^6 \times 3^4$
(b)	$\sqrt[2]{2^{12} \times 3^8}$	(q)	$2^4 \times 3^3$
(c)	$\sqrt[3]{2^{12} \times 3^9}$	(r)	$2^4 \times 3^6$
(d)	$\sqrt[2]{2^8 \times 3^{12}}$	(s)	$2^3 \times 3^4$

Short Answer Type Questions

17. Find the value of $3^{2^{7^{0^{8}}}}$.

18. What is the least natural number that should be multiplied to 3456 so that the product is a perfect square?

19. Evaluate the following.
    (i) $(-5)^3$
    (ii) $(-2)^6$
    (iii) $(3/11)^3$
    (iv) $(2/3)^1 (2/3)^2 (2/3)^3$

20. Find the value of an exponential expression whose exponent is the smallest composite number and base is the smallest odd prime number.

21. Simplify the following.
    (i) $(3/11)^5 \times (3/11)^6 \times (3/11)^{13}$
    (ii) $[(10)^{14} \times (5)^{17} \times (2)^{20}] \div [(10)^{13} \times (5)^{15} \times (2)^{17}]$

22. Simplify $[3^3 + 4^3 + 5^3]^2$ and express in exponential form.

23. What should be multiplied to $2^3 \times 3 \times 5$ so that the product is equal to 3600?

24. By what should $3^3 \times 5^4 \times 7^3$ be divided so that the quotient is equal to 11025?

25. Simplify: $2^6 \times 2^3 + 2^{19} \div 2^{13} - 2^{11} \div 2^2$

26. Simplify: $\{7^2 \times 7^3\} \div 7^8 \times 7^2 + 4^2 - 3^2$

27. Find the square root of the following.
    (i) 2025 (ii) $(2)^{36} \times (3)^{62} \times (7)^{34}$

28. Find the square root of the following.
    (i) $256 \div 289$ (ii) $(625)(361)$

29. Simplify:
    (i) $\sqrt{196} - \sqrt{81}$
    (ii) $(\sqrt{484} + \sqrt{64}) \div (\sqrt{400} - \sqrt{121})$

30. Find the cube root of the following.
    (i) 27000 (ii) $(2)^{63} \times (3)^{66} \times (7)^{69}$

31. Find the cube root of the following.
    (i) $(512) \div 1331$ (ii) $(343)\ (1728)$

32. (i) $\sqrt{10.24}$ (ii) $\sqrt{0.1225}$

33. (i) $\sqrt[3]{1.728}$ (ii) $\sqrt[3]{0.729}$

34. If a painting of area 144 sq. m covers the area of a square frame, then what is the length of the frame?

35. Find the cube of the following:
    (i) 13 (ii) −13

36. Write the exponent of 4 so that the result is 1024.

37. Identify the base and exponent of the following:
    (i) $-(2)^4$ (ii) $(-2)^4$

Essay Type Questions

38. A number, x is both perfect square and perfect cube. What are the possible digits in the unit's place of x?

PRACTICE QUESTIONS COMPETITION WING

Level 1: Apply Your Concepts

***Direction for questions from 1 to 5:* Fill in the blanks**

1. The value of $\sqrt{26^2 - 10^2}$ is _____.
2. The least natural number greater than 1, which is both a perfect square and a perfect cube is _____.
3. $[(999)^9 \times (999)^{90} \times (999)^{900}] \div (999)^{998} =$ _____.
4. $(2^2)^3 - (-2^3)^2 =$ _____.
5. $[99^1 + 98^2 + 97^3 + \ldots\ldots\ldots + 3^{97} + 2^{98} + 1^{99}]^0 =$ _____.
6. Which of the following is(are) perfect cube(s)?
   (a) 1000 (b) 1331
   (c) 1728 (d) All of these
7. The total surface area of a solid cube is equal to 6 times the square of the edge of the cube. If the total surface area of the cube is 726 sq cm. Find the length of the edge of the cube in cm. Also find the cost of coloring a face of the solid cube at the rate of ₹1.5 per sq. cm.
8. Find the difference between $\left(2^3\right)^2$ and 2^{3^2}.
9. The exponential form of 2527?
   (a) $11^2 \times 17$ (b) $13^2 \times 3^5$
   (c) $19^2 \times 7$ (d) $19^2 \times 7^2$
10. $\sqrt{0.64} - \sqrt{0.0064} + \sqrt{6.4} \div \sqrt{0.064} =$ _____.
    (a) 10.88 (b) 9.88
    (c) 9.72 (d) 10.72
11. $\sqrt[3]{2\sqrt{0.25}} =$ _____.
    (a) 0.5 (b) 0.05
    (c) 0.005 (d) 1
12. The area of a square shaped tile is equal to the square of the length of the side of the tile and it is equal to 1.44 sq. ft. Find the length of the side of the tile in feet.

Level 2: Review Your Concepts

13. In a school, there are certain number of students. The number of students in each section is equal to the number of sections in the school. The total number of students is equal to 1024. If each student contributes ₹150 to a charity, what is the total amount collected from each section.
14. $\left[\left\{\left(\dfrac{2}{3}\right)^{-2} \times \left(\dfrac{256}{625}\right)^{\frac{1}{2}}\right\}^{\frac{-1}{2}} \div \left(\left(\dfrac{4}{3}\right)^{-2}\right)^{3}\right] \times \left(\dfrac{1}{0.1}\right)^{-1} =$
    (a) $\dfrac{4^5}{3^7}$ (b) $\dfrac{4^5}{3^7}$ (c) $\dfrac{4^6}{3^5}$ (d) $\dfrac{3^5}{4^6}$
15. A farmer wants to convert his rectangular field into a square shaped field of the same area. The length and the breadth of the field is 54 m and 24 m, respectively. After conversion, what is the side of the square field?
    (a) 24 m (b) 36 m (c) 48 m (d) 54 m

Level 3: Assess Your Concepts

16. Find the two positive integers such that if 1998 is written as a product of these integers, their difference is as small as possible.
17. Show that $\left(2^{13} + 2^{12} - 2^{11} - 2^{10}\right)$ is a perfect square.
18. Arrange 5^6, 3^9, and 2^{12} in the ascending order.

ANSWER KEYS

Crossword

Across

2. Side 3. Exponent 6. Two 8. Cube 10. Positive

Down

1. Edge 4. Negative 5. Three 7. One 9. Base

Classroom Wing

Very Short Answer Type Questions

1. (d) 2. (b) 3. (d) 4. (d) 5. (c)
6. (a) → (r); (b) → (q); (c) → (s); (d) → (p) 7. 15 8. 100 9. 729
10. 39 11. 7 12. (b) 13. (d) 14. (b) 15. (c)
16. (a) → (s); (b) → (p); (c) → (q); (d) → (r)

Short Answer Type Questions

17. 9 18. 6 19. (i) –125; (ii) 64; (iii) $\frac{27}{1331}$; (iv) $\frac{64}{729}$
20. 81 21. (i) $(3/11)^{24}$; (ii) $(5)^3 \times (2)^4$ 22. $2^6 \times 3^6$ 23. 30 24. 525
25. 2^6 26. $7\frac{1}{7}$ 27. (i) 45; (ii) $(2)^{18} \times (3)^{31} \times (7)^{17}$ 28. (i) 16/17; (ii) 475
29. (i) 5(ii) $\frac{10}{3}$ 30. (i) 30; (ii) $(2)^{21} \times (3)^{22} \times (7)^{23}$ 31. (i) $\frac{8}{11}$; (ii) 84 32. (i) 3.2; (ii) 0.35
33. (i) 1.2; (ii) 0.9 34. 12m 35. (i) 2197; (ii) -2197 36. 5
37. (i) 2,4 (ii) -2,4

Essay Type Questions

38. 0, 1, 4, 5, 6, 9

Competition Wing

Level 1: Apply Your Concepts

1. 24 2. 64 3. 999 4. 0 5. 1 6. (d)
7. ₹181.5 8. 448 9. (c) 10. (d) 11. (d) 12. 1.2

Level 2: Review Your Concepts

13. ₹4800 14. (a) 15. (b)

Level 3: Assess Your Concepts

16. 37 and 54 17. $2^{13} + 2^{12} - 2^{11} - 2^{10}$ 18. $2^{12} < 5^6 < 3^9$

Hints and Explanations

CLASSROOM WING

Very Short Answer Type Questions

1. $729 = 27^2$
$784 = 28^2$
$841 = 29^2$
All the given numbers are perfect squares.
Hence, the correct option is (d).

2. Given number is -5^5.
Base = 5 and exponent = 5.
The required sum is 5 + 5 = 10.
Hence, the correct option is (b).

3. $2^6 = 64 = 4^3$ and $3^4 = 9^2$
Hence, the correct option is (d).

4. $3^6 - 3^4 \times 3^2 = 3^6 - 3^{4+2} = 3^6 - 3^6 = 0$
Hence, the correct option is (d).

5. $2^{12} = 4096$; $4^6 = 4096$; $16^3 = 4096$; $8^5 = 2^{15}$
Hence, the correct option is (c).

6. (a) $[2^9 \times 2^{12}] \div 2^5 = 2^{21} \div 2^5 = 2^{21-5} = 2^{16} \rightarrow$ (r)
(b) $[2^{19} \times 2^{14}] \div 2^{20} = 2^{33} \div 2^{20} = 2^{33-20} = 2^{13} \rightarrow$ (q)
(c) $[2^{17} \times 2^{18}] \div 2^{16} = 2^{35} \div 2^{16} = 2^{35-16} = 2^{19} \rightarrow$ (s)
(d) $[2^6 \times 2^{12}] \div 2^8 = 2^{18} \div 2^8 = 2^{18-8} = 2^{10} \rightarrow$ (p)
Therefore, the correct match is:
(a) → (r); (b) → (q); (c) → (s); (d) → (p)

7. $\sqrt{9^2 + 12^2} = \sqrt{81 + 144} = \sqrt{225} = \sqrt{15^2} = 15$.

8. The square of the smallest two-digit natural number, is $10^2 = 100$.

9. The cube of the greatest single digit natural number is $9^3 = 729$.

10. The sum of the square roots of all the 2-digit perfect squares
$= \sqrt{16} + \sqrt{25} + \sqrt{36} + \sqrt{49} + \sqrt{64} + \sqrt{81}$
$= 4 + 5 + 6 + 7 + 8 + 9$
$= 39$

11. The sum of the cube roots of all the 2-digit perfect cubes
$= \sqrt{27} + \sqrt{64}$
$= 3 + 4$
$= 7$

12. $1^2 = 1^3$
Hence, the correct option is (b).

13. 91 is not a perfect square.
Hence, the correct option is (d).

14. $\sqrt{9 + 7} = \sqrt{16} = 4$ is a true statement.
Hence, the correct option is (b).

15. $\sqrt[3]{829 - 486} = \sqrt[3]{343} = \sqrt[3]{7^3} = 7$
Hence, the correct option is (c).

16. (a) $\sqrt[3]{2^9 \times 3^{12}} = 2^{9/3} \times 3^{12/3} = 2^3 \times 3^4 \rightarrow$ (s)
(b) $\sqrt[2]{2^{12} \times 3^8} = 2^{12/2} \times 3^{8/2} = 2^6 \times 3^4 \rightarrow$ (p)
(c) $\sqrt[3]{2^{12} \times 3^9} = 2^{12/3} \times 3^{9/3} = 2^4 \times 3^3 \rightarrow$ (q)
(d) $\sqrt[2]{2^8 \times 3^{12}} = 2^{8/2} \times 3^{12/2} = 2^4 \times 3^6 \rightarrow$ (r)
Therefore, the correct match is:
(a) → (s), (b) → (p), (c) → (q), (d) → (r)

Short Answer Type Questions

17. $3^{2^{7^{0^8}}} = 3^{2^{7^0}}$
$= 3^{2^1}$
$= 3^2 = 9$.

18. $3456 = 2^2 \times 864$
$= 2^2 \times 2^2 \times 216$
$= 2^2 \times 2^2 \times 2^2 \times 54$
$= 2^2 \times 2^2 \times 2^2 \times 2 \times 27$
$= 2^2 \times 2^2 \times 2^2 \times 2 \times 3 \times 3^2$.
The required number is 2×3 i.e., **6**.

19. (i) $(-5)^3 = (-5)(-5)(-5) = -125$

(ii) $(-2)^6 = (-2)(-2)(-2)(-2)(-2)(-2) = 64$

(iii) $\left(\frac{3}{11}\right)^3 = \left(\frac{3}{11}\right)\left(\frac{3}{11}\right)\left(\frac{3}{11}\right) = \frac{27}{1331}$

(iv) $\left(\frac{2}{3}\right)^1\left(\frac{2}{3}\right)^2\left(\frac{2}{3}\right)^3$

$= \left(\frac{2}{3}\right)\left(\frac{2}{3}\right)\left(\frac{2}{3}\right)\left(\frac{2}{3}\right)\left(\frac{2}{3}\right)\left(\frac{2}{3}\right) = \frac{64}{729}$

20. The exponent is the smallest composite number which is 4 and the base is the smallest odd prime number which is 3.

The required expression is $3^4 = 81$.

21. (i) We have $a^m \times a^n = a^{m+n}$

$(3/11)^5 \times (3/11)^6 \times (3/11)^{13} = (3/11)^{5+6+13}$

$= (3/11)^{24}$

(ii) We have $a^m \div a^n = a^{m-n}$

$[(10)^{14} \times (5)^{17} \times (2)^{20}] \div [(10)^{13} \times (5)^{15} \times (2)^{17}]$

$= (10)^{14-13} \times (5)^{17-15} \times (2)^{20-17}$

$= (10)^1 \times (5)^2 \times (2)^3 = (5 \times 2) \times (5)^2 \times (2)^3$

$= (5)^{1+2} \times (2)^{1+3} = (5)^3 \times (2)^4$

22. $[3^3 + 4^3 + 5^3]^2 = [27 + 64 + 125]^2$

$= [216]^2 = [2^3 \times 3^3]^2$

$= [2^3 \times 3^3][2^3 \times 3^3]$

$= 2^{3+3} \times 3^{3+3} = 2^6 \times 3^6$

23. Let the required number be

$a \times (2^3 \times 3 \times 5) = 3600$.

Hence, $a = 2^4 \times 3^2 \times 5^2/2^3 \times 3 \times 5 = 30$.

24. Let the required number be

$3^3 \times 5^4 \times 7^3/a = 11025 = 3^2 \times 5^2 \times 7^2$

Hence, $a = 525$.

25. $2^6 \times 2^3 + 2^{19} \div 2^{13} - 2^{11} \div 2^2$

$= 2^6 \times 2^3 + 2^{19-13} - 2^{11-2} = 2^6 \times 2^3 + 2^6 - 2^9$

$= 2^{6+3} + 2^6 - 2^9 = 2^9 + 2^6 - 2^9 = 2^6$

26. $\{7^2 \times 7^3\} \div 7^8 \times 7^2 + 4^2 - 3^2$

$= \{7^{2+3}\} \div 7^8 \times 7^2 + 4^2 - 3^2$

$= 7^5 \div 7^8 \times 7^2 + 4^2 - 3^2$

$= 7^7 \div 7^8 + 16 - 9 = 1 \div 7 + 7$

$= \frac{1}{7} + 7 = 7\frac{1}{7}$

27. (i) $2025 = 3^4 \times 5^2$

$\sqrt{2025} = 3^{4/2} \times 5^{2/2}$

$= 3^2 \times 5$

$= 45$

(ii) $(2)^{36} \times (3)^{62} \times (7)^{34}$

$\sqrt{(2)^{36} \times (3)^{62} \times (7)^{34}}$

$= (2)^{36/2} \times (3)^{62/2} \times (7)^{34/2}$

$= (2)^{18} \times (3)^{31} \times (7)^{17}$

28. (i) $256 \div 289 = 2^8 \div 17^2$

$\sqrt{256 \div 289} = \sqrt{2^8 \div 17^2}$

$= 2^{8/2} \div 17^{2/2}$

$= 2^4 \div 17$

$= 16/17$

(ii) $(625)(361) = 5^4 \times 19^2$

$\sqrt{(625)(361)} = \sqrt{5^4 \times 19^2}$

$= 5^{4/2} \times 19^{2/2}$

$= 5^2 \times 19 = 475$

29. (i) $\sqrt{196} - \sqrt{81}$

$= 14^{2/2} - 9^{2/2}$

$= 14 - 9 = 5$

(ii) $(\sqrt{484} + \sqrt{64}) \div (\sqrt{400} - \sqrt{121})$

$(22^{2/2} + 8^{2/2}) \div (20^{2/2} - 11^{2/2})$

$(22 + 8) \div (20 - 11) = 30 \div 9$

$= \frac{10}{3}$

30. (i) $27000 = (27)(1000)$

$= (3)^3(10)^3$

$\sqrt{27000} = \sqrt[3]{3^3 \times 10^3}$

$= (3)^{3/3}(10)^{3/3} = 3(10)$

$= 30$

(ii) $\sqrt[3]{(2)^{63} \times (3)^{66} \times (7)^{69}}$

$= (2)^{63/3} \times (3)^{66/3} \times (7)^{69/3}$

$= (2)^{21} \times (3)^{22} \times (7)^{23}$

31. (i) $\sqrt[3]{512 \div 1331}$

$= \sqrt[3]{8^3 \div 11^3}$

$= 8^{3/3} \div 11^{3/3}$

$= \dfrac{8}{11}$

(ii) $\sqrt[3]{(343)(1728)}$

$= \sqrt[3]{7^3 \times 12^3}$

$= (7^{3/3})\ (12^{3/3})$

$= (7)\ (12) = 84$

32. (i) $\sqrt{10.24}$

$= \sqrt{(1024/100)}$

$= \sqrt{\dfrac{2^{10}}{10^2}}$

$= 2^{10/2}/10^{2/2}$

$= 2^5/10$

$= 32/10 = 3.2$

(ii) $\sqrt{0.1225}$

$= \sqrt{(1225/10000)}$

$= \sqrt{(5^2 \times 7^2)/10^4}$

$= (5^{2/2} \times 7^{2/2})/10^{4/2}$

$= (5 \times 7)/100$

$= 35/100 = 0.35$

33. (i) $\sqrt[3]{1.728} = \sqrt[3]{(1728/1000)}$

$= \sqrt[3]{(2^6 \times 3^3)/10^3}$

$= (2^{6/3} \times 3^{3/3})/10^{3/3}$

$= (2^2 \times 3)/10$

$= 12/10 = 1.2$

(ii) $\sqrt[3]{0.729}$

$= \sqrt[3]{(729/1000)}$

$= \sqrt[3]{3^6/10^3}$

$= 3^{6/3}/10^{3/3}$

$= 3^2/10$

$= 9/10 = 0.9$

34. Area covered by the square painting is 144 sq. m.

We know, area of square = $(\text{side})^2$

$144 = (\text{side})^2$

$12 = \text{side}$

∴ The length of the frame = 12 m

35. (i) $13 \times 13 \times 13 = 2197$

(ii) $(-13) \times (-13) \times (-13) = -2197$

36. $1024 = 4 \times 4 \times 4 \times 4 \times 4 = 45$

Exponent = 5

37. (i) Base = 2; Exponent = 4

(ii) Base = −2; Exponent = 4

Essay Type Questions

38. Given that x is both perfect square and perfect cube.

Units Digit of a number	0	1	2	3	4	5	6	7	8	9
Units Digit of Square of the number	0	1	4	9	6	5	6	9	4	1
Units Digit of Cube of the number	0	1	8	7	4	5	6	3	2	9

We know that the resulting unit's digits are the unit's digits of cube of square of a number or square of cube of a number.

Units Digit of a number	0	1	2	3	4	5	6	7	8	9
Units Digit of Square of the number	0	1	4	9	6	5	6	9	4	1
Units Digit of Cube of the number	0	1	8	7	4	5	6	3	2	9
Unit's digit of x	0	1	4	9	6	5	6	9	4	1

The possible units digits of x are: 0, 1, 4, 5, 6, 9.

COMPETITION WING

Level 1: Apply Your Concepts

1. $\sqrt{26^2 - 10^2} = \sqrt{676 - 100} = \sqrt{576} = \sqrt{24^2} = 24.$

2. The required number is 2^6 i.e., **64**.

3. $[(999)^9 \times (999)^{90} \times (999)^{900}] \div (999)^{998}$
$= [(999)^{9+90+900}] \div (999)^{998}$
$= (999)^{999} \div (999)^{998} = (999)^{999-998} = 999$

4. $(2^2)^3 - (-2^3)^2 = (4)^3 - (-8)^2 = 64 - 64 = 0$

5. $[99^1 + 98^2 + 97^3 + \ldots\ldots\ldots + 3^{97} + 2^{98} + 1^{99}]^0 = 1,$ since $a^0 = 1$.

6. $1000 = 10^3$
$1331 = 11^3$
$1728 = 12^3$
Hence, all the given numbers are perfect cubes.
Hence, the correct option is (d).

7. Given that the total surface area a cube is equal to 6 times the square of the edge of the cube.
The total surface area of the cube = 726 sq cm.
Area of a face = Square of the edge = 726/6 = 121.
The length of the edge of the cube = $\sqrt{121}$ = 11 cm.
The cost of coloring a face of the cube = (area of a face) (Cost per sq. cm.) = (121) (₹1.5) = ₹181.5

8. $\left(2^3\right)^2 = 2^{3\times 2} \qquad \left[\left(a^m\right)^n = a^{m\times n}\right]$
$= 2^6 = 64.$
$2^{3^2} = 2^9 = 512.$
Now $2^{3^2} - \left(2^3\right)^2 = 512 - 64 = 448.$

9. $2527 = 7 \times 361$
$= 7 \times 19^2.$
Hence, the correct option is (c).

10. $\sqrt{0.64} - \sqrt{0.0064} + \sqrt{6.4} \div \sqrt{0.064}$
$= \sqrt{0.64} - \sqrt{0.0064} + \sqrt{\dfrac{6.4}{0.064}}$
$= \sqrt{0.64} - \sqrt{0.0064} + \sqrt{\dfrac{64 \times 1000}{64 \times 10}}$
$= \sqrt{0.64} - \sqrt{0.0064} + \sqrt{100}$
$= \sqrt{\dfrac{64}{100}} - \sqrt{\dfrac{64}{10000}} + 10$
$= \dfrac{8}{10} - \dfrac{8}{100} + 10$
$= 10.72$
Hence, the correct option is (d).

11. $\sqrt[3]{2\sqrt{0.25}} = \sqrt[3]{2\sqrt{0.5 \times 0.5}}$
$= \sqrt[3]{2 \times 0.5}$
$= \sqrt[3]{1}$
$= 1$
Hence, the correct option is (d).

12. Given that the area of a square shaped tile (the square of the side) = 1.44 sq. ft.
∴ The length of the side of the tile = $\sqrt{1.44}$
$= \sqrt{(144/100)} = \sqrt{\left(\dfrac{12^2}{10^2}\right)} = 12/10 = 1.2$ ft

Level 2: Review Your Concepts

13. Given that the number of students in each section is equal to the number of sections in the school.
Let the number of students in each section be.
The number of sections = a
The total number of students = 1024.
$a \times a = 1024 = 32 \times 32.$
$a = 32$
The number of students in each section = 32
The total amount collected from each section = 32(₹150) = ₹4800

14. $\left[\left\{\left(\dfrac{2}{3}\right)^{-2} \times \left(\dfrac{256}{625}\right)^{\frac{1}{2}}\right\}^{\frac{-1}{2}} \div \left(\left(\dfrac{4}{3}\right)^{-2}\right)^3\right] \times \left(\dfrac{1}{0.1}\right)^{-1}$
$= \left[\left(\left(\dfrac{2}{3}\right)^{-2}\right)^{\frac{-1}{2}} \times \left(\left(\dfrac{256}{625}\right)^{\frac{1}{2}}\right)^{\frac{-1}{2}} \div \left(\dfrac{4}{3}\right)^{-6}\right] \times \left(\dfrac{1}{0.1}\right)^{-1}$
$= \left[\left(\dfrac{2}{3}\right) \times \left(\dfrac{256}{625}\right)^{\frac{-1}{4}} \div \left(\dfrac{4}{3}\right)^{-6}\right] \times \left(\dfrac{1}{0.1}\right)^{-1}$

$$= \left[\left(\frac{2}{3}\right) \times \left(\frac{625}{256}\right)^{\frac{1}{4}} \div \left(\frac{3}{4}\right)^{6}\right] \times \left(\frac{1}{0.1}\right)^{-1}$$

$$= \left[\left(\frac{2}{3}\right) \times \left(\frac{5^4}{4^4}\right)^{\frac{1}{4}} \times \left(\frac{4}{3}\right)^{6}\right] \times \left(\frac{1}{0.1}\right)^{-1}$$

$$= \left[\left(\frac{2}{3}\right) \times \left(\frac{5}{4}\right) \times \left(\frac{4}{3}\right)^{6}\right] \times (10)^{-1}$$

$$= \left[\frac{2 \times 5 \times 4^6}{3 \times 4 \times 3^6}\right] \times \left(\frac{1}{10}\right)$$

$$= \frac{4^5}{3^7}$$

Hence, the correct option is (a).

15. Let the length and the breadth of the rectangle be l and b, respectively.

Let the side of square be 'a'.

Given, $a \times a = l \times b$

$a^2 = 54 \times 24$

$a^2 = 1296$

$a = \sqrt{1296}$

$a = 36$ m

Hence, the correct option is (b).

Level 3: Assess Your Concepts

16. The difference of the two factors has to be as small as possible, so, these two integers have to be as close to $\sqrt{1998}$ as possible. (Now, we know that $45^2 = 2025$, therefore, the factors should be as close to 44 and 45 as possible).

Looking at the prime factors of $1998 = 2 \times 3^2 \times 37$

We observe that 37 is quite close to 44.

This is a suitable number as there lies no other number between 38 and 44 that happens to be factor of 1998. So, the two factors are 37 and $2 \times 3^2 = 54$, and the difference is $54 - 37 = 17$.

Therefore, the two numbers are 37 and 54.

17. $2^{13} + 2^{12} - 2^{11} - 2^{10} = 2^{10}\left(2^3 + 2^2 - 2^1 - 1\right)$

$$= 2^{10}\left(2^3 + 2^2 - 2^1 - 1\right)$$
$$= 2^{10}(8 + 4 - 2 - 1)$$
$$= 2^{10}(9)$$
$$= 2^{5 \times 2} \times 3^2$$
$$= \left(2^5\right)^2 \times 3^2$$
$$= (32)^2 \times 3^2$$
$$= (32 \times 3)^2 = (96)^2$$

Hence, $2^{13} + 2^{12} - 2^{11} - 2^{10}$ is a perfect square.

18. Given: 5^6, 3^9, and 2^{12}

To compare such numbers, we need to equate either bases or exponents.

As the bases are the distinct primes, we need to equate the exponents.

The HCF (6, 9, and 12) = 3.

$5^6 = 5^{2 \times 3} = \left(5^2\right)^3 = 25^3$

$3^9 = 3^{3 \times 3} = \left(3^3\right)^3 = 27^3$

$2^{12} = 2^{4 \times 3} = \left(2^4\right)^3 = 16^3$

The ascending order of the numbers is: $16^3 < 25^3 < 27^3$.

i.e., $2^{12} < 5^6 < 3^9$.

CHAPTER

5

Ratio and Proportion

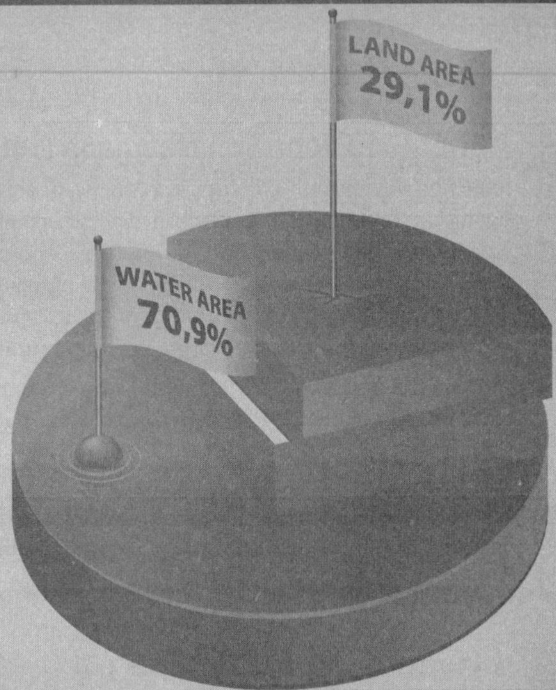

Remember

Before beginning this chapter, you should be able to:

- Recall division of numbers
- Compare numbers
- Recall units of different measures

Key Ideas

After completing this chapter, you should be able to:

- Understand terms of a ratio
- Define properties of a ratio
- Understand simplest form of a ratio
- Describe proportion

Scientific Crypt

A Tribute to John von Neumann (1903-1957)

John von Neumann, a Hungarian-American polymath, made significant contributions to mathematics, physics, computer science, engineering, and economics. His visionary concepts, including stored-program architecture and self-replicating machines, played a crucial role in shaping the digital age. His exceptional intellect and innovative ideas left an enduring impact on various fields.

Born in Budapest in 1903, John von Neumann showed extraordinary mathematical talent from a young age, publishing significant papers by the age of 19. He pursued mathematics at the University of Berlin, completing his Ph.D. in Budapest. His studies in Göttingen under David Hilbert influenced his contributions to mathematics and science, including set theory.

Von Neumann's contributions to mathematics, including set theory, operator theory, and game theory, laid the foundation for numerous scientific disciplines. He crafted the mathematical structure of quantum mechanics, uncovering the mystery of the quantum world. During World War II, he worked on the Manhattan Project and played an instrumental role in nuclear physics and the design of nuclear weapons. Von Neumann's work laid the foundation for the modern computing architecture known as the Von Neumann architecture. He was a key figure in the U.S. defence establishment during the Cold War and advocated for the policy of mutually assured destruction.

FUN TIME

CROSSWORD

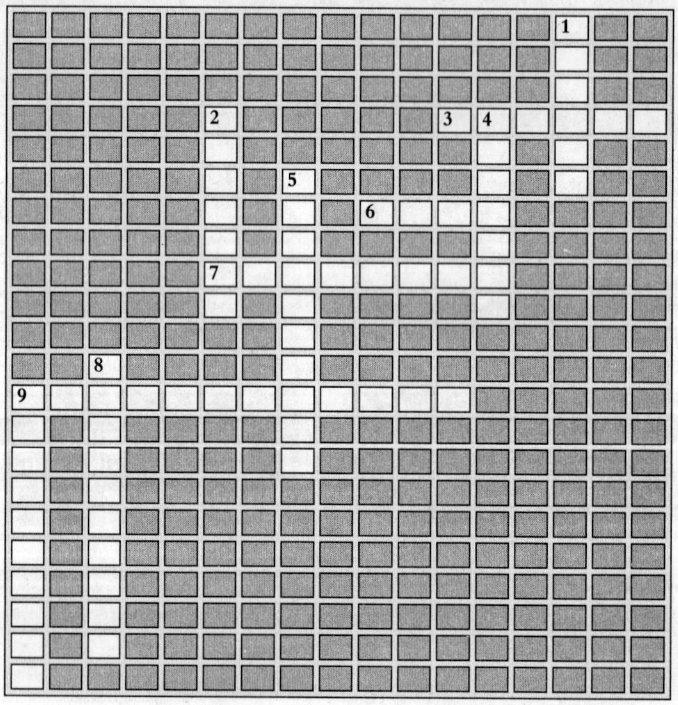

Across

3. When a change in one quantity directly results in a similar change in a second quantity, the two quantities are in _______ proportion.
6. The ratio of two quantities can be found only when both the quantities are of the _______ kind.
7. The first and the fourth terms in proportion are called _______.
9. The values of a, b, c, and d are respectively known as the first, second, third, and the fourth _______.

Down

1. A unique number approximately equal to 1.618 is known as _______ ratio.
2. The value of a ratio remains the same if both its terms are multiplied or _______ by the same non-zero quantity.
4. When an increase in one quantity results in a decrease in another, or vice versa, then the two quantities are in _______ proportion.
5. The value of a ratio remains unchanged if both its terms are _______ or divided by the same non-zero quantity.
8. For a given ratio a : b, 'b' is referred to as the _______.
9. The equality of two ratios is called _______.

INTRODUCTION

While making a cup of coffee, we determine particular quantities of water, sugar, milk, etc. We keep this fraction in mind to give the coffee a flawless taste. And, this is how the concept of ratio and proportion is used frequently in day-to-day life. In Mathematics, we use the knowledge of this concept to solve numerous problems.

Ratio

In our daily life, we come across different situations where we have to compare quantities such as heights, weights, distance or time. We can compare two quantities of the same kind in two ways by subtracting the smaller from the bigger or by dividing one by the other.

> **Info Bytes!**
> Ratio has no units.

Example: Let us take two numbers such as 2 and 3. We may say that 2 is 1 less than 3. This comparison was made by subtracting the two numbers.

We may also say that 2 is two thirds of 3. This comparison was made by dividing the two numbers. Comparison by division is called a **ratio**.

> **Konnect**
> The ratio of two quantities can be found only when both the quantities are of the same kind. The ratio between 1 metre and 5 seconds cannot be found, as the quantities given are not of the same kind.

Terms of a Ratio

For a given ratio $a : b$, we say that a is the **first term** or **antecedent** and b is the **second term** or **consequent**.

Example: In the ratio 3 : 4, 3 is the antecedent while 4 is the consequent.

Properties of a Ratio

The value of a ratio remains the same, if both the terms of the ratio are multiplied or divided by the same non-zero quantity.

Simplest Form of a Ratio

The ratio of two or more quantities is said to be in the simplest form, if the highest common factor (HCF) of the quantities is 1. If the HCF of the quantities is not 1, then each quantity of the ratio is divided by HCF to convert the ratio into its simplest form.

Example: (i) Let us suppose that there are three numbers such as 6, 9 and 12. The HCF of the numbers is 3. Dividing each numbers of 6, 9 and 12 by 3, the results obtained are 2, 3 and 4. The ratio of 6, 9 and 12, in the simplest form is 2 : 3 : 4.

(ii) Suppose $a : b = 3 : 4$, then $a : b$ is equal to 3 : 4 or 6 : 8 or 9 : 12 and so on.

EXAMPLE 5.1 Write the following ratios in their simplest forms.

(I) 49 : 77 (II) $\frac{11}{13} : \frac{7}{8}$

SOLUTION

(I) 49 : 77 = 7 : 11

(II) $\frac{11}{13} : \frac{7}{8}$

The LCM of 13 and 8 is 104.

$$\left(\frac{11}{13}\times 104\right) : \left(\frac{7}{8}\times 104\right) = 88 : 91$$

EXAMPLE 5.2 Divide the amount ₹640 in the ratio 9 : 7.

SOLUTION

The sum of the terms of the ratio 9 + 7 = 16

The required amounts are $\frac{9}{16}$ (₹640) and $\frac{7}{16}$ (₹640), i.e., ₹360 and ₹260.

EXAMPLE 5.3 240 mL of water is added to 9600 mL of milk. Find the ratio of milk and water in the solution.

SOLUTION

960 mL : 240 mL = 960 : 240 = 96 : 24 = 4 : 1

Proportion

The equality of two ratios is called **proportion**.

Example: If $a : b = c : d$, i.e., $\frac{a}{b} = \frac{c}{d}$, then a, b, c and d are said to be in proportion.

Konnect

- The values of a, b, c and d are respectively known as the first, second, third and the fourth proportional.
- The first and the fourth terms are called **extremes** while the second and the third terms are called **means.**
- The product of extremes = The product of means, i.e., $ad = bc$.

EXAMPLE 5.4 Check whether the following are in proportion or not.

(I) 2, 4, 6, 8 **(II)** 12, 18, 10, 15

SOLUTION

(I) Product of extremes = 2 × 8 = 16

Product of means = 4 × 6 = 24

16 ≠ 24

∴ 2, 4, 6, 8 are not in proportion.

(II) Product of extremes = 12 × 15 = 180

Product of means = 18 × 10 = 180

Product of extremes = Product of means

∴ 12, 18, 10, 15 are in proportion.

EXAMPLE 5.5 Find the value of x, if 3, 24, 5 and x are in proportion.

SOLUTION

Given that 3, 24, 5, x are in proportion.

Product of extremes = Product of means

$3 \times x = 24 \times 5$

$3x = 120$

$x = \frac{120}{3} \Rightarrow x = 40$

EXAMPLE 5.6 In a milk solution, water and milk are in the ratio of 2 : 15. If the quantity of pure milk is 6 L, then find the quantity of water in the solution.

SOLUTION

Let the quantity of water be x L.

$2 : 15 :: x : 6 \Rightarrow 2 \times 6 = 15 \times x \Rightarrow 12 = 15x$

$\therefore x = \frac{12}{15} = \frac{4}{5} = 0.8 \text{ L} = 800 \text{ mL}$

$\therefore$ The quantity of water in the solution = 800 mL.

Direct and Inverse Proportions

When a decrease or increase in a quantity directly results in corresponding decrease or increase in second quantity, then the two quantities are in **direct proportion**.

Example: At a speed of 10 km/h in 2 h, a car travels 20 km. If the car moves at a speed of 20 km/h, it will cover 40 km in 2 h. Hence, 10 : 20 : : 20 : 40

When an increase in a quantity results in corresponding decrease in second quantity or *vice versa*, then the two quantities are in **inverse proportion**.

Example: A group of 12 workers take 12 days to construct a 4-km long highway. When two such groups work together, they complete the highway in 6 days. Hence, ratio of workers is inverse of ratio of time taken for construction.

Info Bytes!

The Golden Ratio is a unique number approximately equal to 1.618. Famous-building, Parthenon in Greece has theGolden Ratio in it.

POINTS TO REMEMBER

- Comparison by division is called a ratio.
- For a given ratio $a : b$, we say that a is the first term or antecedent and b is the second term or consequent.
- The equality of two ratios is called proportion.
- The first and the fourth terms in proportion are called extremes while the second and the third terms are called means.
- When a decrease or increase in a quantity directly results in corresponding decrease or increase in second quantity, then the two quantities are in direct proportion.
- When an increase in a quantity results in corresponding decrease in second quantity or vice versa, then the two quantities are in inverse proportion.

PRACTICE QUESTIONS CLASSROOM WING

Very Short Answer Type Questions

Direction for questions from 1 to 5: **Select the correct alternative from given choices.**

1. If a, b, c and d are in proportion, then which of the following is true?
   (a) $ac = bd$ (b) $bc = ad$
   (c) $cd = ab$ (d) $ab = cd$

2. Which of the following is equivalent to 5 : 7?
   (a) 25 : 35 (b) 35 : 49
   (c) 60 : 84 (d) All of these

3. Given that $c > 0$. Which of the following is equal to $a : b$?
   (a) $(a + c) : (b + c)$
   (b) $(a - c) : (b - c)$
   (c) $\frac{a}{c} : \frac{b}{c}$
   (d) All the above

4. The ratio of 75 paise to ₹10 is ______.
   (a) 15 : 2 (b) 3 : 40
   (c) 3 : 4 (d) 75 : 100

5. The ratio of 10 m to 1 km is ______.
   (a) 10 : 1
   (b) 1 : 10
   (c) 1 : 100
   (d) 100 : 1000

Direction for question 6: **Match Column A with Column B.**

6.

	Column A		Column B
(a)	$\frac{1}{3} : \frac{2}{5}$	(p)	20 : 3
(b)	$\frac{3}{4} : \frac{5}{2}$	(q)	3 : 10
(c)	$\frac{2}{3} : \frac{3}{5}$	(r)	5 : 6
(d)	$\frac{4}{3} : \frac{1}{5}$	(s)	10 : 9

Direction for questions from 7 to 11: **Fill in the blanks.**

7. The simplified form of $\frac{6}{7} : \frac{15}{14}$ is ______.

8. If $3 : 8 = 12 : x$, then the value of x is ______.

9. If p, q, r and s are in proportion, then $\frac{p}{q}$ = ______.

10. If 3, x, 6, 12 are in proportion, then x = ______.

11. If $x : 5 :: 4 : 20$, then x = ______.

Direction for questions from 12 to 14: **Select the correct alternative from given choices.**

12. Which of the following is true?
   (a) 2, 5, 7, 10 are in proportion.
   (b) 4 : 3 : : 8 : 6
   (c) If $a : b = c : d$, then $b : c = d : a$.
   (d) None of the above

13. If $x : 12 :: 12 : 18$, then x is ______.
   (a) 6 (b) 8
   (c) 10 (d) 4

14. If $\frac{1}{2} : \frac{1}{3} :: \frac{1}{4} : x$, then x is ______.
   (a) $\frac{1}{8}$ (b) $\frac{1}{6}$
   (c) $\frac{1}{12}$ (d) $\frac{1}{16}$

Direction for question 15: **Match Column A with Column B.**

15.

	Column A		Column B
(a)	$x : 5 :: 2 : 3$	(p)	$\frac{6}{5}$
(b)	$2 : x :: 4 : 3$	(q)	$\frac{15}{2}$
(c)	$2 : 5 :: x : 3$	(r)	$\frac{10}{3}$
(d)	$2 : 5 :: 3 : x$	(s)	$\frac{3}{2}$

Short Answer Type Questions

16. Find the ratio of the following and express them in the simplest form.
    (i) 360 mL, 500 mL (ii) 4 h 20 min, 6 h

17. Express the following in the simplest form.
    (i) $4\frac{1}{5}:2\frac{3}{4}$ (ii) $2\frac{3}{8}:3\frac{5}{6}$

18. Find the greatest ratio of the following.
    (i) 1 : 6; 3 : 8 (ii) 9 : 16; 5 : 12

19. Divide ₹2353 among A, B and C in the ratio $\frac{1}{2}:\frac{1}{3}:\frac{1}{4}$.

20. If the cost 175 of oranges is ₹p, find the cost of 35 oranges.

21. There are three numbers which are in the ratio $3:\frac{4}{7}:\frac{2}{5}$. If the sum of the numbers is 278, then find the three numbers.

22. In a school, there are 720 students. If there are 300 boys, then find the ratio of the number of girls to that of boys.

23. Check whether the following sets of numbers are in proportion or not in the given order.
    (i) 2, 3, 2016, 2019 (ii) 12, 15, 32, 40

24. Find the value of x in each of the following proportions.
    (i) 17 : 68 : : 7 : x (ii) 14 : 42 : : x : 27

25. Arrange the following sets of numbers in the order such that they should be in proportion. Hence, find the product of extremes.
    (i) 45, 9, 27, 15 (ii) $\frac{1}{6},\frac{1}{15},\frac{1}{40},\frac{4}{9}$

26. In Rahul's house every person eats 3 mangoes. There are 8 members in Rahul's house. If Rahul brings 24 mangoes, what is the ratio of the numbers representing the persons and the mangoes in proportion?

27. A student Gaurav of weight 50 kg secured 150 marks. Another student Saurav of weight 40 kg also wrote the same exam. If their weights were in proportion to their marks, how much did Saurav score the exam?

28. A and B's savings are in proportion to the ratio of their incomes. A's income is ₹12,000 and his savings is ₹4000. If B's savings is ₹12,000, then find the income of B.

29. Find the ratio of the following:
    (i) 12 g and 120 g
    (ii) 360 L and 504 L

30. Ram and Sham are told by their mother to share 68 chocolates in the ratio 6 : 11 respectively. How many chocolates do each one of them gets?

31. Are the following ratios are in proportion?
    (i) 3.2 : 4 and 8 : 10
    (ii) 1 : 2 and 2 : 1

32. Find the value of the term a in the following proportion.
    6 : 18 : : a : 54

33. Find the value of x in each of the following.
    (i) 3: 5 : : x : 25 (ii) x : 6 : : 12 : 24

Essay Type Questions

34. (i) The ratio of the areas of two squares is 1 : 4. If the area of the first square is 9 sq. units, then the area of the other square is ______ (in sq. units).
    (a) 16 (b) 36
    (c) 64 (d) 49

    (ii) The length and the breadth of a rectangle are in the ratio 12 : 5. If the length of the rectangle is 48 cm, then the breadth of the rectangle is ______.
    (a) 20 cm (b) 30 cm
    (c) 40 cm (d) 50 cm

35. Amar earns ₹50000 per month and saves 40% of his earnings. If he gets ₹10000 hike in his earnings and saves 50% of it, what will be the ratio of expenditure and savings after the hike.

PRACTICE QUESTIONS COMPETITION WING

Level 1: Apply Your Concepts

Direction for questions from 1 to 5: **Fill in the blanks.**

1. A comparison between two quantities which is of the same kind and expressed in the same unit, it is obtained by dividing one of them by the other is called their ______.
2. The simplified form of $5^2 : 5^5$ is ______.
3. 12, 14, 18, and 21 are proportion. (True/False)
4. Consider the ratio 2 : 3. The consequent and antecedent are doubled and tripled respectively. The resultant ratio is ______.
5. The ratio of $3^2 : 3^0$ is ______.
6. A sweet maker mixes sugar, milk and other ingredients in the ratio 4 : 9 : 3. In 2 kg of such sweet, find the quantity of sugar.
7. In the construction of a building, the volume of the walls is in proportion to the cost of construction. If a wall of volume 24 m^3 costs ₹18,600, then find the cost of construction of a wall of volume 36 m^3.
8. *P* and *Q*'s expenditures are in proportion to the ratio of their incomes. *P*'s income is ₹32000 and his expenditure is ₹24000. If *Q*'s expenditure is ₹36000, then find the income of Q.
   (a) ₹42000 (b) ₹39000
   (c) ₹48000 (d) ₹45000
9. Which of the following is the ratio of 2 kg 750 g and 1 kg 125 g?
   (a) 11:3 (b) 17:7
   (c) 22:9 (d) All of these
10. The simplest form of 114:133?
    (a) 2 : 3 (b) 6 : 7
    (c) 12 : 13 (d) 16 : 17
11. Can the following measures be compared using the concept of ratio?
    (i) The length (in cm) of the soft drink can in the freezer and temperature inside the freezer in °C.
    (ii) Average weight (in kg) of boys in a class and average weight (in kg) of girls in that class.

Level 2: Review Your Concepts

12. Mr. Keshav wants to distribute papaya to his three daughters in the ratio 3 : 5 : 7, such that the eldest daughter gets the highest share, and the youngest daughter gets the least share. If the eldest daughter gets 300 g more than that of the youngest, then find the total weight of the papaya distributed.
13. If $x - 10$, $x - 8$, $x - 5$, and $x - 2$ are in proportion, find the value of x.
14. At a given point of time, the heights of trees are in proportion to the lengths of the shadows of the trees. A tree of height 25.6 m casts a shadow of 32 m. If the shadow of another tree at that point of time is 48 m, then find the height of that tree.
15. If 3 kg 500 g : 7 kg :: 27 kg : *m* kg, then *m* =
    (a) 36 (b) 360
    (c) 540 (d) 54
16. In an exam the marks secured by Manish and Nagesh are in the ratio 5 : 4. If Manish secured 12 marks more than Nagesh, then how many marks did Nagesh secure in that exam?
    (a) 108 (b) 48
    (c) 60 (d) 16

Level 3: Assess Your Concepts

17. In a basket, the number of blue, white and yellow balls are in the ratio 5: 8 : 11. If there are a total of 1200 balls, then find the number of white balls.

18. Savings of A and B are in proportion to the ratio of their incomes. A's income is ₹15,000 and his savings is ₹5000. If B's savings is ₹15,000, then find the income of B.

19. Divide 126 into three parts proportional to 1, 2 and 3. Find the smallest part?

20. The sum of two numbers is 84. If the two numbers are in the ratio 4:3, find the two numbers.

21. If $4a = 3b$, find $(7a + 9b) :(4a + 5b)$.

AT

ANSWER KEYS

Crossword

Across

3. Direct 6. Same 7. Extremes 9. Proportional

Down

1. Golden 2. Divided 4. Inverse 5. Multiplied 8. Consequent
9. Proportion

Classroom Wing

Very Short Answer Type Questions

1. (b) 2. (d) 3. (c) 4. (b) 5. (c)
6. (a) → (r); (b) → (q); (c) → (s); (d) → (p) 7. 4 : 5 8. 32 9. $\frac{r}{s}$
10. 6 11. 1 12. (b) 13. (b) 14. (b)
15. (a) → (r); (b) → (s); (c) → (p); (d) → (q)

Short Answer Type Questions

16. (i) 18 : 25; (ii) 13 : 18 17. (i) 84 : 55; (ii) 57 : 92 18. (i) 3 : 8; (ii) 9 : 16
19. ₹1086, ₹724 and ₹543 20. $\frac{p}{5}$ 21. 210, 40, 28 22. 7 : 5
23. (i) Not in proportion; (ii) In proportion 24. (i) 28; (ii) 9 25. (i) 720; (ii) $\frac{1}{12}$
26. Yes 27. 120 marks 28. ₹36,000 29. (i) 1 : 10; (ii) 5 : 7 30. 24; 44
31. (i) Yes; (ii) No 32. 18 33. (i) 15; (ii) 3

Essay Type Questions

34. (i) (b); (ii) (a) 35. 7 : 5

Competition Wing

Level 1: Apply Your Concepts

1. Ratio 2. 1 : 125 3. True 4. 1 : 1 5. 9 : 1 6. 500 g
7. ₹27,900 8. (c) 9. (c) 10. (b) 11. (i) No; (ii) Yes

Level 2: Review Your Concepts

12. 1125 g 13. 20 14. 38.4 m 15. (d) 16. (b)

Level 3: Assess Your Concepts

17. 400 18. ₹45000 19. 21 20. 48,36 21. 57:32

Hints and Explanations

CLASSROOM WING

Very Short Answer Type Questions

1. Given that a, b, c and d are in proportion.
$ad = bc$
($\because$ The product of extremes = the product of means)
Hence, the correct option is (b).

2. $25:35 = \frac{25}{5}:\frac{35}{5} = 5:7.$
$35:49 = \frac{35}{7}:\frac{49}{7} = 5:7.$
$60:84 = \frac{60}{12}:\frac{84}{12} = 5:7.$
Hence, the correct option is (d).

3. $a/c : b/c = a:b$
Hence, the correct option is (c).

4. 75 paise : ₹10 = 75 : 1000 = 25 × 3 : 25 × 40
= 3 : 40
Hence, the correct option is (b).

5. 10 m : 1 km = 10 m : 1000 m
10 × 1 : 10 × 100 = 1 : 100
Hence, the correct option is (c).

6. (a) $\frac{1}{3}:\frac{2}{5} = 5:6 \rightarrow$ (r)
(b) $\frac{3}{4}:\frac{5}{2} = 3:10 \rightarrow$ (q)
(c) $\frac{2}{3}:\frac{3}{5} = 10:9 \rightarrow$ (s)
(d) $\frac{4}{3}:\frac{1}{5} = 20:3 \rightarrow$ (p)
Therefore, the correct match is:
(a) → (r), (b) → (q), (c) → (s), (d) → (p)

7. The simplified form of
$\frac{6}{7}:\frac{15}{14} = \frac{6 \div 3}{7 \div 7}:\frac{15 \div 3}{14 \div 7} = 2:\frac{5}{2} = 4:5.$

8. Given that $3:8 = 12:x$.
$3x = 8 \times 12$
($\because$ The product of extremes = the product of means)
$x = \frac{96}{3} = 32.$

9. p, q, r, s are in proportion.
$p:q::r:s$
$\frac{p}{q} = \frac{r}{s}$

10. 3, x, 6, 12 are in proportion.
$\frac{3}{x} = \frac{6}{12} \Rightarrow \frac{3}{x} = \frac{3}{6}$
$\Rightarrow x = 6.$

11. $x:5::4:20$
$\Rightarrow \frac{x}{5} = \frac{4}{20}$
$\frac{x}{5} = \frac{1}{5}$
$\Rightarrow x = 1$

12. (a) 2, 5, 7, 10
Product of extremes = 2 × 10 = 20
Product of means = 5 × 7 = 35
$2 \times 10 \neq 5 \times 7$
(b) $4:3::8:6$
$\Rightarrow \frac{4}{3} = \frac{8}{6}$ (True)
(c) a, b, c, d are in proportion.
$\Rightarrow \frac{a}{b} = \frac{c}{d} \Rightarrow bc = ad$
$\frac{b}{c}$ need not be equal to $\frac{d}{a}$
Hence, the correct option is (b).

13. $x:12::12:18$
Product of extremes = Product of means
$\Rightarrow 18 \times x = 12 \times 12$

$\Rightarrow x = \frac{12}{18} \times 12 = \frac{12 \times 2}{3}$

$x = 8$

Hence, the correct option is (b).

14. $\frac{1}{2} : \frac{1}{3} :: \frac{1}{4} : x$

$\frac{1}{2} \times x = \frac{1}{3} \times \frac{1}{4}$

$x = \frac{1}{3} \times \frac{1}{4} \times 2$

$x = \frac{1}{6}$

Hence, the correct option is (b).

15. (a) $x : 5 :: 2 : 3$

$\frac{x}{5} = \frac{2}{3}$

$\Rightarrow x = \frac{10}{3} \rightarrow$ (r)

(b) $2 : x :: 4 : 3$

$\Rightarrow \frac{2}{x} = \frac{4}{3}$

$\Rightarrow x = 2 \times \frac{3}{4} = \frac{6}{4} = \frac{3}{2} \rightarrow$ (s)

(c) $2 : 5 :: x : 3$

$\Rightarrow \frac{2}{5} = \frac{x}{3}$

$\Rightarrow x = \frac{2}{5} \times 3 = \frac{6}{5} \rightarrow$ (p)

(d) $2 : 5 :: 3 : x$

$\frac{2}{5} = \frac{3}{x}$

$\Rightarrow x = 3 \times \frac{5}{2}$

$x = \frac{15}{2} \rightarrow$ (q)

Therefore, the correct match is:

(a) → (r), (b) → (s), (c) → (p), (d) → (q)

Short Answer Type Questions

16. (i) 360 ml, 500 ml

360 : 500 = 36 : 50

= 2 × 18 : 2 × 25 = 18 : 25

(ii) 4 h 20 min : 6 h

= (4 × 60 + 20) : 6 × 60 = 260 : 360

= 26 : 36 = 13 : 18

17. (i) $4\frac{1}{5} : 2\frac{3}{4}$

$= \frac{21}{5} : \frac{11}{4} = 84 : 55$

(ii) $2\frac{3}{8} : 3\frac{5}{6} = \frac{19}{8} : \frac{23}{6}$

LCM of 8 and 6 is 24.

$= \frac{19}{8} \times 24 : \frac{23}{6} \times 24 = 57 : 92$

18. (i) $\frac{1}{6} : \frac{3}{8}$

LCM of 6 and 8 is 24.

$\frac{1}{6} \times 24 : \frac{3}{8} \times 24$

$= 4 : 9 = \frac{1}{6} < \frac{3}{8}$

∴ 3 : 8 is greater.

(ii) $\frac{9}{16} : \frac{5}{12}$

LCM of 16, 12 is 48.

$\frac{9}{16} \times 48 : \frac{5}{12} \times 48 = 27 : 20$

$\frac{9}{16} > \frac{5}{12}$

∴ 9 : 16 is greater.

19. The ratio of the shares of A, B and C = $\frac{1}{2} : \frac{1}{3} : \frac{1}{4}$

$= \frac{1}{2} \times 12 : \frac{1}{3} \times 12 : \frac{1}{4} \times 12$ [LCM of 2, 3, and 4 is 12]

= 6 : 4 : 3.

Total amount = ₹2353.

The share of A = $\frac{6}{6+4+3} \times 2353$

$= \frac{6}{13} \times 2353$

= 6 × 181 = ₹1086.

The share of B = $\frac{4}{13} \times 2353$

= 4 × 181 = ₹724.

The share of C $= \frac{3}{13} \times 2353$

$= 3 \times 181 = ₹543.$

Hence, the ratio of the shares of A, B and C are ₹1086, ₹724, and ₹543.

20. Given that the cost of 175 oranges is ₹p.

Let the cost of 35 oranges be x.

$175 : p = 35 : x$.

We know that the product of extremes = the product of means.

$175 \times x = p \times 35$

$x = \frac{p \times 35}{175}$

$x = \frac{p}{5}$.

21. Ratio of the numbers

$= \frac{3}{1} : \frac{4}{7} : \frac{2}{5} = 105 : 20 : 14$

The required numbers are

$\frac{105}{105+20+14} \times 278, \frac{20}{105+20+14} \times 278,$

$\frac{14}{105+20+14} \times 278$

The three numbers are 210, 40, 28.

22. Total number of students = 720

Number of girls = 720 − 300 = 420

Ratio of the number of girls to that of boys

= 420 : 300 = 7 × 60 : 5 × 60 = 7 : 5

23. (i) 2, 3, 2016, 2019

$2 \times 2019 = 4038$

$3 \times 2016 = 6048$

$\therefore 2 \times 2019 \neq 3 \times 2016$

Hence, 2, 3, 2016 and 2019 are not in proportion.

(ii) 12, 15, 32, 40

$12 \times 40 = 480$

$15 \times 32 = 480$

$\therefore 12 \times 40 = 15 \times 32$

Hence, 12, 15, 32 and 40 are in proportion.

24. (i) $17 : 68 : : 7 : x$

$\Rightarrow \frac{17}{68} = \frac{7}{x}$

$\therefore \ x = 28$

(ii) $14 : 42 : : x : 27$

$\frac{14}{42} = \frac{x}{27}$

$\frac{1}{3} = \frac{x}{27}$

$\therefore x = 9$

25. (i) $45 \times 15 = 675$

$9 \times 27 \neq 675$

$45 \times 9 = 405$

$27 \times 15 = 405$

$\Rightarrow 45 : 27 :: 15 : 9$

∴ 45, 27, 15, 9 are in proportion.

∴ Product of extremes = 405.

(ii) $\frac{1}{6}, \frac{1}{15}, \frac{1}{40}, \frac{4}{9}$

$\frac{1}{6} \times \frac{4}{9} = \frac{2}{27}$

$\frac{1}{15} \times \frac{1}{40} \neq \frac{2}{27}$

$\frac{1}{6} \times \frac{1}{15} = \frac{1}{90}$

$\frac{4}{9} \times \frac{1}{40} = \frac{1}{90}$

$\frac{1}{6} : \frac{4}{9} :: \frac{1}{40} : \frac{1}{15}$

$\therefore \frac{1}{6}, \frac{4}{9}, \frac{1}{40}, \frac{1}{15}$ are in proportion.

∴ Product of extremes $= \frac{1}{6} \times \frac{1}{15} = \frac{1}{90}$.

26. Given that: 1 person eats 3 mangoes.

The ratio of the number of person to mangoes is 1 : 3.

Now, 1 : 3 :: 8 : 24

∴ The number of persons and that of mangoes are in proportion.

27. Let the marks obtained by Saurav be x.

$50 : 40 : : 150 : x$

$\frac{50}{40} = \frac{150}{x} \Rightarrow \frac{5}{4} = \frac{150}{x}$

$x = 150 \times \frac{4}{5} \Rightarrow x = 120$

∴ Saurav got 120 marks.

28. Incomes of A and B are ₹12000 and ₹x, respectively.

Savings of A and B are ₹4000, ₹12000.

$\therefore$ 12000 : x = 4000 : 12000

$$\frac{12000}{x} = \frac{4000}{12000} \Rightarrow \frac{12000}{x} = \frac{1}{3}$$

$\Rightarrow x$ = ₹36000

$\therefore$ Income of B is ₹36000.

29. (i) 12 : 120 = 1 : 10

(ii) 360 : 504 = 5 : 7

30. Ram and Sham shares 68 chocolates in the ratio 6 : 11.

Ram gets: 68 × 6/(11+6)= 68 × 6/17 = 4 × 6 = 24

Sham gets: 68 × 11/(11+6)= 68 × 11/17 = 4 × 11 = 44

Ram gets 24 chocolates and Sham gets 44 chocolates.

31. (i) 3.2 : 4 : : 8 : 10

Product of extremes = 3.2 × 10 = 32

Product of means = 4 × 8 = 32

$\therefore$ 3.2 : 4 and 8 : 10 are in proportion.

(ii) 1 : 2 : : 2 : 1

Product of extremes = 1 × 1 = 1

Product of means = 2 × 2 = 4

$\therefore$ 1 : 2 and 2 : 1 are not in proportion.

32. Given that: 6 : 18 : : a : 54 are in proportion.

$a \times 18 = 54 \times 6$

$$a = \frac{54 \times 6}{18}$$

$a = 18$

33. (i) $3/5 = x/25 \Rightarrow 5x = 75 \Rightarrow x = 15$.

(ii) $x/6 = 12/24 \Rightarrow 24x = 72 \Rightarrow x = 3$.

Essay Type Questions

34. (i) Let the area of other square be x.

$1 : 4 = 9 : x$

$$\frac{1}{4} = \frac{9}{x}$$

$x = 9 \times 4$

$x = 36$ sq. units

Hence, the correct option is (b).

(ii) Let the breadth of the rectangle be x.

$12 : 5 = 48 : x$

$$\frac{12}{5} = \frac{48}{x}$$

$$x = \frac{48}{12} \times 5$$

$x = 4 \times 5$

$x = 20$ cm

Hence, the correct option is (a).

35. Monthly earnings of Amar = ₹50000.

Monthly savings = 40% of ₹50000 = ₹20000.

New earnings = ₹50000 + ₹10000 = ₹60000

New savings = ₹20000 + 50% of ₹10000 = ₹20000 + ₹5000 = ₹25000.

New Expenditure = ₹60000 - ₹25000 = ₹35000.

The required ratio = ₹35000 : ₹25000 = **7 : 5**.

COMPETITION WING

Level 1: Apply Your Concepts

1. Ratio

2. The simplified form of $5^2 : 5^5 = \frac{5^2}{5^2} : \frac{5^5}{5^2}$

$= 1 : 5^3 = 1 : 125.$

3. $12 \times 21 = 252.$

$14 \times 18 = 252.$

$\Rightarrow 12 \times 21 = 14 \times 18$

So, 12, 14, 18, and 21 are proportion.

Hence, the given statement is **true**.

4. The required ratio is $3 \times 2 : 2 \times 3 = 6 : 6 = 1 : 1$

5. $3^2 : 3^0 = 9 : 1$

6. 2 kg Sweet : Sugar : Milk : Others = 4 : 9 : 3

Weight of sugar in 2 kg of sweet

$= \frac{4}{4+9+3} \times 2 = \frac{4}{16} \times 2 = \frac{1}{2}$ kg = 500 g

7. Given, 24 : 36 : : 18600 : x

$\frac{24}{36} = \frac{18600}{x} \Rightarrow x = \frac{18600}{24} \times 36$

$x = 18{,}600 \times \frac{3}{2} \Rightarrow x = 9300 \times 3 \Rightarrow x =$ ₹27900

8. P and Q's expenditures are in proportion to the ratio of their incomes.

$\Rightarrow$ P's expenditure : P's income = Q's expenditure : Q's income

$\Rightarrow$ ₹24000 : ₹32000 = ₹36000 : Q's income

$\Rightarrow 32000 \times 36000 = 24000 \times$ Q's income

$\Rightarrow$ Q's income $= \frac{32000 \times 36000}{24000} =$ ₹48000

Hence, the correct option is (c).

9. The ratio of 2 kg 750 g and 1 kg 125 g is 2750 : 1125.

$= \frac{2750}{25} : \frac{1125}{25}$

$= 110 : 45$

$= \frac{110}{5} : \frac{45}{5}$

$= 22 : 9$

Hence, the correct option is (c).

10. The simplest form of $114 : 133 = \frac{114}{19} : \frac{133}{19} = 6 : 7.$

Hence, the correct option is (b).

11. (i) No (ii) Yes

Level 2: Review Your Concepts

12. [7/(3 + 5 + 7) - 3/(3 + 5 + 7)] of total weight = 300 grams

(7/15 – 3/15) of total weight = 300 grams

= 4/15 of total weight = 300 grams

Hence, total weight = (300)(15)/4 = 1,125 grams.

13. Given that $x-10$, $x-8$, $x-5$, and $x-2$ are in proportion.

$(x-10)(x-2) = (x-8)(x-5)$

$x^2 - 12x + 20 = x^2 - 13x + 40$

$\boldsymbol{x} = 20.$

14. Given, 32 : 48 : : 25.6 : x

$\frac{32}{48} = \frac{25.6}{x} \Rightarrow \frac{2}{3} = \frac{25.6}{x}$

$x = 25.6 \times \frac{3}{2} = 38.4$ m

15. Given, 3 kg 500 g : 7 kg :: 27 kg : m kg

3 kg 500 g = 3000 g + 500 g = 3500 g; 7 kg = 7000 g; 27 kg = 27000 g; m kg = 1000 m g

$\Rightarrow 3500 : 7000 :: 27000 : 1000\,m$

$\Rightarrow 7000 \times 27000 = 3500 \times 1000\,m$

$\Rightarrow m = \frac{7000 \times 27000}{3500 \times 1000}$

$\Rightarrow m = 54$

Hence, the correct option is (d).

16. Let the marks secured by Manish and Nagesh be $5x$ and $4x$, respectively.

Given, $5x = 4x + 12$

$5x - 4x = 12 \Rightarrow x = 12$

Therefore, the marks secured by Nagesh $= 4x = 4 \times 12 = 48.$

Hence, the correct option is (b).

Level 3: Assess Your Concepts

17. The ratio of the number of blue balls, white balls, and yellow balls

= 5 : 8 : 11

Total number of balls is 1200

Number of white balls = $\frac{8}{5+8+11} \times 1200$

= $\frac{8}{24} \times 1200 = 400$.

18. Incomes of A and B are ₹15,000, ₹x.

Savings of A and B are ₹5000, ₹15000

∴ 15000: x = 5000 : 15000

$\frac{15000}{x} = \frac{5000}{15000} \Rightarrow \frac{15000}{x} = \frac{1}{3}$

⇒ x = ₹45000

∴ Income of B is ₹45000

19. The three numbers can be expressed as x, $2x$ and $3x$.

Now, by adding these values together, we get

$x + 2x + 3x = 126$

or $6x = 126$

Divide each side by 6, we get

$x = \frac{126}{6}$ or $x = 21$

So, the smallest part is 21.

(Note: the other parts are 42 and 63).

20. As the two numbers are in the ratio 4:3, let their actual values be $4x$ and $3x$.

As the sum of two numbers is 84, we have $4x + 3x = 84$

$\Rightarrow 7x = 84$

$\Rightarrow x = (84/7) = 12$.

Hence, $4x = 48$ and $3x = 36$.

Alternatively, the two numbers are $(4/7) \times 84$ and $(3/7) \times 84$, i.e., 48 and 36 respectively since the ratio of the two numbers is 4:3.

21. It is given that $4a = 3b$,

Hence, $(a/b) = (3/4)$

$\Rightarrow a = 3k$ and $b = 4k$, where k is the common factor of a and b.

Required expression $(7a + 9b) : (4a + 5b)$

$= [(7 \times 3k) + (9 \times 4k)] : [(4 \times 3k) + (5 \times 4k)]$

$= (21k + 36k) : (12k + 20k)$

$= 57k : 32\,k = 57 : 32$

CHAPTER

6

Percentages and their Applications

Remember

Before beginning this chapter, you should be able to:

- Recall equivalent fractions
- Compare fractions and decimals

Key Ideas

After completing this chapter, you should be able to:

- Express percentage as fraction and fraction as percentage
- Compare percentages
- Understand SP, CP, profit, loss, discount
- Understand simple interest

Scientific Crypt

A Tribute to Luca Pacioli: Renaissance Mathematician (1447-1517)

Luca Pacioli was a mathematician who lived in the heart of Italy during the Renaissance (1447–1517). People were rediscovering art, science, and, of course, mathematics at this time.

Luca Pacioli was a significant figure who contributed significantly to the world of mathematics. He attended some of the best universities and even worked with famous people such as Leonardo da Vinci.

Pacioli's most important work, "Summa de Arithmetica," was about more than just difficult math problems. Instead, it was a guide for merchants at the time. Merchants are individuals who buy and sell goods. They had to do all of their math by hand back when there were no calculators or computers.

Consider yourself a merchant attempting to determine how much to charge for an item or how much you've earned after selling many items. This is where percentages come into play. If a merchant purchased a vase for 10 gold coins and wanted to sell it for a profit, he would use percentages to determine the new price.

FUN TIME

CROSSWORD

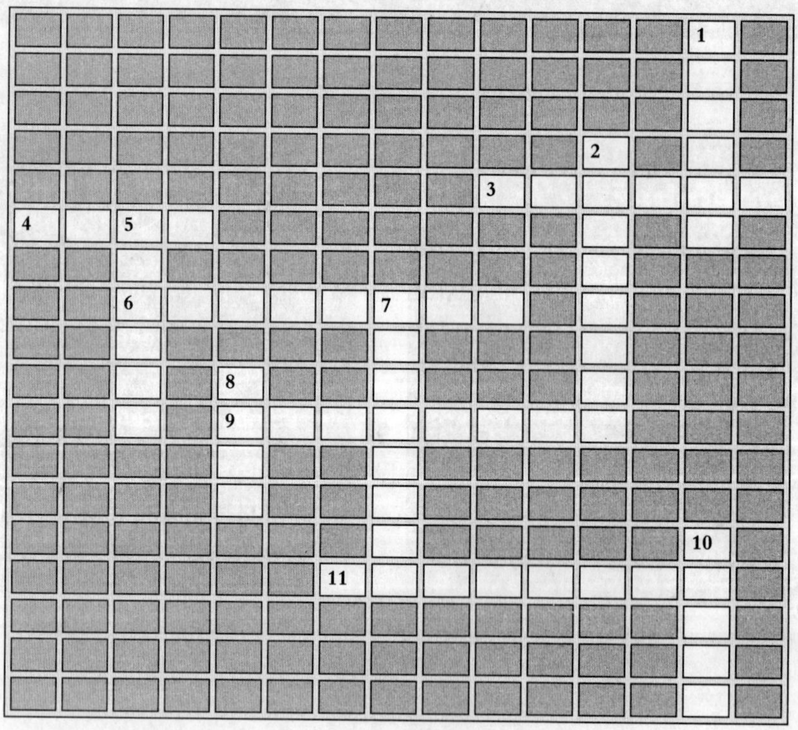

Across

3. The amount left after all expenses are deducted from the total revenue is known as _______ profit.
4. The outcome if the selling price is lower than the cost price.
6. The time at which the principal amount of a loan or bond becomes due and is repaid to the investor and interest payments stop.
9. Ongoing expenses of a business that aren't directly tied to producing a specific product or service, but can affect profit.
11. When a percentage represents a reduction from an original amount.

Down

1. What one makes if the selling price is higher than the cost price.
2. Interest on both the initial principal and the accumulated interest from previous periods on a deposit or loan is known as __________ interest.
5. The interest type where the principal stays constant throughout the loan period is know as ________ interest.
7. When a percentage signifies growth from the starting value.
8. The price at which an item is originally purchased is know as ______ price.
10. A fraction where the denominator is 100.

INTRODUCTION

Mathematics is a language of numbers and symbols. Most of us must have seen the symbol % (per cent) on daily basis. When we receive our report card, we see the percentage obtained. For example, if a student obtains 80%, it means that he overall scored 80 parts from 100. In this chapter, we shall learn the concept of percentage and solve the problems based on it.

Percentages

The term 'per cent' means 'for every hundred'.

A fraction, in which the denominator is 100, is a **percentage**. The denominator, i.e., 100 is denoted by a special symbol %, which is read as per cent.

Examples: 10/100 = 10%

25/100 = 25%

$x/100 = x\%$

Since any ratio is a fraction, each ratio can also be expressed as a percentage.

Example: A ratio of 1/2 can be converted to a percentage figure as $\frac{1}{2} = \frac{1(50)}{2(50)} = \frac{50}{100}$ = 50%

Info Bytes!

The term 'per cent' is derived from the Latin term per centum which means per hundred. It's interesting that even though percentages are used globally, the concept has its roots in ancient language.

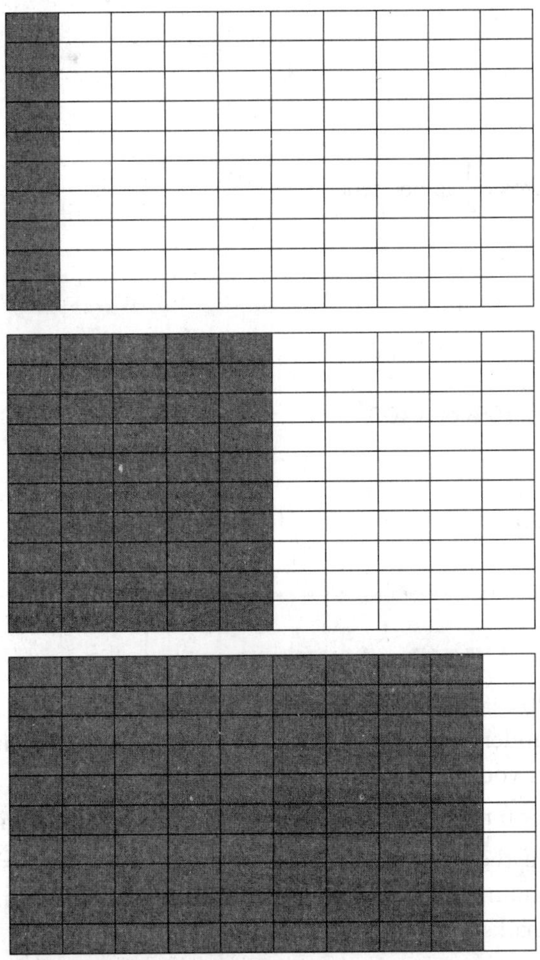

Figure 6.1 Representation of 10%, 50%, 90%

Expressing x% as a Fraction

Any percentage can be expressed as a decimal fraction by dividing the percentage figure by 100. As $x\% = x$ out of $100 = x/100$. So, 75% = 75 out of 100 = 75/100 = 3/4 or 0.75.

Expressing the Fraction a/b as a Decimal and as a Percentage

Any fraction can be expressed as a decimal and any decimal fraction can be converted into percentage by multiplying it by 100.

Examples: 1/2 = 0.5 = 50%

1/4 = 0.25 = 25%

1/5 = 0.2 = 20%

1/3 = 0.33… = 33.33…%

EXAMPLE 6.1 Express 40% as a fraction.

SOLUTION

$$40\% = \frac{40}{100} = \frac{4}{10} = \frac{2}{5}$$

$\therefore$ 40% as a fraction is $\frac{2}{5}$.

EXAMPLE 6.2 Express 77% as a decimal.

SOLUTION

$$77\% = \frac{77}{100} = 0.77$$

EXAMPLE 6.3 Express $\frac{1}{4}$ as per cent.

SOLUTION

$$\frac{1}{4} = \left(\frac{1}{4}\right) \times 100\% = 25\%.$$

EXAMPLE 6.4 Find 35% of 1400.

SOLUTION

$$35\% \text{ of } 1400 = \left(\frac{35}{100}\right) \times 1400 = 490.$$

Percentage, a Relative Value

When you obtain 16 marks out of 20 marks in your maths unit test, this would be an absolute value. Let us say that you got 80% in the maths unit test, it is understood that you got 80 marks out of 100 marks. However, if the maximum marks for the unit test is 50, then the marks you got is 80% of 50 or (80/100)50 = 40.

Hence, the actual score depends upon the maximum marks of the unit test and varies with the maximum marks.

Percentage, a Relative Value, if the maximum score is 60, then 80% of 60 = 48. If the maximum marks are 70, then 80% of 70 = 56. As the maximum marks vary, your marks may also vary. Hence, percentage is seen as a relative or comparative value. If the maximum marks are 100, your score is 80.

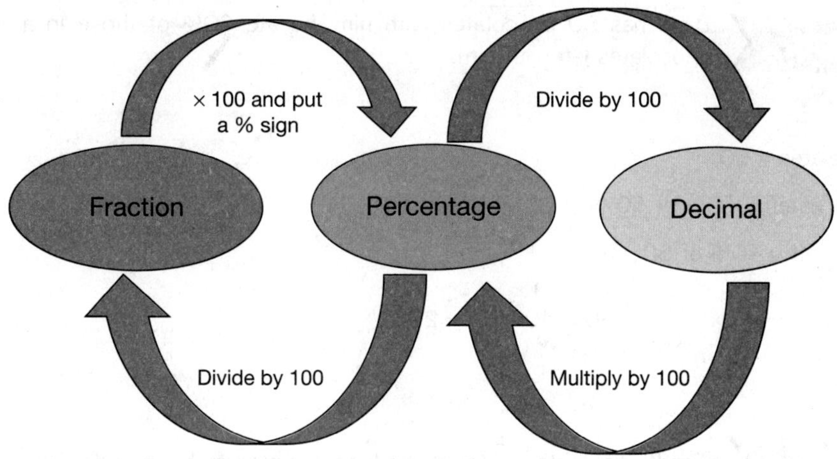

Figure 6.2 Conversions between decimal, fraction and percentage

EXAMPLE 6.5

Represent the following decimals as percentages.

(I) 3.80 **(II)** 0.96

SOLUTION

(I) $3.80 = 3.80 \times 100 \times \frac{1}{100} = 3.80 \times 100\% = 380\%$

(II) $0.96 = 0.96 \times 100 \times \frac{1}{100} = 0.96 \times 100\% = 96\%$

EXAMPLE 6.6

Represent the following percentages as fractions.

(I) 140% **(II)** 8.5%

SOLUTION

(I) $140\% = 140 \times \frac{1}{100} = 14 \times \frac{1}{10} = \frac{7}{5}$

(II) $8.5\% = 8.5 \times \frac{1}{100} = \frac{85}{1000} = \frac{17}{200}$

EXAMPLE 6.7

Represent the following fractions as percentages.

(I) $\frac{3}{8}$ **(II)** $\frac{8}{3}$

SOLUTION

(I) $\frac{5}{8} = \frac{5}{8} \times 100 \times \frac{1}{100} = \frac{5}{8} \times 100\% = 5 \times 12.5\% = 62.5\%$

(II) $\frac{8}{5} = \frac{8}{5} \times 100 \times \frac{1}{100} = \frac{8}{5} \times 100\% = 8 \times 20\% = 160\%$

EXAMPLE 6.8 Banti has 50 chocolates with him, he ate 60% of those in a week. Find the number of chocolates left with him.

SOLUTION

Total number of chocolates = 50

Number of chocolates eaten = 60% of 50

Number of chocolates left = 40% of 50

$$= 40 \times \frac{1}{100} \times 50 = 40 \times \frac{1}{2} = 20$$

EXAMPLE 6.9 Chanti distributed $\frac{3}{4}$th of his birthday cake to his friends. Find the percentage of the cake distributed to his friends.

SOLUTION

Fraction of the cake distributed = $\frac{3}{4}$

$$\frac{3}{4} = \frac{3 \times 25}{4 \times 25} = \frac{75}{100}$$

$$= 75 \times \frac{1}{100} = 75\%$$

Profit, Loss and Discount

The concept of percentage finds numerous applications in commercial Mathematics. When we go shopping, we frequently come across terms like sale, discount, price, etc. Let us understand the basic terms related to profit, loss and discount.

> **Info Bytes!**
> Profit isn't just about money. In broader terms, profit means gaining more than what you started with. So, if you started with 5 apples and ended up with 8, your 'apple profit' would be 3 apples.

Profit and Loss

When a person buys an article for a certain price and then sells it for a different price, he makes a **profit** or incurs a **loss**.

Cost Price

The price at which an article is purchased is called its **cost price** (CP).

Selling Price

The price at which an article is sold is called its **selling price** (SP).

If the selling price of an article is greater than its cost price, we say that there is a profit (or) gain (p) and if it is less, we say that there is a loss (ℓ).

If $p < 0$, then there is a loss. If SP = CP, then there is no profit and no loss. Profit or loss is generally expressed as a percentage of the cost price.

Discount

Nowadays we know that the competition is very high in any business. So, in order to cope up with this competition and also to boost the sale of goods, shopkeepers offer rebate to customers. The rebate offered is called **discount**. Discount is always calculated on the market price (MP) of the article.

1. Discount = MP – SP
2. Discount Percentage = $\frac{\text{Discount}}{\text{MP}} \times 100\%$

Overheads

All the expenditure incurred on transportation, repairs, etc., (if any) are categorized as **overheads**. These overheads are always included in the cost price of the article.

EXAMPLE 6.10 The cost price of an article is ₹450. It is sold for ₹495. Find the profit percentage.

SOLUTION

CP = ₹450; SP = ₹495

SP > CP and SP – CP = profit

Profit = ₹(495 – 450) = ₹45

$$\text{Profit percentage} = \frac{\text{Profit}}{\text{CP}} \times 100\%$$

$$= \frac{45}{450} \times 100\% = 10\%$$

EXAMPLE 6.11 A book is sold at a profit of 20%. If its cost price is ₹20, then find its selling price.

SOLUTION

CP of the book = ₹20

Profit percentage = 20%

Profit = 20% of ₹20

$$= 20 \times \frac{1}{100} \times ₹20 = ₹4$$

Selling price = CP + Profit

= ₹(20 + 4) = ₹24

EXAMPLE 6.12 A shopkeeper sold an article for ₹280. If its cost price is ₹300, then find his loss percentage.

SOLUTION

CP of the article = ₹300

SP of the article = ₹280

SP < CP and loss = CP – SP = ₹(300 – 280) = ₹20

$$\text{Loss percentage} = \frac{\text{Loss}}{\text{CP}} \times 100\%$$

$$= \frac{20}{300} \times 100\% = 6\frac{2}{3}\%$$

EXAMPLE 6.13 The cost price of an article is ₹500. The article is marked as ₹700. If the shopkeeper sold it at a discount of 30%, then find the profit or loss percentage.

SOLUTION

The cost price of the article = ₹500

The marked price of the article = ₹700

Discount = 30% of 700 = $\frac{30}{100} \times 700$ = ₹210

Selling price = Marked price – Discount = ₹(700 – 210)

SP = ₹490

∴ SP < CP and loss = CP – SP

Loss = ₹(500 – 490) = ₹10

Loss percentage = $\frac{\text{Loss}}{\text{CP}} \times 100\%$

$= \frac{10}{500} \times 100\% = 2\%$

Simple Interest

Interest is the money paid by a borrower to the lender which is received by the lender for a specific time period until repayment is done.

Example: If person A borrows ₹100 from person B, for a period of one year on the condition that he would repay ₹110 at the end of a year, the additional money of ₹10 is the interest. A is the borrower and B is the lender and ₹100 is the principal.

The definitions for specific terms which are used frequently are given below:

Principal or Sum

The money borrowed from an agency or an individual for a certain period of time is called the **principal** or **sum**.

> **Konnect**
>
> Simple interest is like a rent on money. If you borrowed money, or if you lend it to someone, simple interest is the 'fee' for using that money over a period of time. Think of it as the cost of borrowing or the reward for lending.

Amount

The principal together with the interest is called the **amount**, i.e., Amount (A) = Principal (P) + Interest (I).

Rate of Interest

The interest on principal per annum is called the **rate of interest** per annum.

Simple Interest

If the principal remains the same for the entire loan period, then the interest paid is called **simple interest**.

Formula for the Computation of Simple Interest

Let P be the principal in rupees, R be the rate of interest and T denotes the number of years. Then, Simple Interest (SI) = PTR/100.

Also, Amount (A) = Principal (P) + Simple Interest (SI) $= P + \frac{PTR}{100} = P\left(1 + \frac{RT}{100}\right)$

EXAMPLE 6.14 Principal = ₹25000. Amount after 2 years is ₹30000. Find the rate of interest per annum.

SOLUTION

Interest = Amount – Principal

= ₹(30000 – 25000) = ₹5000

Rate of interest = $\frac{5000}{25000} \times 100\% = 20\%$

EXAMPLE 6.15 How much simple interest is to be paid on a loan of ₹20000 at 18% per annum for a period of 3 years?

SOLUTION

P = ₹20000, R = 18%, T = 3 years

$SI = \frac{PTR}{100}$

$SI = \frac{20000 \times 3 \times 18}{100} = 600 \times 18 =$ ₹10800

∴ Interest to be paid at the end of 3 years = ₹10800

EXAMPLE 6.16 The simple interest on a sum of ₹12000 is ₹1440. Find the amount after 5 years.

SOLUTION

Interest for one year = ₹1440

Interest for five years = ₹(1440 × 5) = ₹7200

∴ Amount = Principal + Interest

Amount after five years = ₹12000 + ₹7200 = ₹19200

EXAMPLE 6.17 Mr Abhishek paid ₹360 as an interest for 8 months at 18% p.a. Find the principal value of the loan taken by him.

SOLUTION

Let the principal be P.

R = 18% p.a.

$T = 8 \text{ months} = \frac{8}{12} \text{ years} = \frac{2}{3} \text{ years}$

$SI = \frac{PTR}{100}$

$360 = P \times \frac{2}{3} \times \frac{18}{100}$

$P = \frac{360 \times 3 \times 100}{2 \times 18} = 10 \times 300 =$ ₹3000

POINTS TO REMEMBER

- ✔ A fraction, in which the denominator is 100, is a percentage.
- ✔ When a person buys an article for a certain price and then sells it for a different price, he makes a profit or incurs a loss.
- ✔ The price at which an article is purchased is called its cost price (CP).
- ✔ The price at which an article is sold is called its selling price (SP).
- ✔ The money borrowed from an agency or an individual for a certain period of time is called the principal.
- ✔ The principal together with the interest is called the amount.
- ✔ The interest on principal per annum is called the rate of interest per annum.
- ✔ If the principal remains the same for the entire loan period, then the interest paid is called simple interest.

DW

PRACTICE QUESTIONS CLASSROOM WING

Very Short Answer Type Questions

***Direction for questions from 1 to 5:* Select the correct alternative from the given choices.**

1. Which of the following is the equivalent percentage to 1.5?
   (a) 150% (b) 100%
   (c) 50% (d) 25%

2. What is the value of 50% of 75 + 150% of 75?
   (a) 375 (b) 300
   (c) 225 (d) 150

3. 100% of x is equal to ______.
   (a) $100x$ (b) $0.1x$
   (c) $0.01x$ (d) x

4. 15% of 50 is equal to ______.
   (a) 50% of 30 (b) 100% of 30
   (c) 7.5% of 25 (d) 100% of 7.5

5. 10% of 20% of 100 is equal to ______.
   (a) 30% of 100 (b) 2% of 100
   (c) 15% of 100 (d) 200% of 100

***Direction for question 6:* Match Column A with Column B.**

6.

Column A	Column B
(a) 45%	(p) $\frac{3}{2}$
(b) 75%	(q) $\frac{9}{20}$
(c) 125%	(r) $\frac{3}{4}$
(d) 150%	(s) $\frac{5}{4}$

***Direction for questions from 7 to 11:* Fill in the blanks.**

7. A person borrowed ₹10000 and paid back ₹11000. The interest paid by the borrower is ____.

8. If the selling price is less than the cost price, then there is a ______ in this transaction.

9. If the cost price of an article is ₹55 and the selling price is ₹44, then the loss in this transaction is ______ and the loss % is ______.

10. If the cost price is equal to the selling price, then there is ______.

11. If the profit on selling an article is ₹50 and the cost price of the article is ₹500, then the profit percentage is ______.

***Direction for questions from 12 to 15:* Select the correct alternative from the given choices.**

12. Which of the following is true?
    (a) 10% profit on cost price of ₹450 is ₹50.
    (b) If loss % on the cost price of ₹400 is 25%, then the selling price is ₹300.
    (c) Selling price – Loss = Cost price
    (d) Profit – Cost price = Selling price

13. The percentage of loss is calculated on the ______.
    (a) Selling price (b) Cost price
    (c) Marked price (d) None of these

14. Discount = ______.
    (a) Cost price + Selling price
    (b) Selling price – Marked price
    (c) Marked price – Cost price
    (d) Marked price – Selling price

15. If an article is sold for ₹150 at a loss of ₹50, then which of the following is true?
    (a) 20% loss
    (b) 10% loss
    (c) 25% loss
    (d) 50% loss

***Direction for question 6:* Match Column A with Column B.**

16.

Column A	Column B
(a) CP = ₹200, SP = ₹210	(p) 5% profit
(b) CP = ₹400, SP = ₹500	(q) 10% profit
(c) CP = ₹700, SP = ₹770	(r) 20% profit
(d) CP = ₹800, SP = ₹960	(s) 25% profit

Direction for questions 17 to 21: **Fill in the blanks.**

17. Amount = ______ + Interest.

18. The money taken as loan is called ______.

19. The additional money to be paid for using others money is called ______.

20. The money paid to the money lender which includes the interest and the principal is called ______.

21. The simple interest on ₹1000 at 10% p.a. for 10 years is ______.

Direction for questions 22 to 26: **Select the correct alternative from the given choices.**

22. If $I = \frac{PTR}{100}$ then T = ______.

(a) $\frac{PT}{100}$ (b) $\frac{100IR}{P}$

(c) $\frac{PR}{100I}$ (d) $\frac{100I}{PR}$

23. Interest on ₹500 at 12% p.a. for 1 year is ______.

(a) 50 (b) 60

(c) 70 (d) 80

24. Interest on a certain sum is ₹456 and the amount is ₹2988. The principal is ₹______.

(a) 2532 (b) 2522

(c) 3444 (d) 2352

25. A sum of ₹4700 is doubled in 6 years under simple interest at a certain rate of interest. The interest is ₹______.

(a) 2350 (b) 4700

(c) 9400 (d) Cannot be determined

26. The simple interest on ₹550 at the rate of 5% p.a. for 2 years is ______.

(a) ₹55 (b) ₹27.50

(c) ₹125 (d) ₹12.50

Direction for question 27: **Match Column A with Column B.**

27.

	Column A (in ₹)		Column B (in ₹)
(a)	P = 256, I = 23	(p)	A = 289
(b)	P = 265, I = 34	(q)	A = 279
(c)	P = 258, I = 31	(r)	A = 269
(d)	P = 257, I = 12	(s)	A = 299

Short Answer Type Questions

28. If an amount is doubled in 5 years, what is the rate of interest per annum?

29. If the cost price of 125 apples is ₹1875 and they are sold at two apples for ₹34, find the loss/profit percentage.

30. How much interest will be paid at rate of 6% per annum on a borrowing of ₹800 for 2 years?

31. Find the values of 72% of 250 and 37.5% of 800.

32. Find the value 62% of 19 + 38% of 19.

33. Convert $\frac{12}{25}$ and $4\frac{2}{3}$ into percentages.

34. Express (i) 0.05 (ii) 5.0 into percentages.

35. If 10% of a number x is 25, then find the value of 20% of x.

36. If $\frac{3}{5}$ of a number 'R' is equal to 30, then find 40% of R.

37. If 20% of x + 40% of $\frac{x}{2}$ + 20% of $3x$ = 100, then find the value of x.

38. In a tray, there are 240 eggs. Raju sold 24 eggs from it and he used 12 eggs for himself. Find the percentage of remaining eggs in the tray.

39. Saritha added 0.5 litre of water to 2 litres of pure milk. Find the percentage of pure milk in the solution.

40. CP = ₹990 and Loss = ₹220. Find the selling price and the percentage of loss.

41. CP = ₹800, MP = ₹1000 and SP = ₹900. Find the percentage of (i) discount and (ii) profit.

42. The percentage of profit made on selling an article is 12%. If the cost price of the article is ₹1200, then find the profit.

43. The loss incurred on selling an article for ₹720 is ₹360. Find the loss percentage.

44. Anish spends ₹3000 from his pocket money of ₹5000 and saves the rest. What is the percentage of the money that he has saved?

45. How much will be the amount to be paid after 2 years on a borrowing of ₹4000 at an interest of 10% per annum?

Essay Type Questions

46. For the better living of future generations, the CM of a state in India encourages his team and the people of his state to plant trees in the state. The number of plants increases every year by 5% over its previous year. If the number of trees in the state at the beginning year 2021 was 10, 00,00,000. What would be the number of trees of the state at the beginning of the year 2022?

47. A fruit seller purchased 100 kg of guavas at ₹40 per kg. Of which 20 kg of guavas are spoiled. If he sells the remaining at the rate of ₹90 per kg, find his profit/loss percentage.

PRACTICE QUESTIONS COMPETITION WING

Level 1: Apply Your Concepts

Direction for questions from 1 to 5: **Fill in the blanks.**

1. The value of 100% of 100 is ________.
2. The profit or loss percentage is always calculated on the selling price of the article. (True/False)
3. $\frac{1}{5}$ of x is ______ % of x.
4. 0.25 of x is equal to ______ % of x.
5. 60% is equal to ______.
6. Which of the following is equivalent to $16\frac{2}{3}\%$?
   (a) 5 : 6 (b) 2 : 3
   (c) 1 : 3 (d) 1 : 6
7. The value of 10% of 10 is a. Which of the following is equal to 100% of 10?
   (a) a (b) 10 a
   (c) 100 a (d) 1000 a
8. An article is sold at a discount of 25%. Find the marked price of the article if its selling price is ₹1200.
   (a) ₹1600 (b) ₹900
   (c) ₹1425 (d) ₹1500

Level 2: Review Your Concepts

9. Find the value of 28.5% of 37 + 37% of 71.5.
10. If the selling price of an article is three-fourth of the cost price, find the loss percentage on selling the article.
11. The population of a city increases every year 8% over its previous year. If the population of the city at the beginning of the year 2015 was 15,00,000. What would be the population of the city at the beginning of the year 2016?

Level 3: Assess Your Concepts

12. A circle is inscribed in a square of side 28 cm. Find the percentage of the area occupied by the circle in the square.
13. A gold smith takes 250 grams of copper to 2 kg of pure gold to make ornaments. Find the percentage of copper in the mixture.
14. Abhinav took loan of ₹1,00,000 at the rate of 8% pa simple interest and lent this money to his friend at 12% simple interest for 5 years. If he cleared the loan in five years, then find his profit in this transaction.
15. The MRP printed on a chocolate was 30% less than its suggested retail price on an online store. Shalu purchased the chocolate for half the MRP at a Mega-Sale-day. What percent of the suggested retail price did Shalu pay?
16. In 1991, Anjana's salary was ₹30000 and Bhavana's salary was ₹40000. In 1990, Anjana's salary was 40% of the sum of the salaries of Anjana and Bhavana in 1991. What was the percentage increase in Anjana's salary from 1990 to 1991?
17. 56% of a number is 448. What is 98% of the same number?

AT

ANSWER KEYS

Crossword

Across

3. Profit 4. Loss 6. Maturity 9. Over head 11. Decrease

Down

1. Profit 2. Compound 5. Simple 7. Increase 8. Cost
10. Percentage

Classroom Wing

Very Short Answer Type Questions

1. (a) 2. (d) 3. (d) 4. (d) 5. (b)
6. (a) → (q), (b) → (r), (c) → (s), (d) → (p) 7. 1000 8. Loss
9. ₹11; 20% 10. No profit and no loss 11. 10% 12. (b) 13. (b)
14. (d) 15. (c) 16. (a) → (p), (b) → (s), (c) → (q), (d) → (r)
17. Principal 18. Principal 19. Interest 20. Amount 21. ₹1000 22. (d)
23. (b) 24. (a) 25. (b) 26. (a)
27. (a) → (q), (b) → (s), (c) → (p), (d) → (r)

Short Answer Type Questions

28. 20% 29. $13\frac{1}{3}\%$ 30. ₹96 31. (i) 180; (ii) 300 32. 19
33. (i) 48%; (ii) $466\frac{2}{3}\%$ 34. (i) 5%; (ii) 500% 35. 50 36. 20
37. 100 38. 85% 39. 80% 40. ₹770; $22\frac{2}{9}\%$
41. (i) 10%; (ii) 12.5% 42. ₹144 43. $33\frac{1}{3}\%$ 44. 40%
45. ₹4800

Essay Type Questions

46. 10,50,00,000 47. 80%

Competition Wing

Level 1: Apply Your Concepts

1. 100 2. false 3. 20 4. 25 5. 3/5 6. (d)
7. (b) 8. (a)

Level 2: Review Your Concepts

9. 37 10. 25% 11. ₹16,20,000

Level 3: Assess Your Concepts

12. 550/7% 13. 100/9% 14. ₹20,000 15. 35% 16. 7.14% 17. 784

Hints and Explanations

CLASSROOM WING

Very Short Answer Type Questions

1. $1.5 = 1.5 \times 100\% = 150\%$.

Hence, the correct option is (a).

2. 50% of $75 + 150\%$ of $75 = 200\%$ of 75

$$= \frac{200}{100} \times 75 = 150.$$

Hence, the correct option is (d).

3. 100% of $x = \frac{100}{100} \times x = x$

Hence, the correct option is (d).

4. 15% of $50 = 15 \times \frac{1}{100} \times 50 = 15 \times \frac{1}{2} = 7.5$

$= 7.5 \times 100\%$

$= 100\%$ of 7.5

Hence, the correct option is (d).

5. 10% of 20% of $100 = \frac{10}{100} \times \frac{20}{100} \times 100$

$= \frac{200}{100} = 2$

$= 2 \times \frac{1}{100} \times 100$

$= 2\%$ of 100

Hence, the correct option is (b).

6. (a) $45\% = \frac{45}{100} = \frac{9}{20} \rightarrow$ (q)

(b) $75\% = \frac{75}{100} = \frac{3}{4} \rightarrow$ (r)

(c) $125\% = \frac{125}{100} = \frac{5}{4} \rightarrow$ (s)

(d) $150\% = \frac{150}{100} = \frac{3}{2} \rightarrow$ (p)

Therefore, the correct match is:

(a) → (q), (b) → (r), (c) → (s), (d) → (p)

7. Principal is ₹10000 and the amount paid back is ₹11000.

The interest = ₹11000 - ₹10000 = **₹1000.**

8. Loss

9. Loss = ₹(55 – 44) = ₹11

$$\text{Loss } \% = \frac{11}{55} \times 100\% = \frac{1}{5} \times 100\% = 20\%$$

10. No profit and no loss.

11. Profit = ₹50; CP = ₹500

$$\text{Profit percentage} = \frac{50}{500} \times 100\% = \frac{50}{5}\% = 10\%$$

12. (a) 10% on ₹450 is ₹45.

(b) 25% on ₹400 = $\frac{25}{100} \times$ ₹400 = ₹100

∴ Selling price = ₹(400 – 100) = ₹300

Hence, the correct option is (b).

13. The % of loss or % of profit is calculated on the cost price of the article.

Hence, the correct option is (b).

14. Discount = Marked price – Selling price

Hence, the correct option is (d).

15. SP = ₹150, Loss = ₹50

CP = ₹(150 + 50) = ₹200

$$\text{Loss } \% = \frac{50}{200} \times 100\% = 25\%$$

Hence, the correct option is (c).

16. (a) Profit % $= \frac{10}{200} \times 100\% = 5\% \rightarrow$ (p)

(b) Profit % $= \frac{100}{400} \times 100\% = 25\% \rightarrow$ (s)

(c) Profit % $= \frac{70}{700} \times 100\% = 10\% \rightarrow$ (q)

(d) Profit % $= \frac{160}{800} \times 100\% = 20\% \rightarrow$ (r)

Therefore, the correct match is:

(a) → (p), (b) → (s), (c) → (q), (d) → (r)

17. Principal

18. Principal

19. Interest

20. Amount

21. $I = \frac{PTR}{100} = \frac{1000 \times 10 \times 10}{100} = ₹1000$

22. $T = \frac{100I}{PR}$

Hence, the correct option is (d).

23. $I = \frac{PTR}{100} = \frac{500 \times 1 \times 12}{100} = 60$

Hence, the correct option is (b).

24. $P = A - I$

$= ₹(2988 - 456) = ₹2532$

Hence, the correct option is (a).

25. $A = P + I$ and $A = 2P$

$I = P$

$\therefore I = ₹4700$

Hence, the correct option is (b).

26. $I = \frac{PTR}{100}$

$I = \frac{550 \times 2 \times 5}{100}$

$= ₹55$

Hence, the correct option is (a).

27. $A = P + I$

(a) 256 + 23 = 279 → (q)
(b) 265 + 34 = 299 → (s)
(c) 258 + 31 = 289 → (p)
(d) 257 + 12 = 269 → (r)

Therefore, the correct match is:
(a) → (q), (b) → (s), (c) → (p), (d) → (r)

Short Answer Type Questions

28. Given that an amount is doubled in 5 years.

Interest in 5 years = 100%.

Interest in 1 year $= \frac{100\%}{5} = 20\%$

Rate of interest = 20%.

29. Given that the cost price of 125 apples is ₹1875.

The cost price of 1 apple $= \frac{₹1875}{125} = ₹15$.

Also given that the selling price of 2 apples $= ₹34$.

The selling price of 1 apple $= \frac{₹34}{2} = ₹17$.

As CP is lesser than SP, there is a profit in the transaction.

Profit $= ₹17 - ₹15 = ₹2$.

Profit % $= \frac{\text{Profit}}{\text{CP}} \times 100\%$

$= \frac{₹2}{₹15} \times 100\% = 13\frac{1}{3}\%$.

Hence, the percentage of profit $= 13\frac{1}{3}\%$.

30. Interest to be paid $= 800 \times \frac{6}{100} \times 2$

$= 96$

31. (i) 72% of 250

$= 72 \times \frac{1}{100} \times 250$

$= 72 \times \frac{1}{2} \times 5 = 36 \times 5$

$= 180$

(ii) 37.5% 800

$= 37.5 \times \frac{1}{100} \times 800 = 37.5 \times 8 = 300$

32. 62% of 19 + 38% of 19

$= 100\%$ of $19 = \frac{100}{100} \times 19 = 19$

33. (i) $\frac{12}{25}$

$= \frac{12}{25} \times 100 \times \frac{1}{100} = \frac{12}{25} \times 100\%$

$= 12 \times 4\% = 48\%$

(ii) $4\frac{2}{3} = \frac{4 \times 3 + 2}{3} = \frac{14}{3}$

$\Rightarrow \frac{14}{3} \times 100 \times \frac{1}{100}$

$= \frac{14}{3} \times 100\% = \frac{1400}{3}\% = 466\frac{2}{3}\%$

34. (i) $0.05 = 0.05 \times 100 \times \frac{1}{100} = 0.05 \times 100\% = 5\%$

(ii) $5.0 = 5.0 \times 100 \times \frac{1}{100} = 500\%$

35. 10% of a number x is 25.

2 × 10% of the number x is 2 × 25.

20% of the number x is 50.

36. $\frac{3}{5} \times R = 30$

$R = 30 \times \frac{5}{3}$

$R = 50$

$40\% \text{ of } R = \frac{40}{100} \times 50$

$= 20$

37. 20% of x + 40% of $\frac{x}{2}$ + 20% of $3x$ = 100

20% of x + 20% of x + 60% of x = 100

(20% + 20% + 60%) of x = 100

100% of x = 100

$\Rightarrow x = 100$

38. 24 is 10% of 240.

12 is 5% of 240.

Hence, (100 – 15)% = 85% of eggs are remaining in the tray.

39. The quantity of milk in the solution = 2 litres

Total quantity of the solution

= 2 + 0.5 = 2.5 litres

Percentage of milk in the solution

$= \frac{2}{2.5} \times 100\% = \frac{20}{25} \times 100\% = 80\%$

40. CP = ₹990, Loss = ₹220

SP = CP – Loss = ₹(990 – 220) = ₹770

$\text{Loss } \% = \frac{\text{Loss}}{\text{CP}} \times 100\%$

$= \frac{220}{990} \times 100\% = \frac{2}{9} \times 100\%$

$= \frac{200}{9}\% = 22\frac{2}{9}\%$

41. CP = ₹800, MP = ₹1000, SP = ₹900

Discount = MP – SP = ₹(1000 – 900)

= ₹100

(i) $\text{Discount } \% = \frac{\text{Discount}}{\text{Marked price}} \times 100\%$

$= \frac{100}{1000} \times 100\% = 10\%$

(ii) Profit = SP – CP = ₹(900 – 800) = ₹100

$\text{Profit } \% = \frac{\text{Profit}}{\text{CP}} \times 100\%$

$= \frac{100}{800} \times 100\% = 12.5\%$

42. CP = ₹1200, Profit = 12% CP

Profit = 12% of ₹1200

$= \frac{12}{100} \times ₹1200 = ₹144$

43. SP = ₹720, Loss = ₹360

CP = SP + Loss = ₹720 + ₹360

= ₹1080

$\therefore \text{Loss percentage} = \frac{\text{Loss}}{\text{CP}} \times 100\%$

$= \frac{360}{1080} \times 100\% = \frac{1}{3} \times 100\%$

$= 33\frac{1}{3}\%$

44. Total money = ₹5000

Amount spent = ₹3000

Amount saved = ₹2000

Percentage of money saved

= (Amount saved/total amount) × 100%

= (2000/5000) × 100

= 40%

45. Interest to be paid $= 4000 \times \frac{10}{100} \times 2 = 800$

Amount to be paid = 4000 + 800

= ₹4800

Essay Type Questions

46. The number of trees in the state at the beginning year 2021 = 10,00,00,000.

Percentage increase = 5%.

The number of plants to be planted during 2021 = 5% of 10,00,00,000.

$= \frac{5}{100} \times 10{,}00{,}00{,}000.$

= 50,00,000.

The number of trees of the state at the beginning of the year 2022

= 10,00,00,000 + 50,00,000.

= 10,50,00,000.

47. The total CP of guavas = 100(₹40) = ₹4000.

The total SP of guavas = 80(₹90) = ₹7200 (since 20 kg of guavas are spoiled).

As the SP is more than CP, the fruit seller obtained a profit.

Profit = SP - CP = ₹7200 - ₹4000 = ₹3200.

The percentage of profit $= \dfrac{\text{Profit}}{\text{CP}} \times 100\%$.

$= \dfrac{3200}{4000} \times 100\% = 80\%$.

COMPETITION WING

Level 1: Apply Your Concepts

1. 100% of 100 = $\frac{100}{100} \times 100 = 100$.

2. We know that the profit or loss percentage is always calculated on the cost price of the article.
The profit or loss percentage is always calculated on the selling price of the article - this is a **false** statement.

3. $\frac{1}{5}$ of $x = \frac{x}{5} \times 100\% = 20\%$ of x

4. 0.25 of $x = 0.25 \times 100\%$ of $x = 25\%$ of x

5. $60\% = \frac{60}{100} = \frac{6}{10} = \frac{3}{5}$

6. $16\frac{2}{3}\% = \frac{50}{3}\%$

$= \frac{50}{3 \times 100} = \frac{1}{6} = 1:6$.

Hence, the correct option is (d).

7. Given that 10% of 10 is a.
Now 100% of 10 = 10 × 10% of 10
= 10 × a = 10 a.

Hence, the correct option is (b).

8. Given, discount = 25% of MP
SP = ₹1,200

⇒ MP – discount = 1200

⇒ MP – 25% of MP = 1200

⇒ 75% of MP = 1200

⇒ MP = $1200 \times \frac{100}{75} = 1600$

Therefore, marked price of the article = ₹1,600.

Hence, the correct option is (a).

Level 2: Review Your Concepts

9. 28.5% of 37 + 37% of 71.5
= 28.5% of 37 + 71.5% of 37
= (28.5 + 71.5)% of 37
= 100% of 37

$= \frac{100}{100} \times 37 = 37$.

10. Let the cost price of the article be ₹x.

Given that the selling price of an article is three-fourth of the cost price.

The selling price = ₹$\frac{3x}{4}$.

As CP is more than SP, there is a loss in the transaction.

Loss = ₹x – ₹$\frac{3x}{4}$ = ₹$\frac{x}{4}$

Loss % = $\frac{\text{Loss}}{\text{CP}} \times 100\%$

$= \frac{₹\frac{x}{4}}{₹x} \times 100\% = 25\%$.

Hence, the percentage of loss = 25%.

11. The population at the beginning of 2015 is 15,00,000.

The population at the beginning of 2016

$= \frac{8}{100} \times 15{,}00{,}000 + 15{,}00{,}000$

= 1,20,000 + 15,00,000

= 16,20,000

Level 3: Assess Your Concepts

12. Side of the square = 28 cm.
As the circle is inscribed in the square, the diameter of the circle is equal to the side of the square.

The radius of the circle = $\frac{28}{2}$ cm = 14 cm.

Area of the square = 28 × 28 sq cm.

Area of the circle = $\frac{22}{7} \times 14 \times 14$ sq cm
= 22 × 2 × 14 sq cm

The percentage of the area occupied by the circle in the square = $\frac{22 \times 2 \times 14}{28 \times 28} \times 100\%$.

$= \frac{550}{7}\%$.

13. The weight of copper = 250 grams.
The weight of gold = 2 kg = 2000 grams.
The total weight of mixture = 2250 grams.
The percentage of copper in the mixture

$= \frac{250}{2250} \times 100\%$.

$= \frac{100}{9}\%$.

14. **Case-1:**

Principal = ₹1,00,000.

Rate of interest = 8% pa.

Time period = 5 years.

$$\text{Interest} = \frac{PTR}{100} = \frac{100000 \times 5 \times 8}{100} = ₹40{,}000.$$

Amount to be paid by Abhinav to clear the loan = ₹1,00,000 + ₹40,000 = ₹1,40,000.

Case-2:

Principal = ₹1,00,000.

Rate of interest = 12% pa.

Time period = 5 years.

$$\text{Interest} = \frac{PTR}{100} = \frac{100000 \times 5 \times 12}{100} = ₹60{,}000.$$

Amount to be received by Abhinav from his friend = ₹1,00,000 + ₹60,000 = ₹1,60,000.

Abhinav's profit in the transaction = ₹1,60,000 – ₹1,40,000 = ₹20,000.

15. Let the retail price of the chocolate = ₹100

Since, the MRP of the chocolate is 30% off of ₹100, it must be $= 100 - (100 \times 0.30) = (100 - 30) = 70$

Now, Shalu bought it at 50% of the retail price, i.e., 50% of ₹70 = 0.50 × 70 = ₹35

Therefore, the percent Shalu paid for the chocolate, of the suggested retail price is $\frac{35}{100} = 35\%$

16. Anjana's salary in 1990

= (30000 + 40000) × 0.4 = ₹28000

Percentage increase in Anjana's salary

$$= \frac{30000 - 28000}{28000} \times 100$$

= (1/14) × 100 = 7.14%

17. Let the number be n.

Given (56/100) × n = 448

⇒ n = 800

∴ 98% of 800 = (98/100) (800) = 784

Alternate method:

Given 56% of a number is 448.

$$\therefore 98\% \text{ of the number} = \frac{98 \times 448}{56} = 784$$

CHAPTER

7

Algebra

Remember

Before beginning this chapter, you should be able to:

- Know numbers and symbols
- Write expressions in numbers and symbols

Key Ideas

After completing this chapter, you should be able to:

- Learn terms of an expression
- Define polynomial and types of polynomials
- Understand addition and subtraction of polynomials
- Understand multiplication and division of a polynomials with a monomial
- Describe linear equation, simple equation, properties of equations
- Solve equation in one variable

Scientific Crypt

A Tribute to Amalie Emmy Noether (1882-1935)

Emmy Noether, the German mathematician behind Noether's Theorem, reshaped modern physics and algebra, despite battling the gender bias of her time. Her brilliance shone through, rewriting not only the rules of mathematics but also transcending societal barriers.

Born on March 23, 1882, in Erlangen, Germany, Emmy Noether's life embodies resilience and intellectual prowess. In an era entrenched with gender bias, she pursued her mathematical passion with unwavering determination. Overcoming societal norms, she audited classes and pursued higher education, guided by her mathematician father's support. Her academic journey defied convention, leading to a bachelor's degree in mathematics in 1903, followed by a PhD in 1907.

Her breakthroughs emerged in abstract algebra and theoretical mathematics. Noether's contributions revolutionized algebraic structures, particularly ring theory and group theory. Her name graces "Noetherian rings" and "Noetherian modules," underscoring her profound influence. Collaborating with luminaries like David Hilbert and Felix Klein solidified her position among the academic elite.

FUN TIME

CROSSWORD

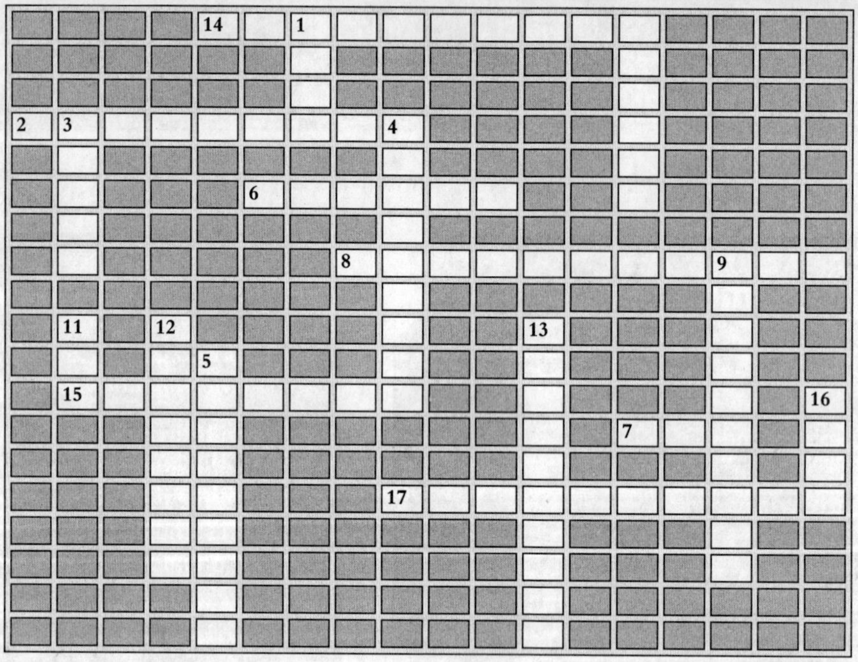

Across

2. A sentence verifiable as true or false is known as mathematical ___________.
6. Terms having different literal coefficients are known as _____ terms.
7. Abbreviation for the left side of an equality sign.
8. In the term $9 \times x^4$, 9 is referred to as the ______.
14. An algebraic expression where variables have only non-negative integer powers.
15. An expression containing only one term.
17. In Mathematics, the _______ value depends on the values of the variables forming the expression.

Down

1. Terms having the same literal coefficients are known as _____ terms.
3. Several parts of an expression, separated by '+' or '–' signs.
4. An expression containing three terms.
5. The value or values found after resolving an equation.
9. A combination of constants and variables connected by '+' or '–' or '×' or '÷' signs algebriac _______.
10. _______ equation is an equation where the highest index of the unknowns is one.
11. ______ of polynomials is achieved by adding numerical coefficients of like terms.
12. An expression containing two terms.
13. ______ of polynomials is achieved by subtracting numerical coefficients of like terms.
16. Sentences true for some variable values and false for others are known as ______ sentences.

INTRODUCTION

A mathematical phrase that has various components like numbers, letters and some symbols is called an **algebraic expression**. In this chapter, we will learn what these components are called in an expression and how are they used.

Algebraic Expressions

In this chapter, we shall look at various algebraic concepts and their definitions such as constant, variable, terms, like terms, algebraic expression, application of four fundamental operations, i.e., addition, subtraction, multiplication and division. Apart from this, we shall also discuss the methods of solving simple equations.

Info Bytes!

The word 'algebra' is dervied from the Arabic word 'al-jabr'.

Constant

A number having a fixed numerical value is called a **constant**.

Example: 2, 3, 7, –8, 1.4, $\frac{2}{3}$, etc.

Variable

A number which can take various numerical values is known as a **variable**.

Example: x, y, z, etc.

A number which is a power of another variable where the power is not zero is also a variable.

Example: x^3, y^2, z^4, etc.

A number which is the product of a constant and a variable is also a variable.

Example: $5x^4$, $8x^3$, $-8x$, etc.

A combination of two or more variables separated by a '+' sign or a '–' sign is also a variable.

Example: $x^2 - y^4 + z^6$, $x^3 + y^3 + z^2$, etc.

Algebraic Expression

A combination of constants and variables connected by '+' or '–' or '×' or '÷' signs is known as an **algebraic expression**.

Example: $8x^2 + 5$, $4x^3 + 2xy - 8xy^2 + 6$, etc.

Terms

Several parts of an algebraic expression, separated by '+' or '–' signs are called the **terms of the expression**.

Example: In the expression, $8x - 14y + 9$, we say that $8x$, $-14y$ and 9 are terms.

Coefficient of a Term

Consider the term $9x^4$. In this case, 9 is called the **numerical coefficient** of x^4 and x^4 is said to be the **literal coefficient** of 9.

In case of $6xy$, the numerical coefficient is 6 and the literal coefficient is xy.

Like Terms

The terms having the same literal coefficients are called **like terms**.

Examples: (i) $2x^4$, $-6x^4$ and $9x^4$ are like terms.

(ii) $18x^2y^3$, $-15x^2y^3$ and $17x^2y^3$ are like terms.

Konnect

Algebraic expressions are mathematical phrases that can include numbers, variables, and operation symbols. Think of them like the sentences of math.

Unlike Terms

The terms having different literal coefficients are called **unlike terms.**

Example: $-13x^2$, $17x^3$, $14x^4$ are unlike terms.

Polynomial

An algebraic expression in which the variables involved have only non-negative integer powers is called a **polynomial.**

Example: $3y + 4x^2 - 7$, $2x^3 + 4y^2 - 8x + 9$, etc.

The expression $5x^4 - 7x^{-3} + 9x^2 - 3x^{5/2}$ is not a polynomial since it has powers of x which are negative and fractions.

A polynomial that contains only one variable is known as a **polynomial in that variable.**

Example: $8x + 15$ is a polynomial in the variable x and $2y^2 + 2y^3$ is a polynomial in the variable y.

A polynomial that contains two variables, say x and y is known as a **polynomial in two variables.**

Example: $x^3y^2 - 2x^4y^3 + 5xy$ is a polynomial in x and y variables.

Degree of a Polynomial in One Variable

The highest exponent of the variable in a polynomial of one variable is called the **degree of the polynomial.**

Examples: (i) $x^4 - 5x^2 - x + 7$ is a polynomial of degree 4.
(ii) $7x^9 - 3x^6 + 7x^3 - x^2 - 5$ is a polynomial of degree 9.

Types of polynomials with respect to the number of terms:

1. **Monomial:** An expression containing only one term is called a **monomial.**
   Examples: $3x$, $5x^2y$, $6xyz$, etc.
2. **Binomial:** An expression containing two terms is called a **binomial.**
   Examples: $2x - 3y$, $5x^2y^2 - 7$, $xy - 3y$
3. **Trinomial:** An expression containing three terms is called a **trinomial.**
   Examples: $2x - 3y + 4z$, $3xy^2 - xy + 5$.

Table 7.1 Common algebraic terms

Term	Notation
Variable	x
Variable term	$7x$
Constant	4
Constant term	45
Algebraic expression	$7x - 45$
Algebraic statement	$7x - 45 = 4$

Value of an Expression

In Mathematics, we come across many situations where we need to find out the value of an expression. The value of an expression purely depends upon the values of the variables that form the expression.

Examples: When $x = 6$, the value of the expression $3x - 2$ is $3 \times 6 - 2 = 16$.
And the value of $8x + y$, when $x = 1$ and $y = -2$ is $8(1) - 2 = 8 - 2 = 6$.

EXAMPLE 7.1 Find the number of terms in the following expressions:

(I) $4x^3y$ (II) $5x^4 - y^3$ (III) $2x^4 - y^2 + 3$

SOLUTION

(I) $4x^3y$ has one term.

(II) $5x^4 - y^3$ has two terms.

(III) $2x^4 - y^2 + 3$ has three terms.

EXAMPLE 7.2 Name the following algebraic expressions with respect to the number of terms.

(I) $5x^2y - 5x + 7$ (II) $5xy - 3$ (III) $-3x$

SOLUTION

(I) $5x^2y - 5x + 7$ has three terms, hence it is a trinomial.

(II) $5xy - 3$ has two terms, hence it is a binomial.

(III) $-3x$ has one term, hence it is a monomial.

EXAMPLE 7.3 Name the following algebraic expressions with respect to the number of terms.

(I) $2 \times 5 \times 9 \times x \times x \times x \times x \times y \times y \times y$

(II) $2 \times 3 \times 7 \times 13 \times x \times x \times x \times y \times y \times y \times y$

(III) $5 \times 9 \times x \times x \times x \times x \times x \times y \times y \times y \times y$

SOLUTION

(I) $2 \times 5 \times 9 \times x \times x \times x \times x \times y \times y \times y = 2(5)(9)x^4y^3$

(II) $2 \times 3 \times 7 \times 13 \times x \times x \times x \times y \times y \times y \times y = 2(3)(7)(13)x^3y^4$

(III) $5 \times 9 \times x \times x \times x \times x \times x \times y \times y \times y \times y = 5(9)x^5y^4$

Operations on Polynomials

Let us understand the various operations, such as addition, subtraction, multiplication and division, which are performed on polynomials.

Addition of Polynomials

The sum of two or more polynomials can be obtained by arranging the terms and then adding the numerical coefficients of like terms.

Info Bytes!

When you add or subtract polynomials, you're just grouping and combining like terms. It's like organizing toys into the right boxes.

EXAMPLE 7.4 Let $A = 3x^2 - 7xy + 6$ and $B = 7xy - 5x^2 + 15$.

Find: (I) $A + B$ (II) $2A + B$

SOLUTION

(I) $A + B = (3x^2 - 7xy + 6) + (7xy - 5x^2 + 15)$

$= (3x^2 - 5x^2) + (-7xy + 7xy) + (6 + 15)$

$= -2x^2 + 0 + 21$

$= -2x^2 + 21$

(II) $2A + B = 2(3x^2 - 7xy + 6) + (7xy - 5x^2 + 15)$

$= 6x^2 - 14xy + 12 + 7xy - 5x^2 + 15$

$= 6x^2 - 5x^2 - 14xy + 7xy + 12 + 15$

$= 1x^2 - 7xy + 27$

Subtraction of Polynomials

The difference of two polynomials can be obtained by arranging the terms and subtracting the numerical coefficients of the like terms.

EXAMPLE 7.5 Let $A = 3x^2 - 7xy + 6$ and $B = 7xy - 5x^2 + 15$.

Find: **(I)** $A - B$ **(II)** $3A - 2B$

SOLUTION

(I) $A - B = (3x^2 - 7xy + 6) - (7xy - 5x^2 + 15)$

$= 3x^2 - 7xy + 6 - 7xy + 5x^2 - 15$

$= (3x^2 + 5x^2) + (-7xy - 7xy) + (6 - 15)$

$= 8x^2 - 14xy - 9$

(II) $3A - 2B = 3(3x^2 - 7xy + 6) - 2(7xy - 5x^2 + 15)$

$= 9x^2 - 21xy + 18 - 14xy + 10x^2 - 30$

$= 19x^2 - 35xy - 12$

EXAMPLE 7.6 Simplify: $8m - [3m - \{2m + 3 - 2(4m - 4)\}]$

SOLUTION

$8m - [3m - \{2m + 3 - 2(4m - 4)\}]$

$= 8m - [3m - \{(2m + 3 - 8m + 8\}]$

$= 8m - [3m - \{(2 - 8)m + (3 + 8\}]$

$= 8m - [3m - \{-6m + 11\}]$

$= 8m - [3m + 6m - 11]$

$= 8m - [9m - 11]$

$= 8m - 9m + 11 = 11 - m$

Multiplication of a Polynomial with a Monomial

The result of multiplication of a polynomial is obtained by multiplying each term of the polynomial by the monomial and then taking the algebraic sum of these products.

EXAMPLE 7.7 Multiply $(2x^2 - 4x + 6y)$ by $2xy$.

SOLUTION

$(2x^2 - 4x + 6y)\ (2xy)$

$= 2x^2\ (2xy) - 4x(2xy) + 6y\ (2xy)$

$= 4x^3y - 8x^2y + 12xy^2$

EXAMPLE 7.8 Simplify: $5(2x - 3) - x(3 - 2x) + 2x^2$

SOLUTION

$$\begin{aligned} &5(2x - 3) - x(3 - 2x) + 2x^2 \\ &= 10x - 15 - 3x + 2x^2 + 2x^2 \\ &= 10x - 3x + 2x^2 + 2x^2 - 15 \\ &= 7x + 4x^2 - 15 \\ &= 4x^2 + 7x - 15 \end{aligned}$$

EXAMPLE 7.9 Find the product of polynomial $(x + 2)$ and $(2x + 3)$.

SOLUTION

$$\begin{aligned} &(x + 2)\ (2x + 3) \\ &= x(2x + 3) + 2(2x + 3) \\ &= 2x^2 + 3x + 4x + 6 \\ &= 2x^2 + 7x + 6 \end{aligned}$$

Thus, the sum or product of two or more polynomials is also a polynomial.

Division of a Polynomial by a Monomial

To divide a polynomial by a monomial, we need to divide each term of the polynomial by the monomial.

EXAMPLE 7.10 Divide $16x^3 + 12x^2 + 8x$ by $4x$.

SOLUTION

$$\frac{16x^3 + 12x^2 + 8x}{4x} = \frac{16x^3}{4x} + \frac{12x^2}{4x} + \frac{8x}{4x} = 4x^2 + 3x + 2$$

Equations

We shall understand the various terms and concepts related to equations as given below.

Info Bytes!

Equations are mathematical statements that show the equality of two expressions by connecting them with an equals sign (=).

Algebraic Expressions

Expressions of the form $4x$, $(x + 5)$, $(4x + y)$ are **algebraic expressions**. x and 5 are the terms of $(x + 5)$ and $4x$ and y are the terms of $(4x + y)$. Algebraic expressions are made up of numbers, symbols and basic arithmetic operations.

Mathematical Sentence

Two expressions joined by the equality sign (=) or an inequality sign ($<, >, \leq, \geq$) are **mathematical sentences**.

Examples: $2 + 5 = 7$, $8 - 3 = 5$, $7x - 8 = 4$, $2 + 3 > 4$, $6 - 2 < 8$ are some mathematical sentences. Those which have the equality sign are equations and those which have an inequality sign are inequations.

Mathematical Statement

A mathematical sentence that can be verified as either true or false is a **mathematical statement.**

Example: $15 + 8 = 12 + 11$, this is a true statement. $14 - 3 \geq 17$, this is a false statement.

All sentences involving only numerical expressions can be verified as either true or false. Hence, they are statements.

Open Sentences

Sentences which are true for some values of the variable and false for the other values of the variable are called **open sentences**. When a certain value is substituted for the variable, the sentence becomes a statement, regardless of whether it is true or false.

Example: $2x - 3 = 7$. This is an open sentence. When we substitute 5 for x, we get a true statement. When we substitute any other value, we get a false statement.

An open sentence containing the equality sign is an equation. In other words, an equation is a sentence in which there is an equality sign between two algebraic expressions.

Examples: $2x - 5 = 8$, $3y + 4 = 2$, $x^2 - 7x + 12 = 0$ are equations. Here, x and y are unknown quantities and 2, 5, 8, 3, etc., are known quantities.

Linear Equation

An equation, in which the highest index of the unknowns present is one, is a **linear equation.**

Example: $2x + 3 = 4$, $3x + 4y = 8$ are some linear equations.

Simple Equation

A linear equation which has only one unknown is a **simple equation**. $8x - 3 = 5$ and $4x + 4 = 3x - 6$ are examples of simple equations. The part of an equation which is to the left side of the equality sign is known as the **left-hand side**, it is abbreviated as LHS. The part of an equation which is to the right side of the equality sign is known as the **right-hand side**, abbreviated as RHS. The process of finding the value of an unknown in an equation is called **solving the equation**. The value/values of the unknown found after solving an equation is/are called the **solution**(s) or the **root**(s) of the equation. Before we learn how to solve an equation, let us review the basic properties of equality.

Properties of Equality

1. **Addition Property:** If equal numbers are added to both sides of equality, the equality remains the same. If $x = y$, then $x + z = y + z$.
2. **Subtraction Property:** If equal numbers are subtracted from both sides of equality, the equality remains the same. If $x = y$, then $x - z = y - z$.
3. **Multiplication property:** If both sides of equality are multiplied by the same number, the equality remains the same. If $x = y$, then $(x)(z) = (y)(z)$.
4. **Division Property:** If both sides of equality are divided by a non-zero number, the equality remains the same. If $x = y$, then, $x/z = y/z$ where $z \neq 0$.

Solving an Equation in One Variable

The following steps are involved in solving an equation.

Step 1: Always ensure that the unknown quantities are on the LHS and the known quantities or constants are on the RHS.
Step 2: Add all the terms containing the unknowns on the LHS and all the known values on the RHS so that each side of the equation contains only one term. On the LHS, the number with which the unknown is multiplied is called the coefficient.
Step 3: Divide both sides of the equation by the coefficient of the unknown.

EXAMPLE 7.11

Solve for x: $5x - 6 = 9$

SOLUTION

$5x - 6 = 9$

$5x = 9 + 6$

$x = \frac{15}{5}$

$x = 3$

EXAMPLE 7.12

Solve for x: $\frac{3x}{2} + \frac{x}{3} = x + \frac{x}{6} + 6$

SOLUTION

$\frac{3x}{2} + \frac{x}{3} = x + \frac{x}{6} + 6$

$\frac{3x}{2} + \frac{x}{3} - x - \frac{x}{6} = 6$

$\frac{3 \times 3x + 2 \times x - 6 \times x - 1 \times x}{6} = 6$

$\frac{9x + 2x - 6x - 1x}{6} = 6$

$11x - 7x = 6 \times 6$

$4x = 36$

$x = 9$

EXAMPLE 7.13

The sum of two consecutive odd numbers is 164. Find the numbers.

SOLUTION

Let the two consecutive odd numbers be x and $x + 2$.

Given that: $(x) + (x + 2) = 164$

$2x + 2 = 164$

$2(x + 1) = 164$

$x + 1 = \frac{164}{2}$

$x + 1 = 82$

$x = 82 - 1$

$\Rightarrow x = 81$

$\therefore$ The two consecutive odd numbers are 81 and 83.

EXAMPLE 7.14 The present age of a person is $\frac{1}{3}$ of the present age of his father. If the sum of their ages is 60 years, then find the age of the son.

SOLUTION

Let the present age of father be x years.

$\therefore$ The present age of the son = $\frac{x}{3}$ years.

Given that: $x + \frac{x}{3} = 60$

$\frac{x}{1} + \frac{x}{3} = 60 \Rightarrow \frac{3 \times x + 1 \times x}{3} = 60$

$\frac{3x + x}{3} = 60 \Rightarrow \frac{4x}{3} = 60$

$4x = 60 \times 3 \Rightarrow 4x = 180$

$x = \frac{180}{4}$

$x = 45$

$\therefore$ The age of son = $\frac{1}{3} \times 45 = 15$ years.

POINTS TO REMEMBER

- ✔ A number having a fixed numerical value is called a constant.
- ✔ A number which can take various numerical values is known as a variable.
- ✔ A combination of constants and variables connected by '+' or '–' or '×' or '÷' signs is known as an algebraic expression.
- ✔ The terms having the same literal coefficients are called like terms.
- ✔ The terms having different literal coefficients are called unlike terms.
- ✔ The highest exponent of the variable in a polynomial of one variable is called the degree of the polynomial.
- ✔ An expression containing only one term is called a monomial.
- ✔ An expression containing two terms is called a binomial.
- ✔ An expression containing three terms is called a trinomial.
- ✔ A mathematical sentence that can be verified as either true or false is a mathematical statement.
- ✔ Sentences which are true for some values of the variable and false for the other values of the variable are called open sentences.
- ✔ An equation, in which the highest index of the unknowns present is one, is a linear equation.
- ✔ A linear equation which has only one unknown is a simple equation.

PRACTICE QUESTIONS CLASSROOM WING

Very Short Answer Type Questions

Direction for questions from 1 to 5: **Select the correct alternative from the given choices.**

1. Which of the following is a polynomial?

   (a) $3x - \frac{2}{x}$ (b) $x^2 - \sqrt{3}$

   (c) $\sqrt{x} + 5$ (d) $x + x^{3/2}$

2. The degree of the polynomial

   $8x^7 - 7x^6 + 6x^5 - 15x^3$ is

   (a) 8 (b) 7

   (c) 15 (d) 3

3. Which of the following is a trinomial?

   (a) xyz (b) $x^2 - xy$

   (c) x^3 (d) None of these

4. The numerical coefficient of $2x^5y^3$ is

   (a) 5 (b) 3

   (c) 8 (d) 2

5. The number of second degree terms in the expression $2x^3 - 3x^2y + 5x^2 - 6xy^2 + 8x^2y - 4x^2y^2$ is

   (a) 3 (b) 2

   (c) 1 (d) 4

Direction for question 6: **Match Column A with Column B.**

6.

	Column A (Polynomial)		Column B (Degree of the polynomial)
(a)	$9x^3 + 7x^2 + 6x + 5$	(p)	2
(b)	$\frac{3}{5}x^2 - 7x^4 - 2$	(q)	3
(c)	$8x^5 - 9x^6 + 4$	(r)	4
(d)	$5x^2 - 8x + 3$	(s)	5
		(t)	6

Direction for questions from 7 to 11: **Fill in the blanks.**

7. $3x^2y + 7x^2y =$ _______.

8. $\frac{5}{2}x^2 - \frac{3}{2}x^2 =$ _______.

9. $2017xy - 2xy =$ _______.

10. $\frac{3}{4}(4x - 8) =$ _______.

11. $\frac{2xy - 6x}{2x} =$ _______.

Direction for questions from 12 to 16: **Select the correct alternative from the given choices.**

12. $\frac{2}{3}x + 3x + \frac{1}{3}x =$ _______.

    (a) $4x$ (b) $\frac{5}{3}x$

    (c) $\frac{3}{2}x$ (d) $\frac{5}{2}x$

13. $2x - 2\left(x - \frac{1}{2}\right) =$ _______.

    (a) x (b) $2x$ (c) 2 (d) 1

14. $2x(3 - 2x) =$ _______.

    (a) $6x - 4x^2$ (b) $6x - 2x^2$

    (c) $3 - 4x$ (d) $3 - 4x^2$

15. $\frac{4x^2 - 8x + 10}{2} =$ _______.

    (a) $2x^2 - 4x + 5$ (b) $2x^2 - 8x + 10$

    (c) $2x^2 - 4x + 10$ (d) $2x^2 - 8x + 5$

16. $3x\left(\frac{2}{3}x - \frac{1}{3x}\right) =$ _______.

    (a) $2x^2 - 3$ (b) $2x^2 - 1$

    (c) $2x - 1$ (d) $2x^2 - 2$

Direction for question 17: **Match Column A with Column B.**

17.

Column A	Column B
(a) $\frac{3x}{2}(2x-3)$	(p) $3x^2 - \frac{9x}{2}$
(b) $\frac{2x}{3}(3x-2)$	(q) $\frac{9x^2}{2} - 3x$
(c) $\frac{3x}{2}(3x-2)$	(r) $2x^2 - \frac{4x}{3}$
(d) $\frac{2x}{3}(2x-3)$	(s) $\frac{4x^2}{3} - 2x$

Direction for questions from 18 to 22: **Fill in the blanks.**

18. If $x + 5 = 8$, then $x =$ ________.

19. If $\frac{1}{2}x + \frac{3}{4} = 1$, then $x =$ ________.

20. If $\frac{3x}{5} + \frac{7x}{5} = 2$, then $x =$ ________.

21. If $2x - 5 = 7$, then $x =$ ________.

22. If $12 + x = 18 - x$, then $x =$ ________.

Direction for questions from 23 to 26: **Select the correct alternative from the given choices.**

23. The highest power of the variable in a linear equation is
(a) 0 (b) 1
(c) 2 (d) Can be of any value

24. The number of value(s) of x, which satisfy $7x + 2 = 8x + 2$ is
(a) 0 (b) 1 (c) 2 (d) 3

25. The sum of two consecutive natural numbers is 45. Which of the following represents the above statement?
(a) $(x + 1) + (x + 2) = 45$
(b) $(x) + (x + 1) = 45$
(c) $(x - 1) + x = 45$
(d) All the above

26. The age of a man is 4 times his son's age and the sum of their ages is 60 years. Which of the following represents the above statement?
(a) $x + 60 = 4x$ (b) $4x - x = 60$
(c) $x + 4x = 60$ (d) $4x + 60 = x$

Direction for question 27: **Match Column A with Column B.**

27. $P = 2x + 3y$, $Q = 3y - 2x$, and $R = 2x - 3y$.

Column A	Column B	Column C
1. P + Q	**(a)** a monomial in x	**(e)** $-4x$
2. P × R	**(b)** a monomial in y	**(f)** $4x^2 - 9y^2$
3. P – Q	**(c)** a trinomial in x and y	**(g)** $4x$
4. Q × R	**(d)** a binomial in x and y	**(h)** $6y$
		(i) $-(4x^2 - 12xy + 9y^2)$
		(j) $4x^2 - 12xy + 9y^2$

Short Answer Type Questions

28. Find the product of $(14x)$ and $\left(4x - \frac{5}{7}\right)$.

29. State whether the following statements are true or false.
(i) The coefficient of x in the expression $4xy^2$ is 4.
(ii) The number of terms in the expression $4xy$ is 3.
(iii) $x^2y^3 - xy$ is a binomial.
(iv) $3x^2 - 2x + 2/3$ is not a polynomial.

30. List out the like terms in the following expressions.
(i) $4x^4, -7x^3, 8x^2, 12x^3, -9x^4, -5x, 4x^3, 12x^2$
(ii) $5xy, -3x^2y, 2xy^3, -2x^2y^2, 5x^2y, -3xy, 5x^2y^2$

31. Which of the following algebraic expressions are polynomials?
(i) $x^{1/2} + y^{1/2} + z^{1/2}$ (ii) $x^2 + y^2$
(iii) $\sqrt{x} + 3$ (iv) $\sqrt{5} + x^5$ (v) 2016

32. Write the degree of the following polynomials.
(i) $3x^5 - 7x^2 + 8x - 2x^8 + 10$
(ii) $2x^9 - 3x^2 - 14x^3 - 15x^4$

33. Write the numerical coefficients of the following.
(i) $17x^2y$ (ii) $12xy^3$
(iii) $\frac{3}{5}x$ (iv) $\frac{-3}{2}x^2$

34. If $x = 3$ and $y = 4$, then find the values of
(i) $\frac{3x + 4y}{4y - 3x}$ (ii) $\frac{2x^2 + 5x - 3y}{2y^2 + 5y - 3x}$

35. If $x = 2$ and $y = 3$, then find the values of

(i) $\frac{2x+3y}{4x-3y}$ (ii) $\frac{2x^2-7x+2y}{2y^2-7y+2x}$

36. $A = 3x - 3xy + 9x^2$, $B = 3x + 2xy - 6x^2$ and $C = 3xy - 7x^2 + 3x$. Find the value of A + B – C.

37. Find the product of $(12x)$ and $(5x - \frac{3}{2})$.

38. Find the product of $(2x + 3)$ and $(3x - 2)$.

39. What should be added to $2xy - 3x^2 + 6$ so that the sum is $4x^2 - 7xy + 15$?

40. What should be subtracted from $\frac{3}{2}x - \frac{7}{2}$ so that the difference is $\frac{7x}{2} - \frac{3}{2}$?

41. Simplify: $\frac{8x^2 - 12x^3 + 6x}{2x}$

42. Simplify: $3x - [4x + \{2x - 6(x - \overline{2 - x})\}]$

43. Simplify: $\frac{15}{2}x - \frac{4}{3}[6x^2 - 9x(x - \overline{3 - 2x})]$

44. Solve for x: $3x + 7 = 18x$

45. Solve for x: $\frac{x}{4} = 6x - \frac{5}{4}$

46. Solve for x: $\frac{2x}{3} + 4 = \frac{8}{3}(2x - 6)$

47. Write the following statements in symbolic form.

(i) A number is doubled and added to 6, the result is equal to 14.

(ii) The sum of a number and three fifth of the number is equal to 24.

(iii) Twenty years ago, the age of a man was half of his present age.

48. The sum of three consecutive natural numbers is 90. Find the greatest number.

49. The length of a rectangle is 5 cm more than its breadth. If the perimeter of the rectangle is 42 cm, then find the length of the rectangle.

50. Chintu's pocket money is ₹120. He saves one-third of his expenditure. Find his savings.

51. The sum of the ages of a man and his daughter is 56 years. If the daughter's age is $\frac{1}{3}$ of his father's age, then find the age of the daughter.

52. If $x = 6$ and $y = 5$, then find the values of the following:

(i) $x + y$ (ii) $x - y$

(iii) $3x/2y$ (iv) $3y/2x$

53. If $x = 1$, $y = 2$ and $z = 3$, find the value of $4x^2yz$.

54. Write an algebraic expression that describes the sum of x and 30% of z subtracted from the product of x and y.

55. Ajay buys 8 cookies costing ₹p each. If he gives the shopkeeper ₹50, how much change he gets back?

Essay Type Questions

56. What should be subtracted from $7x^2 - 5x + 11$, so that the difference is $2x^2 + 7x - 9$?

Direction for question 57: **These questions are based on the following data.**

57. Simplify: $\frac{9x^3 - 15x^2 - 12x}{3x}$.

PRACTICE QUESTIONS COMPETITION WING

Level 1: Apply Your Concepts

***Direction for questions from 1 to 5:* Fill in the blanks.**

1. A quantity which has no fixed value is called a/an _____.
2. A quantity which has a fixed numerical value is called a/an ________.
3. A combination of constants and variables connected by one or more fundamental operating signs is a/an ________.
4. The exponents of the variables of a polynomial must be ________ integers.
5. The terms having same literal coefficients are called _____.
6. The cost of a pizza is $2\frac{1}{2}$ times the cost of a burger. If the sum of the costs of one burger and one pizza is ₹105, then find the cost of the burger.
7. Rani has some chocolates with her. If she gives $\frac{2}{5}$ of the chocolates to her brother and $\frac{1}{3}$ of total chocolates to her sister, then she is left with 20 chocolates. Find the number of chocolates that Rani had initially.
8. Rukku has $\frac{3}{4}$ of the number of flowers that Satya has. The number of flowers with Rukku and Satya is 35, then find the number of flowers with Satya.
9. If $A = 2x^3 - 3x^2 - 4x + 5$, $B = 2x^2 - x^3 + x + 1$ and $C = x^2 + x + 2$, then find the degree of A + 2B – C.
   (a) 0 (b) 1 (c) 2 (d) 3
10. Simplify: $3x^2 - [7x - \{5x^2 - (2x - 3)(4x - 2) - 5\} - 2]$
    (a) $9x - 9$ (b) $8x - 9$
    (c) $7x - 9$ (d) $6x - 9$

Level 2: Review Your Concepts

11. A bag consists of ₹1, ₹2 and ₹5 coins. The number of ₹2 coins is equal to twice the number of ₹1 coins. The number of ₹5 is equal to thrice the number of ₹2 coins. If the total amount in the bag is ₹700, then find the total number of coins in the bag.
    (a) 150 (b) 160
    (c) 180 (d) 200
12. Let ABCD be a rectangle of four sides AB = $(2x + 3y + 10)$ cm, BC = $(2x + 3y - 5)$ cm, CD = $(4x + 3y + 6)$ cm and DA = $(2x - 3y + 7)$ cm. Find the perimeter of the rectangle.
    (a) 30 cm (b) 40 cm
    (c) 50 cm (d) 60 cm
13. Mohan has some amount, he gave (1/3)rd of the amount to Vijay, (2/5)th of the remaining amount gave to Suresh and (1/6)th of the remaining amount to Venkat. Finally, Mohan left with ₹3000. What is the sum of amounts received by Suresh and Venkat?
    (a) ₹3000 (b) ₹5000
    (c) ₹7000 (d) ₹8000

Level 3: Assess Your Concepts

***Direction for question 14:* These questions are based on the following data.**

14. The length and breadth of a rectangle A (in cm) are $3x + 4y - 5$ and $2x - 5y$ respectively. B is another rectangle whose measurements are 5 cm more than that of the rectangle A.
    (i) What is the perimeter of the rectangle B?
    (ii) What is the area of the rectangle A?
    (iii) What is the difference between the area of the rectangles A and B?
15. On the Annual day of Ken School, it was planned to distribute some sweets equally among 98 students. But 28 of those students were absent that day. As a result, each of the students present received 4 sweets more. Find the total number of sweets distributed.
16. The sum of three consecutive even numbers is 30. Find the difference of the squares of the extreme numbers.

ANSWER KEYS

Crossword

Across

2. Statement 6. Unlike 7. LHS 8. Coefficient 14. Polynomial 15. Monomial 17. Expression

Down

1. Like 3. Terms 4. Trinomial 5. Solution 9. Expression 10. Linear 11. Sum 12. Binomial 13. Difference 16. Open

Classroom Wing

Very Short Answer Type Questions

1. (b) 2. (b) 3. (d) 4. (d) 5. (c)
6. (a) → (q), (b) → (r), (c) → (t), (d) → (p) 7. $10x^2y$ 8. x^2 9. $2015xy$
10. $3x - 6$ 11. $y - 3$ 12. (a) 13. (d) 14. (a) 15. (a)
16. (b) 17. (a) → (p), (b) → (r), (c) → (q), (d) → (s) 18. 3 19. $\frac{1}{2}$
20. 1 21. 6 22. 3 23. (b) 24. (b) 25. (d)
26. (c) 27. (1) → (b) → (h), (2) → (d) → (f), (3) → (a) → (g), (4) → (c) → (i)

Short Answer Type Questions

28. $= 56x^2 - 10x$ 29. (i) False; (ii) False; (iii) True; (iv) False
30. (i) $4x^4, -9x^4; -7x^3, 12x^3, 4x^3; 8x^2, 12x^2$; (ii) $5xy, -3xy; -3x^2y, 5x^2y; -2x^2y^2, 5x^2y^2$;
31. (ii), (iv), (v) are polynomials 32. (i) 8; (ii) 9 33. (i) 17; (ii) 12; (iii) $\frac{3}{5}$; (iv) $\frac{-3}{2}$
34. (i) 25/7; (ii) 21/43 35. (i) −13; (ii) 0 36. $10x^2 - 4xy + 3x$ 37. $60x^2 - 18x$
38. $6x^2 + 5x - 6$ 39. $7x^2 - 9xy + 9$ 40. $-2x - 2$ 41. $4x - 6x^2 + 3$ 42. $9x - 12$
43. $28x^2 - \frac{57}{2}x$ 44. $\frac{7}{15}$ 45. $\frac{5}{23}$ 46. $\frac{30}{7}$
47. (i) $2x + 6 = 14$; (ii) $x + \frac{3x}{5} = 24$; (iii) $x - 20 = \frac{x}{2}$ 48. 31 49. 13 cm 50. ₹30
51. 14 years 52. (i) 11; (ii) 1; (iii) 9/5; (iv) 5/4 53. 24 54. $xy - (x + 30z/100)$
55. ₹$(50 - 8p)$

Essay Type Questions

56. $5x^2 - 12x + 20$ 57. $3x^2 - 5x - 4$

Competition Wing

Level 1: Apply Your Concepts

1. Variable 2. Constant 3. Algebraic expression 4. Non-negative
5. Like terms 6. ₹30 7. 75 8. 20 9. (b) 10. (a)

Level 2: Review Your Concepts

11. (c) 12. (c) 13. (a)

Level 3: Assess Your Concepts

14. (i) $10x - 2y + 10$, (ii) $6x^2 - 20y^2 - 7xy - 10x + 25y$, (iii) $25x - 5y$ 15. 980 16. 80

Hints and Explanations

CLASSROOM WING

Very Short Answer Type Questions

1. $x^2 - \sqrt{3}$

Hence, the correct option is (b).

2. The degree of the polynomial is the highest exponent of a variable of $8x^7 - 7x^6 + 6x^5 - 15x^3$, i.e., 7.

Hence, the correct option is (b).

3. None of the given expressions are trinomials.

Hence, the correct option is (d).

4. The numerical coefficient of $2x^5y^3$ is 2.

Hence, the correct option is (d).

5. Only $5x^2$ is the second degree term.

Hence, the correct option is (c).

6. (a) $9x^3 + 7x^2 + 6x + 5$: degree = 3 → (q)

(b) $\frac{3}{5}x^2 - 7x^4 - 2$: degree = 4 → (r)

(c) $8x^5 - 9x^6 + 4$: degree = 6 → (t)

(d) $5x^2 - 8x + 3$: degree = 2 → (p)

Therefore, the correct match is:

(a) → (q), (b) → (r), (c) → (t), (d) → (p)

7. $3x^2y + 7x^2y = (3 + 7)\, x^2y = 10x^2y$

8. $\frac{5}{2}x^2 - \frac{3}{2}x^2 = \left(\frac{5}{2} - \frac{3}{2}\right)x^2$

$= \left(\frac{5-3}{2}\right)x^2 = \frac{2}{2}x^2 = x^2$

9. $2017xy - 2xy = (2017 - 2)xy = 2015xy$

10. $\frac{3}{4}(4x - 8) = \frac{3}{4} \times 4x - \frac{3}{4} \times 8 = 3x - 6$

11. $\frac{2xy - 6x}{2x} = \frac{2xy}{2x} - \frac{6x}{2x} = y - 3$

12. $\frac{2}{3}x + 3x + \frac{1}{3}x = \frac{2}{3}x + \frac{1}{3}x + 3x$

$= \frac{2x + x}{3} + 3x = \frac{3x}{3} + 3x = x + 3x = 4x$

Hence, the correct option is (a).

13. $2x - 2\left(x - \frac{1}{2}\right) = 2x - 2x + 2 \times \frac{1}{2}$

$= 0 + 1 = 1$

Hence, the correct option is (d).

14. $2x\,(3 - 2x)$

$= 2x(3) - 2x(2x)$

$= 6x - 4x^2$

Hence, the correct option is (a).

15. $\frac{4x^2 - 8x + 10}{2} = \frac{4x^2}{2} - \frac{8x}{2} + \frac{10}{2}$

$= 2x^2 - 4x + 5$

Hence, the correct option is (a).

16. $3x\left(\frac{2}{3}x - \frac{1}{3x}\right) = 3x \times \frac{2}{3}x - 3x \times \frac{1}{3x}$

$= 2x^2 - 1$

Hence, the correct option is (b).

17. (a) $\frac{3x}{2}(2x - 3) = \frac{3x}{2} \times 2x - \frac{3x}{2} \times 3$

$= 3x^2 - \frac{9x}{2}$ → (p)

(b) $\frac{2x}{3}(3x - 2) = \frac{2x}{3} \times 3x - \frac{2x}{3} \times 2$

$= 2x^2 - \frac{4x}{3}$ → (r)

(c) $\frac{3x}{2}(3x - 2) = \frac{3x}{2} \times 3x - \frac{3x}{2} \times 2$

$= \frac{9x^2}{2} - 3x$ → (q)

(d) $\frac{2x}{3}(2x - 3) = \frac{2x}{3} \times 2x - \frac{2x}{3} \times 3$

$= \frac{4x^2}{3} - 2x$ → (s)

Therefore, the correct match is:

(a) → (p), (b) → (r), (c) → (q), (d) → (s)

18. $x + 5 = 8 \Rightarrow x = 8 - 5 \Rightarrow x = 3$

19. $\frac{1}{2}x + \frac{3}{4} = 1$

$\frac{1}{2}x = 1 - \frac{3}{4}$

$\frac{x}{2} = \frac{4-3}{4}$

$\frac{x}{2} = \frac{1}{4} \Rightarrow x = \frac{1}{4} \times 2 = \frac{1}{2}$

20. $\frac{3x}{5} + \frac{7x}{5} = 2 \Rightarrow \frac{3x+7x}{5} = 2$

$\Rightarrow \frac{10x}{5} = 2 \Rightarrow 2x = 2$

$x = 1$

21. $2x - 5 = 7 \Rightarrow 2x = 7 + 5$

$2x = 12 \Rightarrow x = \frac{12}{2}$

$x = 6$

22. $12 + x = 18 - x$

$x + x = 18 - 12$

$2x = 6$

$x = 3$

23. The highest power of the variable in a linear equation is one.

Hence, the correct option is (b).

24. $7x + 2 = 8x + 2 \Rightarrow x = 0.$

$\therefore$ The number of value of x is 1.

Hence, the correct option is (b).

25. All the given options represent the sum of two consecutive natural numbers.

Hence, the correct option is (d).

26. Let the son's age be x years.

Father's age = $4x$ years

$\therefore x + 4x = 60$

Hence, the correct option is (c).

27. Given that $P = 2x + 3y$, $Q = 3y - 2x$, and $R = 2x - 3y$.

1. $P + Q = 2x + 3y + 3y - 2x = 6y$, a monomial in y. $1 \leftrightarrow b \leftrightarrow h$

2. $P \times R = (2x + 3y)(2x - 3y) = 4x^2 - 9y^2$, a binomial in x and y. $2 \leftrightarrow d \leftrightarrow f$

3. $P - Q = 2x + 3y - (3y - 2x) = 2x + 3y - 3y + 2x = 4x$, a monomial in x. $3 \leftrightarrow a \leftrightarrow g$

4. $Q \times R = (3y - 2x)(2x - 3y)$

$= -(2x - 3y)(2x - 3y)$

$= -(4x^2 - 12xy + 9y^2)$,

a trinomial in x and y. $4 \leftrightarrow c \leftrightarrow i$

Short Answer Type Questions

28. $(14x) \times \left(4x - \frac{5}{7}\right) = 14x \times 4x - 14x \times \frac{5}{7}$

$= 56x^2 - 10x$

29. (i) Coefficient of x in $4xy^2$ is $4y^2$, so the given statement is false.

(ii) The number of terms in the expression $4xy$ is 1, so the given statement is false.

(iii) $x^2y^3 - xy$ is a binominal, so the given statement is true.

(iv) $3x^2 - 2x + \frac{2}{3}$ is a polynomial, so the given statement is false.

30. (i) Like terms: $(4x^4, -9x^4)$, $(-7x^3, 12x^3, 4x^3)$ $(8x^2, 12x^2)$

(ii) Like terms: $(5xy, -3xy)$, $(-3x^2y, 5x^2y)$, $(-2x^2y^2, 5x^2y^2)$

31. (i) $x^{\frac{1}{2}} + y^{\frac{1}{2}} + z^{\frac{1}{2}}$ is not a polynomial since the exponents of the variables are fractions.

(ii) $x^2 + y^2$ is a polynomial.

(iii) $\sqrt{x} + 3$ is not a polynomial, since the variable $\left(\sqrt{x} = x^{\frac{1}{2}}\right)$ has fractional exponent.

(iv) $\sqrt{5} + x^5$ is a polynomial.

(v) 2016 is a polynomial of degree zero. It is a constant polynomial.

32. (i) $3x^5 - 7x^2 + 8x - 2x^8 + 10$ consists of 5 terms and the highest degree term is $-2x^8$. The degree of the polynomial is 8.

(ii) $2x^9 - 3x^2 - 14x^3 - 15x^4$ consists of 4 terms of those the highest degree term is $2x^9$. The degree of the polynomial is 9.

33. (i) In $17x^2y$, the numerical coefficient is 17.

(ii) In $12xy^3$, the numerical coefficient is 12.

(iii) In $\frac{3}{5}x$, the numerical coefficient is $\frac{3}{5}$.

(iv) In $\frac{-3}{2}x^2$, the numerical coefficient is $\frac{-3}{2}$.

34. (i) Given: $x = 3$ and $y = 4$

$$\frac{3x+4y}{4y-3x} = \frac{3(3)+4(4)}{4(4)-3(3)} = \frac{25}{7}.$$

(ii) $$\frac{2x^2+5x-3y}{2y^2+5y-3x} = \frac{2(3)^2+5(3)-3(4)}{2(4)^2+5(4)-3(3)} = \frac{21}{43}$$

35. $x = 2, y = 3$

(i) $$\frac{2x+3y}{4x-3y} = \frac{2\times2+3\times3}{4\times2-3\times3}$$

$$= \frac{4+9}{8-9} = \frac{13}{-1} = -13$$

(ii) $$\frac{2x^2-7x+2y}{2y^2-7y+2x} = \frac{2(2)^2-7(2)+2(3)}{2(3)^2-7(3)+2(2)}$$

$$= \frac{2\times4-14+6}{2\times9-21+4} = \frac{8-8}{18-17} = \frac{0}{1} = 0$$

36. $A + B = (3x - 3xy + 9x^2) + (3x + 2xy - 6x^2)$

$= 9x^2 - 6x^2 - 3xy + 2xy + 3x + 3x$

$= 3x^2 - xy + 6x$

$(A + B) - C = (3x^2 - xy + 6x) - (3xy - 7x^2 + 3x)$

$= 3x^2 - xy + 6x - 3xy + 7x^2 - 3x$

$= 3x^2 + 7x^2 - xy - 3xy + 6x - 3x$

$= 10x^2 - 4xy + 3x$

37. $(12x)\left(5x - \frac{3}{2}\right) = (12x)(5x) - (12x)\left(\frac{3}{2}\right)$

$= 60x^2 - 6x \times 3 = 60x^2 - 18x$

38. $(2x + 3)(3x - 2)$

$= (2x)(3x) - (2x)(2) + 3(3x) - (3)(2)$

$= 6x^2 - 4x + 9x - 6$

$= 6x^2 + 5x - 6$

39. Let $f(x)$ should be added to $2xy - 3x^2 + 6$, so that the sum is $4x^2 - 7xy + 15$.

$f(x) = 4x^2 - 7xy + 15 - (2xy - 3x^2 + 6)$

$= 4x^2 - 7xy + 15 - 2xy + 3x^2 - 6$

$= (4x^2 + 3x^2) + (-7xy - 2xy) + (15 - 6)$

$= 7x^2 - 9xy + 9$

40. Let $f(x)$ should be subtracted from $\frac{3}{2}x - \frac{7}{2}$, so that the difference is $\frac{7x}{2} - \frac{3}{2}$.

$$f(x) = \frac{3x}{2} - \frac{7}{2} - \left(\frac{7x}{2} - \frac{3}{2}\right)$$

$$= \frac{3x}{2} - \frac{7}{2} - \frac{7x}{2} + \frac{3}{2} \Rightarrow \frac{3x}{2} - \frac{7x}{2} - \frac{7}{2} + \frac{3}{2}$$

$$= \frac{3x-7x}{2} + \left(\frac{-7+3}{2}\right) \Rightarrow \frac{-4x}{2} + \left(\frac{-4}{2}\right)$$

$f(x) = -2x - 2$

41. $$\frac{8x^2 - 12x^3 + 6x}{2x} = \frac{8x^2}{2x} - \frac{12x^3}{2x} + \frac{6x}{2x}$$

$= 4x - 6x^2 + 3$

42. $3x - \left[4x + \left\{2x - 6\left(x - \overline{2 - x}\right)\right\}\right]$

$= 3x - [4x + \{2x - 6(x - 2 + x)\}]$

$= 3x - [4x + \{2x - 6x + 12 - 6x\}]$

$= 3x - [4x - 10x + 12]$

$= 3x - [-6x + 12]$

$= 3x + 6x - 12$

$= 9x - 12$

43. $\frac{15}{2}x - \frac{4}{3}\left[6x^2 - 9x(x - \overline{3 - 2x})\right]$

$= \frac{15}{2}x - \frac{4}{3}[6x^2 - 9x(x - 3 + 2x)]$

$= \frac{15}{2}x - \frac{4}{3}[6x^2 - 9x(3x - 3)]$

$= \frac{15}{2}x - \frac{4}{3}[6x^2 - 27x^2 + 27x]$

$= \frac{15}{2}x + \frac{4}{3} \times 21x^2 - \frac{4}{3} \times 27x$

$= \frac{15}{2}x + 28x^2 - 36x = 28x^2 + \frac{15}{2}x - 36x$

$= 28x^2 + \left(\frac{15}{2} - 36\right)x = 28x^2 + \left(\frac{15-72}{2}\right)x$

$= 28x^2 - \frac{57}{2}x$

44. $3x + 7 = 18x \Rightarrow 7 = 18x - 3x$

$7 = 15x \Rightarrow x = \frac{7}{15}$

45. $\frac{x}{4} = 6x - \frac{5}{4} \Rightarrow \frac{5}{4} = 6x - \frac{x}{4}$

$\frac{5}{4} = \frac{24x - x}{4} \Rightarrow \frac{5}{4} = \frac{23x}{4} \Rightarrow 23x = 5$

$x = \frac{5}{23}$

46. $\frac{2x}{3} + 4 = \frac{8}{3}(2x - 6)$

$\frac{2x}{3} + 4 = \frac{16x}{3} - 16 \Rightarrow 4 + 16 = \frac{16x}{3} - \frac{2x}{3}$

$20 = \frac{16x - 2x}{3} \Rightarrow 20 = \frac{14x}{3}$

$20 \times 3 = 14x \Rightarrow 60 = 14x$

$\frac{60}{14} = x \Rightarrow \frac{30}{7} = x$

47. (i) A number is doubled and added to 6, the result is equal to 14.

Let the number be x.

Double the number $= 2x$

It is added to 6.

$\Rightarrow 2x + 6$

The result is equal to 14.

$\Rightarrow 2x + 6 = 14$

(ii) Let the number be x.

$\frac{3}{5}$ of the number $= \frac{3x}{5}$

Given that: $x + \frac{3x}{5} = 24$

(iii) Let the present age of the man be x years. 20 years ago the age of the man $= (x - 20)$ years

Given that: $x - 20 = \frac{x}{2}$

48. Let the three consecutive natural numbers be $(x - 1)$, (x) and $(x + 1)$.

Given that:

$(x - 1) + (x) + (x + 1) = 90$

$x - 1 + x + x + 1 = 90$

$x = \frac{90}{3} \Rightarrow x = 30$

$\therefore$ The three numbers are $30 - 1 = 29$, 30 and $30 + 1 = 31$.

$\therefore$ The greatest number is 31.

49. Let the breadth of the rectangle be x cm.

Length of the rectangle $= (x + 5)$ cm

Perimeter of the rectangle $= 2(\ell + b) = 42$ cm

$2(x + 5 + x) = 42 \Rightarrow 2x + 5 = \frac{42}{2}$

$2x + 5 = 21 \Rightarrow 2x = 21 - 5$

$x = \frac{16}{2} \Rightarrow x = 8$ cm

$\therefore$ Length of the rectangle $= x + 5 = 8 + 5 = 13$ cm

50. Let the expenditure of Chintu be ₹x.

Savings of Chintu $= \frac{1}{3} \times x = \frac{x}{3}$

Chintu's pocket money $= x + \frac{x}{3}$

$x + \frac{x}{3} = 120 \Rightarrow \frac{3x + x}{3} = 120$

$\frac{4x}{3} = 120 \Rightarrow 4x = 120 \times 3$

$x = \frac{120 \times 3}{4} \Rightarrow x = 30 \times 3 \Rightarrow x = 90$

$\therefore$ Savings of Chintu $= \frac{1}{3} x = \frac{90}{3} =$ ₹30

51. Let the father's age be x years.

Daughter's age $= \frac{x}{3}$ years.

Given that:

$x + \frac{x}{3} = 56 \Rightarrow \frac{3x + x}{3} = 56$

$\frac{4x}{3} = 56 \Rightarrow 4x = 56 \times 3$

$x = \frac{56 \times 3}{4} \Rightarrow x = 14 \times 3$

$x = 42$

$\therefore$ The age of the daughter $= \frac{1}{3} \times 42$ years

$= 14$ years

52. (i) $x + y = 6 + 5 = 11$

(ii) $x - y = 6 - 5 = 1$

(iii) $3x/2y = 3(6)/2(5) = 18/10 = 9/5$

(iv) $3y/2x = 3(5)/2(6) = 15/12 = 5/4$

53. $4x^2yz = 4 \times 1 \times 1 \times 1 \times 2 \times 3 = 24$

54. The algebraic expression is $xy - (x + 30z/100)$

55. Total money = ₹50

Money spent on buying cookies = $8p$

Change = ₹$(50 - 8p)$

Essay Type Questions

56.

$$\begin{array}{r} 7x^2 - 5x + 11 \\ 2x^2 + 7x - 9 \\ - \quad - \quad + \\ \hline (-)\ 5x^2 - 12x + 20 \\ \hline \end{array}$$

57. $= \dfrac{9x^3}{3x} - \dfrac{15x^2}{3x} - \dfrac{12x}{3x}.$

$= \dfrac{9 \times x \times x \times x}{3x} - \dfrac{15 \times x \times x}{3x} - \dfrac{12x}{3x}.$

$= 3x^2 - 5x - 4.$

COMPETITION WING

Level 1: Apply Your Concepts

1. variable
2. constant
3. algebraic expression
4. non-negative
5. like terms
6. Let the cost of the burger be ₹x.

   The cost of the pizza $= \left(2\frac{1}{2}\right)(x) = \frac{5}{2}x$

   Given that:

   $\frac{5x}{2} + x = 105 \Rightarrow \frac{5x + 2x}{2} = 105$

   $\frac{7x}{2} = 105 \Rightarrow x = \frac{105 \times 2}{7}$

   $x = 15 \times 2 \Rightarrow x = 30$

   ∴ The cost of the burger = ₹30.

7. Let the number of chocolates with Rani be x.

   Number of chocolates given to her brother $= \frac{2}{5}x$

   Number of chocolates given to her sister $= \frac{1}{3}x$

   Number of chocolates left with her = 20

   $\Rightarrow x - \frac{2x}{5} - \frac{x}{3} = 20 \Rightarrow \frac{15x - 6x - 5x}{15} = 20$

   $\frac{4x}{15} = 20 \Rightarrow 4x = 20 \times 15$

   $x = \frac{20 \times 15}{4} \Rightarrow x = 5 \times 15 \Rightarrow x = 75$

   ∴ The number of chocolates with Rani = 75

8. Let the number of flowers with Satya be x.

   The number of flowers with Rukku $= \frac{3}{4}x$

   Total number of flowers $= x + \frac{3x}{4} = 35$

   $\frac{7x}{4} = 35 \Rightarrow 7x = 35 \times 4$

   $7x = 140 \Rightarrow x = \frac{140}{7} \Rightarrow x = 20$

   The number of flowers with Satya = 20

9. Given that,

   $A = 2x^3 - 3x^2 - 4x + 5$

   $2B = 2(2x^2 - x^3 + x + 1) = 4x^2 - 2x^3 + 2x + 2$

   $C = x^2 + x + 2$

   $A + 2B - C = (2x^3 - 3x^2 - 4x + 5) + (4x^2 - 2x^3 + 2x + 2) - (x^2 + x + 2)$

   $= -3x + 5$

   The degree of A + 2B − C is 1.

   Hence, the correct option is (b).

10. $3x^2 - [7x - \{5x^2 - (2x - 3)(4x - 2) - 5\} - 2]$

    $= 3x^2 - [7x - \{5x^2 - (8x^2 - 4x - 12x + 6) - 5\} - 2]$

    $= 3x^2 - [7x - \{5x^2 - (8x^2 - 16x + 6) - 5\} - 2]$

    $= 3x^2 - [7x - \{5x^2 - 8x^2 + 16x - 6 - 5\} - 2]$

    $= 3x^2 - [7x - \{-3x^2 + 16x - 11\} - 2]$

    $= 3x^2 - [7x + 3x^2 - 16x + 11 - 2]$

    $= 3x^2 - [3x^2 - 9x + 9]$

    $= 3x^2 - 3x^2 + 9x - 9$

    $= 9x - 9$

    Hence, the correct option is (a).

Level 2: Review Your Concepts

11. Let x, y and z be the number of ₹1 coins, ₹2 coins and ₹5 coins, respectively.

    Given, $y = 2x$

    $z = 3y = 3(2x) = 6x$

    $1(x) + 2(y) + 5(z) =$ ₹700

    $1x + 2(2x) + 5(6x) =$ ₹700

    $x + 4x + 30x =$ ₹700

    $35x =$ ₹700 $\Rightarrow x = 20$

    $y = 2 \times 20 = 40$

    $z = 6 \times 20 = 120$

    The total number of coins $= x + y + z$

    $= 20 + 40 + 120 = 180$

    Hence, the correct option is (c).

12. Given, AB $= (2x + 3y + 10)$ cm, BC $= (2x + 3y - 5)$ cm, CD $= (4x + 3y + 6)$ cm and DA $= (2x - 3y + 7)$ cm

    We know that, in a rectangle the opposite sides are equal.

AB = CD

$2x + 3y + 10 = 4x + 3y + 6$

$4x - 2x = 10 - 6$

$2x = 4 \Rightarrow x = 2$

BC = DA

$2x + 3y - 5 = 2x - 3y + 7$

$3y + 3y = 7 + 5$

$6y = 12 \Rightarrow y = 2$

Side AB $= 2x + 3y + 10 = 2(2) + 3(2) + 10$

$= 4 + 6 + 10 = 20$ cm

Side BC $= 2x + 3y - 5 = 2(2) + 3(2) - 5$

$= 4 + 6 - 5 = 5$ cm

Therefore, the perimeter of the rectangle

$= 2(AB + BC) = 2(20 + 5) = 50$ cm

Hence, the correct option is (c).

13. Let the amount with Mohan be 'x'.

The amount received by Vijay = $(1/3)x$

The amount received by Suresh

$= (2/5)\text{th} \times (2/3)\text{rd}\ x$

The amount received by Venkat

$= (1/6)\text{th} \times (3/5)\text{th} \times (2/3)\text{rd}\ x$

The amount left with Mohan

$= (5/6)\text{th} \times (3/5)\text{th} \times (2/3)\text{rd}\ x$

₹3000 $= (5/6)\text{th} \times (3/5)\text{th} \times (2/3)\text{rd}\ x$

₹3000 $= 1/3\ x$

$x =$ ₹9000

The amount received by Suresh

$= (2/5)\text{th} \times (2/3)\text{rd} \times 9000$

= ₹2400

The amount received by Venkat

$=(1/6)\text{th} \times (3/5)\text{th} \times (2/3)\text{rd} \times 9000$

= ₹600

The sum of amounts received by Suresh and Venkat = ₹2400 + ₹600 = ₹3000

Hence, the correct option is (a).

Level 3: Assess Your Concepts

14. Given that the length of the rectangle (in cm) $(l) = 3x + 4y - 5$.

The breadth of the rectangle (in cm) $(b) = 2x - 5y$.

(i) The length of the rectangle B (in cm) $(l_1) = 3x + 4y - 5 + 5 = 3x + 4y$.

The breadth of the rectangle B (in cm) $(b_1) = 2x - 5y + 5$.

The perimeter of the rectangle B (in cm) $= 2(l_1 + b_1)$

$= 2(3x + 4y + 2x - 5y + 5)$

$= 2(5x - y + 5)$

$= 10x - 2y + 10$.

Hence, the perimeter of the rectangle B (in cm) $= 10x - 2y + 10$.

(ii) The length of the rectangle A (in cm) $(l) = 3x + 4y - 5$.

The breadth of the rectangle A (in cm) $(b) = 2x - 5y$.

The area of the rectangle A (in sq cm) $= l \times b$

$= (3x + 4y - 5)(2x - 5y)$

$= 3x(2x - 5y) + 4y(2x - 5y) - 5(2x - 5y)$

$= 6x^2 - 15xy + 8xy - 20y^2 - 10x + 25y$

$= 6x^2 - 20y^2 - 7xy - 10x + 25y$.

Hence, the area of the rectangle A (in sq cm) $= 6x^2 - 20y^2 - 7xy - 10x + 25y$.

(iii) The length of the rectangle B (in cm) $(l_1) = 3x + 4y$.

The breadth of the rectangle B (in cm) $(b_1) = 2x - 5y + 5$.

The area of the rectangle B (in sq cm) $= l_1 \times b_1$

$= (3x + 4y)(2x - 5y + 5)$

$= 3x(2x - 5y + 5) + 4y(2x - 5y + 5)$

$= 6x^2 - 15xy + 15x + 8xy - 20y^2 + 20y$

$= 6x^2 - 20y^2 - 7xy + 15x + 20y$

The difference between the area of the rectangles A and B (in sq cm)

$= (6x^2 - 20y^2 - 7xy + 15x + 20y)$

$-(6x^2 - 20y^2 - 7xy - 10x + 25y)$

$= 15x + 20y + 10x - 25y$

$= 25x - 5y$.

Hence, the required difference (in sq cm) $= 25x - 5y$.

15. Let the total number of sweets distributed be x

$$\frac{x}{98-28} - \frac{x}{98} = 4$$

$$\frac{x}{70} - \frac{x}{98} = 4$$

$$x\left(\frac{98-70}{(70)(98)}\right) = 4$$

$$x = \frac{(4)(70)(98)}{28} = 980.$$

16. Sum of x, $x + 2$, $x + 4 = 30$

i.e., $3x = 24$

$x = 8$

The numbers are 8, 10, 12. The difference of the extreme numbers is $= (12)^2 - (8)^2 = 80$

CHAPTER

8

Geometry

Remember

Before beginning this chapter, you should be able to:

- Know the names of different geometrical figures
- Identify lines and line segments, angles, triangles, rectangles, squares and circles

Key Ideas

After completing this chapter, you should be able to:

- Understand basic concepts: Plane, lines and angles
- Learn about triangles: Types of triangles, properties of triangles, congruence of triangles and construction of triangles
- Learn about circles: Chord, secant, tangent, segment and sector
- Understand symmetry: Line symmetry

Scientific Crypt

A Tribute to Gottfried Wilhelm Leibniz (1646-1716)

Gottfried Wilhelm Leibniz (1646–1716), a German philosopher, mathematician, and innovator renowned for his work on "monads," abstract algebra, calculus, and contributions to metaphysics and logic, left an enduring legacy that shapes diverse fields of human knowledge.

Born in 1646 in Leipzig, Saxony, Holy Roman Empire, amidst the turmoil of the Thirty Years' War, he was largely self-taught and entered the University of Leipzig in 1661. His goal was to reconcile the ideas of modern thinkers like Galileo with those of Aristotle. Leibniz's early work laid the foundation for his concept of monads. He applied his talents to law and politics, serving at courts and engaging in various scientific endeavours. He independently developed calculus and critiqued Descartes' mechanics, introducing the concept of dynamics. Leibniz also explored metaphysical systems, delving into questions about God's role and the nature of reality. His efforts contributed to the establishment of the German Academy of Sciences in Berlin.

Beyond being a philosopher, Leibniz exemplified curiosity and innovation in an era marked by intellectual upheaval. As a mathematician, his seminal achievement was the development of the main principles of differential and integral calculus. His innovations in abstract algebra and group theory laid the groundwork for fundamental concepts such as "Noetherian rings" and "Noetherian modules." Collaborations with luminaries of his time solidified his reputation as a true intellectual luminary.

FUN TIME

CROSSWORD

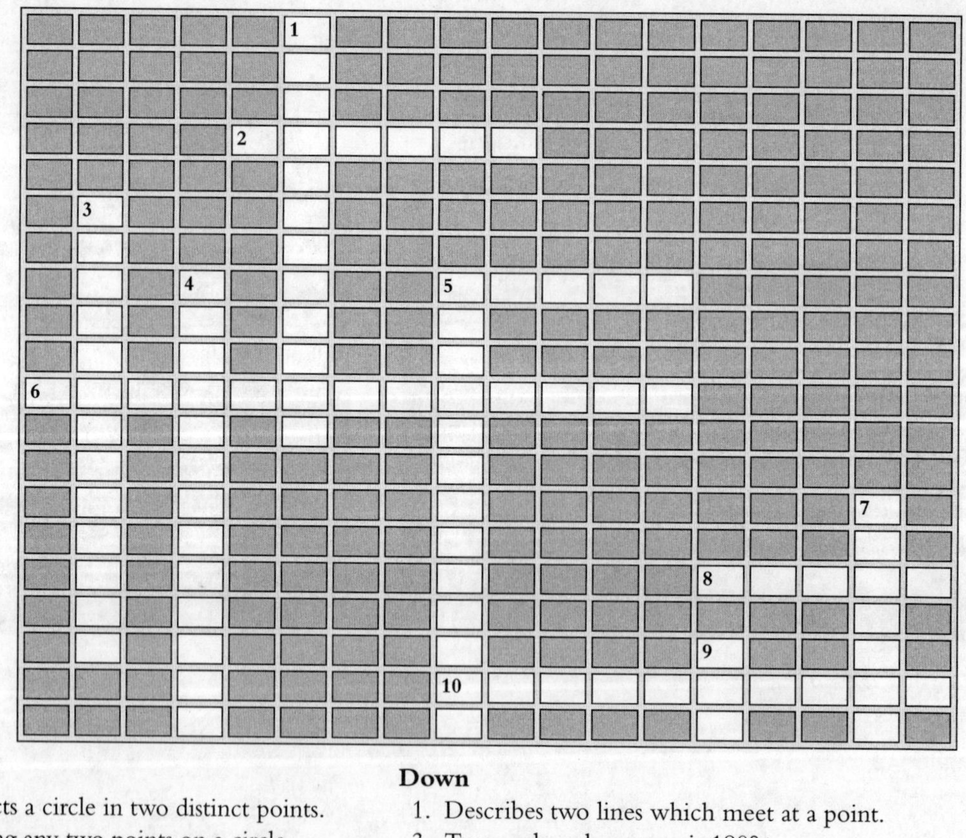

Across

2. A line which intersects a circle in two distinct points.
5. A line segment joining any two points on a circle.
6. Two lines making an angle of 90° with each other.
8. A surface which extends indefinitely in all directions.
10. Describes two or more lines in a plane passing through the same point.

Down

1. Describes two lines which meet at a point.
3. Two angles whose sum is 180°.
4. Two angles whose sum is 90°.
5. The perimeter of a circle; π times the diameter.
7. A line in the plane of a circle that meets the circle in exactly one point.
9. A continuous piece of a circle.

INTRODUCTION

The world is full of different shapes and figures, if you look around yourself you can find objects with various shapes. When we look at the Sun, it is round in shape, but when we look at notebooks, it is square in shape. Mathematics involves numbers, symbols and algebraic expression. Interestingly, study of Maths is not only just about numbers but it also includes shapes. In this chapter, we will learn Geometry which deals with study of various shapes.

Basic Concepts

The term 'geometry' comes form the combination of two Greek words '*Geo*' (Earth) and '*Metria*' (Measure) meaning measurement of the Earth. **Geometry** is the study of properties of lines, angles, polygons and circles. We shall begin with some basic concepts.

Info Bytes!

A polygon is an enclosed figure made up of straight lines!

Table 8.1 Classification of polygons on the basis of number of sides

Number of Sides	Name of the Polygon
3	Triangle
4	Quadrilateral
5	Pentagon
6	Hexagon
7	Heptagon
8	Octagon
9	Nonagon
10	Decagon

Plane

A **plane** is a surface which extends indefinitely in all directions.

Example: the surface of a table is a part of a plane. A black board is a part of a plane.

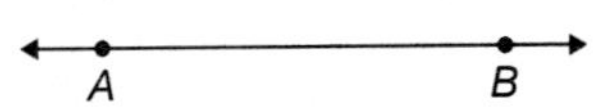

Line

A **line** is a set of infinite points that has no end points and it is infinite in length. The figure given shows a line ℓ that extends to infinity on either side. If A and B are any two points on ℓ, we also denote the line ℓ as $\overleftrightarrow{AB}$, read as line AB.

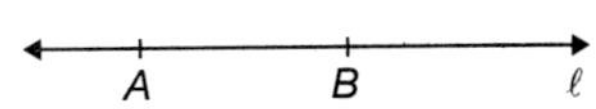

Line Segment

A **line segment** is a part of a line. The line segment has two end points and it has a finite length.

In the given figure, AB is a line segment, it is a part of line ℓ, consisting of the points A, B and all the points of ℓ lie between A and B. The line segment AB is also denoted as $\overline{AB}$. Here, A and B are the end points of $\overline{AB}$.

Info Bytes!

A 'Ray' is like the sun's rays. It starts at one point and goes on infinitely in one direction.

Ray

A **ray** has one end point and it extends infinitely on the other side.

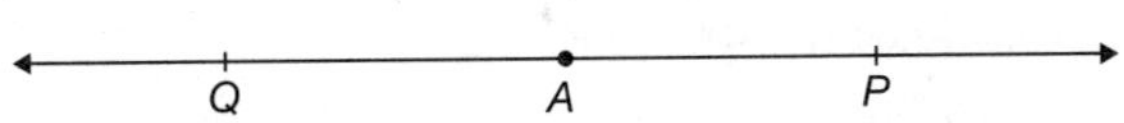

In the above figure, AP is a ray which has only one end point A. The ray AP is denoted as $\overrightarrow{AP}$. $\overrightarrow{AQ}$ is different from $\overrightarrow{AP}$. If A lies between P and Q, $\overrightarrow{AP}$ and $\overrightarrow{AQ}$ are said to be opposite rays.

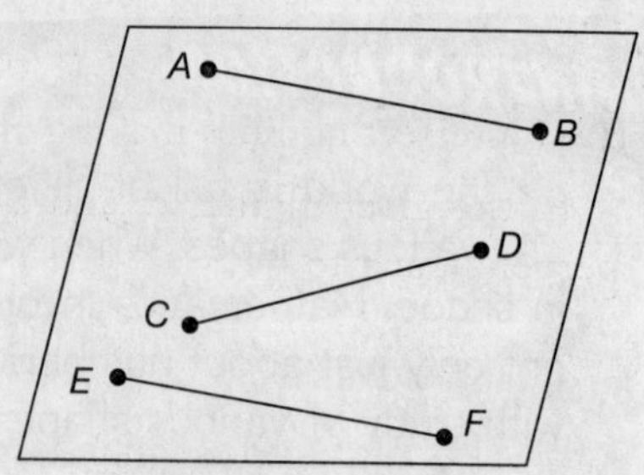

Coplanar Lines

Two or more lines lying in a same plane are called **coplanar lines**.

Intersecting Lines

Two lines which meet at a point are called **intersecting lines**.

In the given figure, ℓ_1 and ℓ_2 are two intersecting lines.

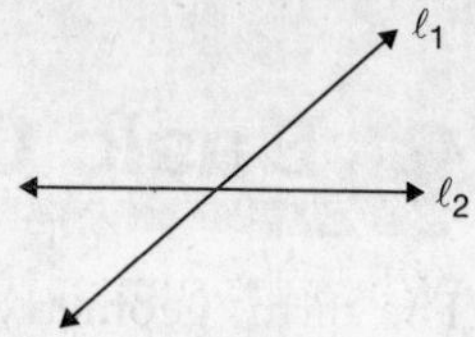

Angle

Two rays which meet at a point are said to form an **angle** at their meeting point.

In the given figure, $\overrightarrow{OQ}$ and $\overrightarrow{OP}$ are two rays which have O as their meeting point and an angle with certain measurement is formed. The point O is called the **vertex** of the angle and $\overrightarrow{OQ}$ and $\overrightarrow{OP}$ are called the **sides** or **arms** of the angle. We denote the angle as $\angle QOP$ or $\angle POQ$ (or sometimes simply as $\angle O$). We see that $\angle QOP = \angle POQ$ (These are the two ways of representing the same angle). A common unit of measurement of angles is the **degree**. This unit is denoted by a small circle placed above and to the right of the number.

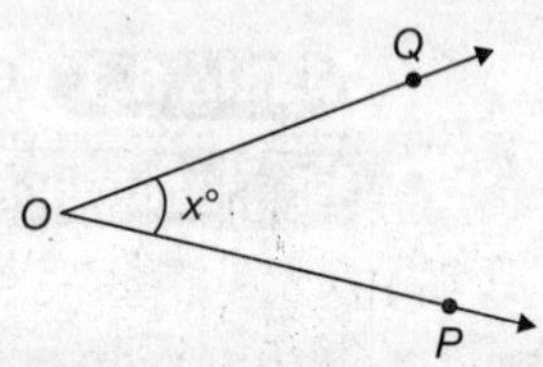

Example: we write $\angle QOP = 34°$ and read it as 34 degrees.

Let the measurement of an angle be $x°$.

1. If $0° < x < 90°$, it is called an **acute angle**.

   Example: In the given figure 8.1 (a), $\angle AOB$ is acute.

2. If $x = 90°$, it is called a **right angle**.

   Example: In the given figure 8.1 (b), $\angle AOC$ is a right angle.

3. If $90° < x < 180°$, it is called an **obtuse angle**.

   Example: In the given figure 8.1 (c), $\angle AOD$ is an obtuse angle.

4. If $x = 180°$, it is the angle of a **straight line** or a **straight angle**.

   Example: In the figure given 8.1 (d), $\angle AOE = 180°$, $\overleftrightarrow{AE}$ is a straight line and O is a point on the line AE.

5. If $180° < x < 360°$, it is called **reflex angle**.

   Example: 200°, 270° and 300°

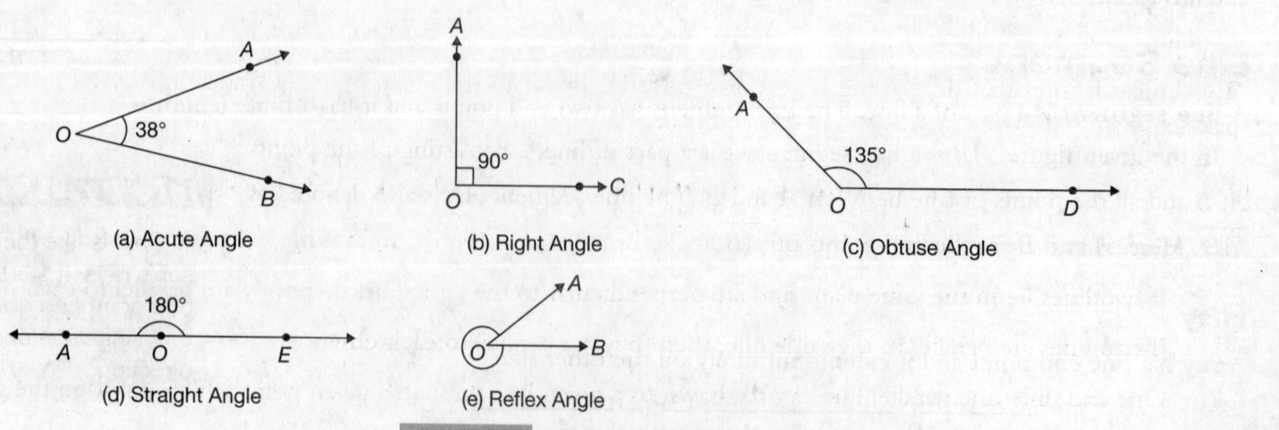

Figure 8.1 Types of angles

Perpendicular Lines

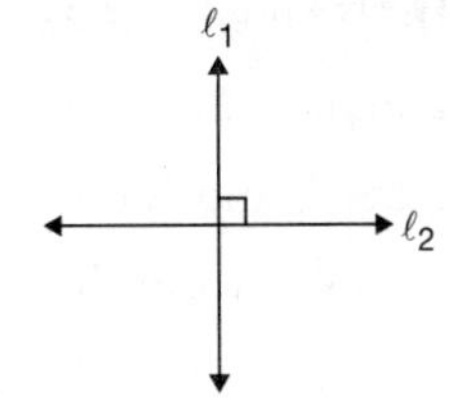

Two intersecting lines making an angle of 90° with each other are called **perpendicular lines**.

In the given figure, ℓ_1 and ℓ_2 are perpendicular lines. We write $\ell_1 \perp \ell_2$ and read this as ℓ_1 is perpendicular to ℓ_2.

Complementary Angles

When the sum of two angles is 90°, the two angles are called **complementary angles**.

Example: If $x + y = 90°$, then $x°$ and $y°$ are called complementary angles.

Supplementary Angles

When the sum of two angles is 180°, the two angles are called **supplementary angles**.

Example: If $a + b = 180°$, then $a°$ and $b°$ are called supplementary angles.

Adjacent Angles

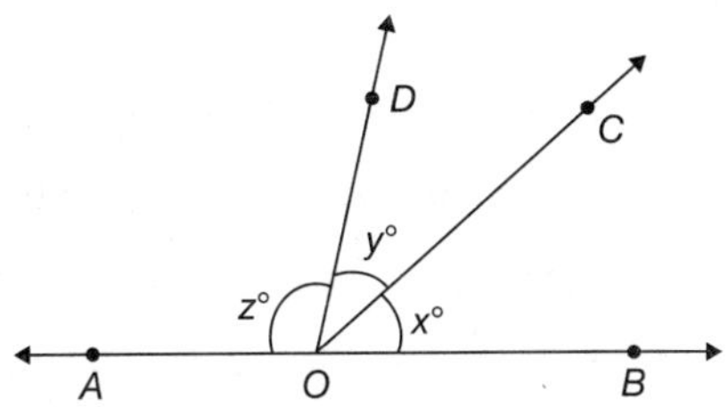

If two angles have a common vertex and a common ray and the other two sides lie on either side of the common ray, then they are said to be **adjacent angles**.

In the given figure, $\angle AOD$ and $\angle DOC$ are adjacent angles. Likewise, $\angle DOC$ and $\angle COB$ are also adjacent angles.

Linear Pair

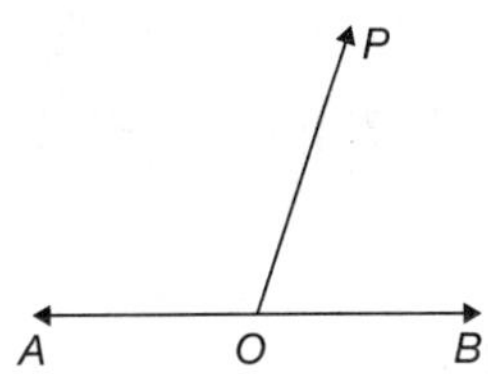

If a pair of angles are adjacent and the non-common rays are opposite to each other, then the angles are said to form a **linear pair**.

Example: If O is a point between A and B and P is a point that does not lie on AB, then $\angle AOP$ and $\angle POB$ form a linear pair. The angles of a linear pair are supplementary.

Vertically Opposite Angles

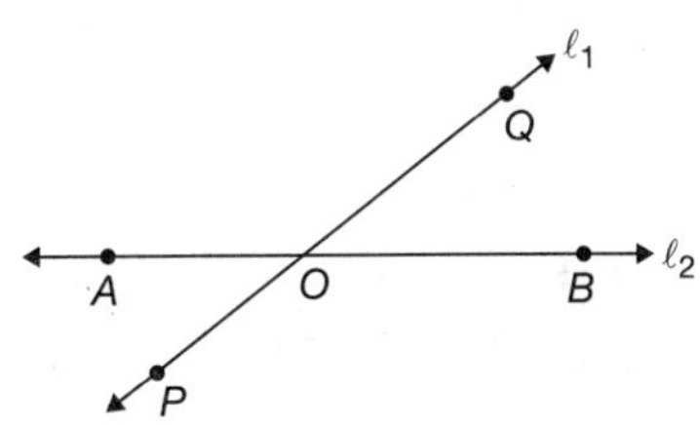

When two lines intersect each other, four angles are formed.

In the given figure, $\overleftrightarrow{AB}$ and $\overleftrightarrow{PQ}$ intersect at O. $\angle AOP$ and $\angle BOQ$ are vertically opposite angles. Similarly, $\angle POB$ and $\angle QOA$ are vertically opposite angles. Vertically opposite angles are equal.

Concurrent Lines

Two or more lines in a plane passing through a same point are called **concurrent lines**.

Parallel Lines

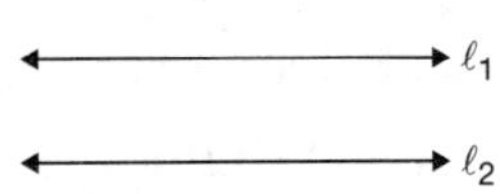

Two coplanar lines that do not meet are called **parallel lines**. In the given figure, l_1 and l_2 are parallel lines. Symbolically, we write $l_1 \parallel l_2$ and read as l_1 is parallel to l_2.

Properties of Parallel Lines

(i) For two given parallel lines, the perpendicular distance between the lines is the same everywhere.

(ii) If two lines lie in the same plane and are perpendicular to the same line, then they are parallel to each other.

(iii) If two lines are parallel to the same line, then they are parallel to each other.

(iv) One and only one parallel line can be drawn to a given line through a given point which is not on the given line.

Transversal

A straight line intersecting a pair of lines in two distinct points is a **transversal** for the two given lines.

Let l_1 and l_2 be a pair of lines and t be a transversal.

As shown in the figure, totally eight angles are formed.

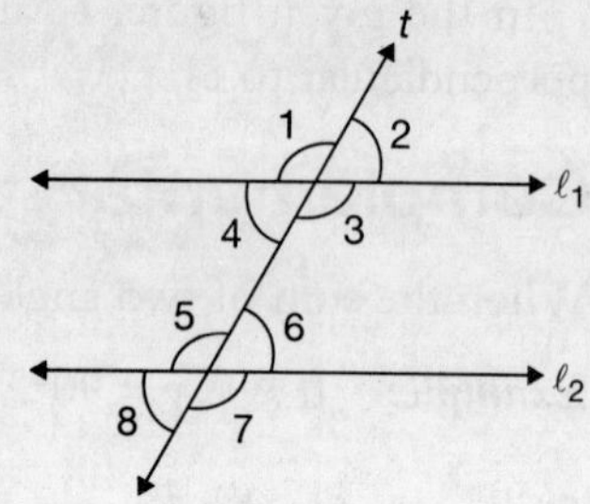

1. $\angle 1$, $\angle 2$, $\angle 7$ and $\angle 8$ are exterior angles and $\angle 3$, $\angle 4$, $\angle 5$ and $\angle 6$ are interior angles.
2. ($\angle 1$ and $\angle 5$), ($\angle 2$ and $\angle 6$), ($\angle 3$ and $\angle 7$) and ($\angle 4$ and $\angle 8$) are pairs of corresponding angles.
3. ($\angle 1$ and $\angle 3$), ($\angle 2$ and $\angle 4$), ($\angle 5$ and $\angle 7$) and ($\angle 6$ and $\angle 8$) are pairs of vertically opposite angles.
4. ($\angle 4$ and $\angle 6$), and ($\angle 3$ and $\angle 5$) are pairs of alternate interior angles.
5. ($\angle 1$ and $\angle 7$) and ($\angle 2$ and $\angle 8$) are pairs of alternate exterior angles.

If l_1 and l_2 are parallel, then

1. Corresponding angles are equal, i.e., $\angle 1 = \angle 5$, $\angle 2 = \angle 6$, $\angle 3 = \angle 7$ and $\angle 4 = \angle 8$.
2. Alternative interior angles are equal, i.e., $\angle 4 = \angle 6$ and $\angle 3 = \angle 5$.
3. Alternative exterior angles are equal, i.e., $\angle 1 = \angle 7$ and $\angle 2 = \angle 8$.
4. Exterior angles on the same side of the transversal are supplementary, i.e., $\angle 1 + \angle 8 = 180°$ and $\angle 2 + \angle 7 = 180°$.
5. Interior angles on the same side of the transversal are supplementary, i.e., $\angle 4 + \angle 5 = 180°$ and $\angle 3 + \angle 6 = 180°$.

EXAMPLE 8.1

$\angle A$ and $\angle B$ are two complementary angles. If $\angle A$ is 24° more than $\angle B$, then find the angles of $\angle A$ and $\angle B$.

SOLUTION

Given that:

$\angle A + \angle B = 90°$

$(\angle B + 24°) + \angle B = 90°$

$2\angle B = (90° - 24°)$

$2\angle B = 66°$

$\angle B = 33°$

$\therefore \angle A = (90° - 33°)$

$\angle A = 57°$

EXAMPLE 8.2

$\angle P$ and $\angle Q$ are two supplementary angles. If $\angle P$ is four-times of $\angle Q$, then find measurement of the angles P and Q.

SOLUTION

Given that:

$\angle P + \angle Q = 180°$

$(4\angle Q) + \angle Q = 180°$

$\angle Q = \frac{180}{5} = 36°$

$\angle Q = 36°$

$\therefore \angle P = 4(36°)$

$\angle P = 144°$

EXAMPLE 8.3 In the given figure, ℓ || *m*, $a = 40°$, then find all the other angles as mentioned in the figure.

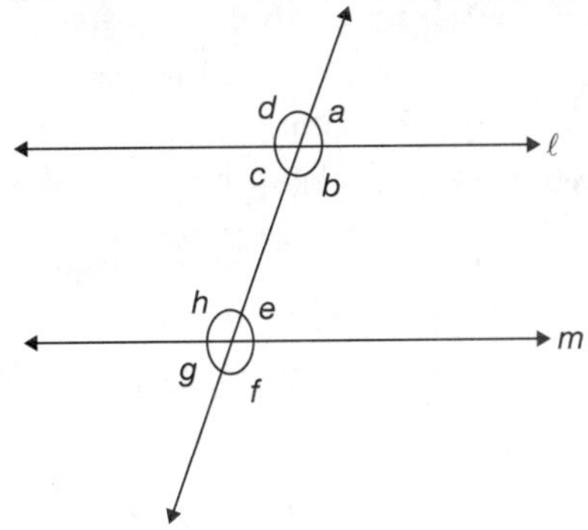

SOLUTION

Given that: $a = 40°$ and $\ell \parallel m$

$b = 180° - 40° = 140°$ (Since *a*, *b* are linear pair)

$b = d = 140°$ (Vertically opposite angles)

$a = c = 40°$ (Vertically opposite angles)

$a = e = 40°$ (Corresponding angles)

$b = f = 140°$ (Corresponding angles)

$h = f = 140°$ (Vertically opposite angles)

$e = g = 40°$ (Vertically opposite angles)

Triangles

A three-sided simple closed figure is a **triangle**. In the given figure, *ABC* is a triangle. It has three sides *AB*, *BC* and *CA*. *A*, *B* and *C* are the three vertices of the triangle. $\angle CAB$, $\angle ABC$ and $\angle BCA$ are its three angles. Triangle *ABC* is denoted as ΔABC.

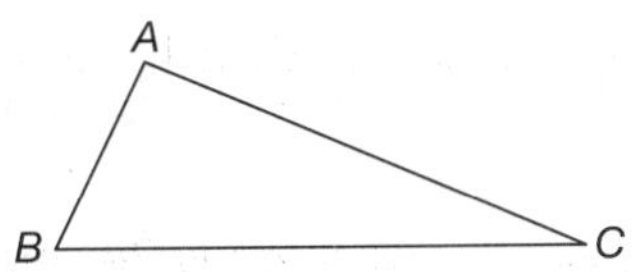

Info Bytes!

- The relationship between triangles and their angles and sides is known as **Trigonometry!**
- Triangles are the only shape that cannot be 'deformed' without changing the lengths of its sides. That's why they're so important in structures like bridges.

Types of Triangles

Based on their sides, triangles can be classified as follows:

1. **Scalene triangle:** A triangle in which no two sides are equal is a **scalene triangle**. In the given triangle 8.2 (a), $AB \neq BC$, $BC \neq CA$, and $CA \neq AB$. Hence, it is a scalene triangle.
2. **Isosceles triangle:** A triangle in which any two sides are equal is an **isosceles triangle**. In the triangle given 8.2 (b), $PQ = PR$. Hence, *PQR* is an isosceles triangle.
3. **Equilateral triangle:** A triangle in which all the three sides are equal is an **equilateral triangle**. In ΔXYZ, $XY = YZ = ZX$. Hence, *XYZ* is an equilateral triangle.

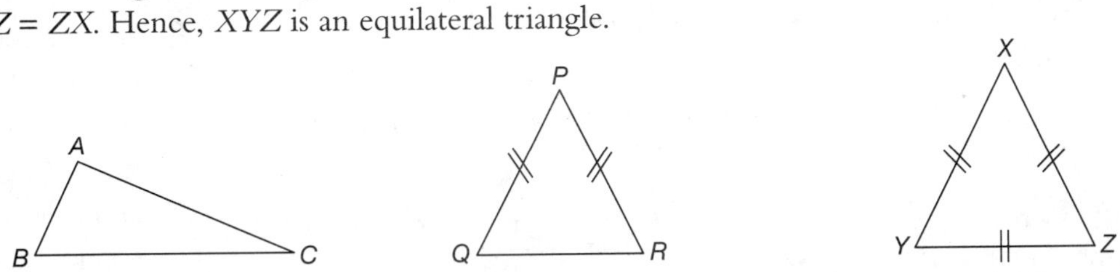

(a) Scalene Triangle (b) Isosceles Triangle (c) Equilateral Triangle

Figure 8.2 Types of Triangle

Based on the angles, triangles can be classified as follows:

1. **Acute-angled triangle:** A triangle in which all the angles are acute is an **acute-angled triangle**.
In such a triangle, the square of the longest side is less than the sum of the squares of other two sides. In the given triangle 8.3 (a), each of the angles *A*, *B* and *C* is less than 90°. Hence, *ABC* is an acute-angled triangle.

2. **Right-angled triangle:** A triangle with a right angle is a **right-angled triangle**. In such a triangle, the square of the longest side and the hypotenuse is equal to the sum of the squares of other two sides. In the given triangle 8.3 (b), $\angle ABC = 90°$. Hence, ABC is a right-angled triangle. In right-angled triangle ABC, if $\overline{AC}$ is the longest side, then $AC^2 = AB^2 + BC^2$.

3. **Obtuse-angled triangle:** A triangle in which one angle is greater than 90° is an **obtuse-angled triangle**. In such a triangle, the square of the longest side is greater than the sum of the squares of the other two sides. In the given triangle 8.3 (c), $\angle ABC > 90°$. Hence, ABC is an obtuse-angled triangle. In an obtuse-angled triangle ABC, if $\overline{AC}$ is the longest side, then $AC^2 > AB^2 + BC^2$.

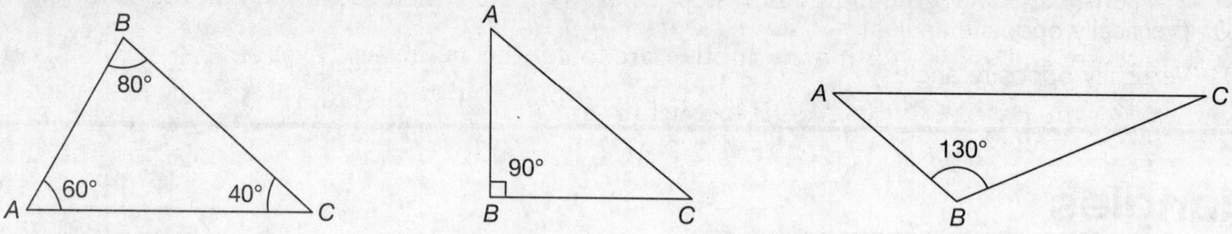

(a) Acute Angled Triangle (b) Right Angled Triangle (c) Obtuse angled triangle

Figure 8.3 Types of Triangle

Isosceles Right-angled Triangle

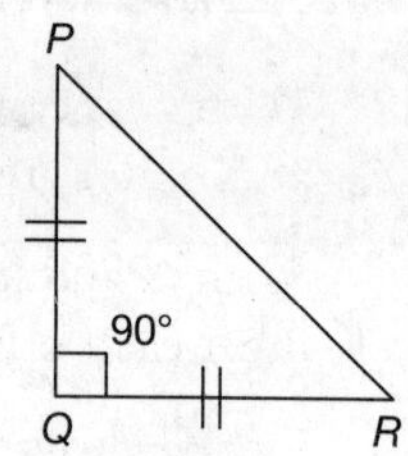

A triangle in which two sides are equal and one angle is 90° is an **isosceles right-angled triangle**.

In the given triangle PQR, $PQ = QR$ and $\angle PQR = 90°$.

$\therefore$ PQR is an isosceles right triangle.

In such a triangle, the ratio of sides PQ, QR and RP is $1 : 1 : \sqrt{2}$.

Given below are the statements of some of the properties of triangles:

1. The sum of the three angles of a triangle is 180°.
2. The exterior angle of a triangle is equal to the sum of the interior angles opposite to it.
3. The sum of any two sides of a triangle is greater than the third side. In ΔPQR, $PQ + QR > PR$, $QR + RP > PQ$ and $RP + PQ > QR$.
4. Difference between any two sides is less than the third side. $PQ - QR < PR$, $QR - RP < PQ$ and $RP - PQ < QR$
5. Angles opposite to equal sides are equal and vice versa. If $\angle P = \angle Q$, then $QR = PR$. If $QR = PR$, then $\angle P = \angle Q$.
6. If the angles are in increasing or decreasing order, the sides opposite to them will also be in the same order. If $\angle P > \angle Q > \angle R$, then $QR > PR > PQ$.

Konnect

1. A scalene triangle can be acute, right or obtuse angled.
2. An isosceles triangle can be acute, right or obtuse angled.
3. An equilateral triangle is always be acute. It cannot contain a right angle or an obtuse angle.

Constructions

We shall now look at the steps of constructing angles and bisector.

Congruent Angles (or) Equal Angles

Given: An angle *PQR*

To construct: $\angle AOB$ equal to $\angle PQR$.

Steps of construction:

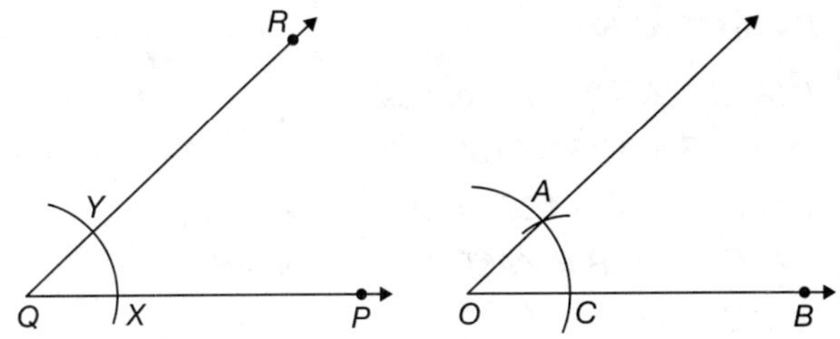

1. Draw a ray *OB*.
2. With *Q* as centre and a suitable radius draw an arc which cuts rays *QP* and *QR* at *X* and *Y*, respectively.
3. With *O* as centre and the same radius as in step (2) draw an arc which cuts ray *OB* at the point *C*.
4. With *C* as centre and *XY* as radius draw another arc to cut the arc in step (2) at *A*.
5. Join *OA* to get the ray *OA*. Now $\angle AOB$ is equal to $\angle PQR$.

Bisector of an Angle

Given: An $\angle MON$

To construct: The bisector of the $\angle MON$

Steps of construction:

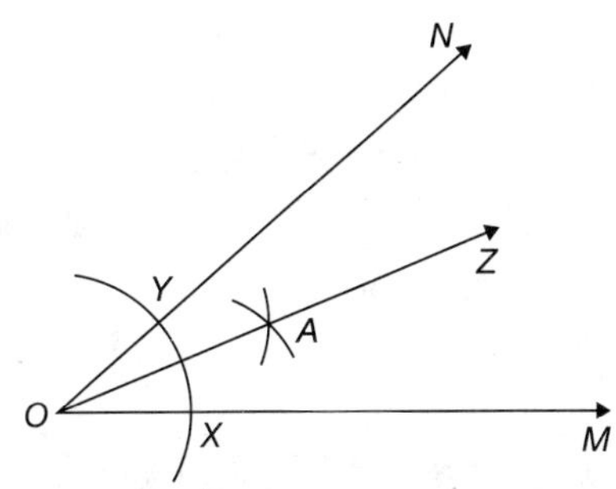

1. With *O* as centre and a suitable radius draw an arc which cuts rays *OM* and *ON* at *X* and *Y*, respectively.
2. With *X* and *Y* as centres and more than half of *XY* as radius, draw two arcs to meet each other at *A*.
3. Join *OA* to get the ray *OA*. Now *OA* is the bisector of the $\angle MON$.

Construction of an Angle 60°

Steps of construction:

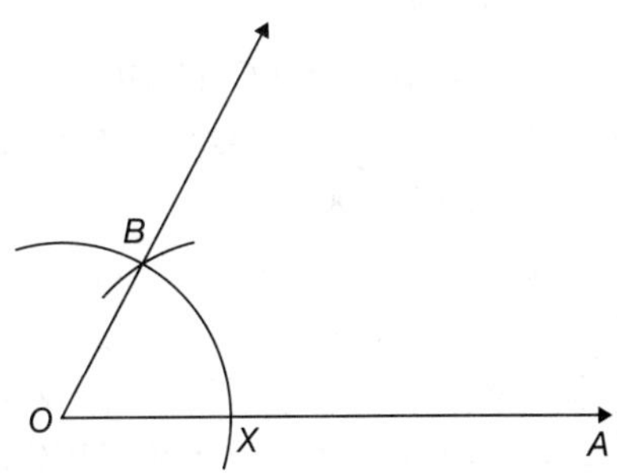

1. Draw a ray *OA*.
2. With *O* as centre and a suitable radius draw an arc which cuts the ray *OA* at *X*.
3. With *X* as centre and the same radius as in step (2), draw an arc to cut the arc in step (2) at *B*.
4. Join *OB* to get the ray *OB*. Now the $\angle BOA$ is 60°.

Construction of an Angle 90°

Steps of construction:

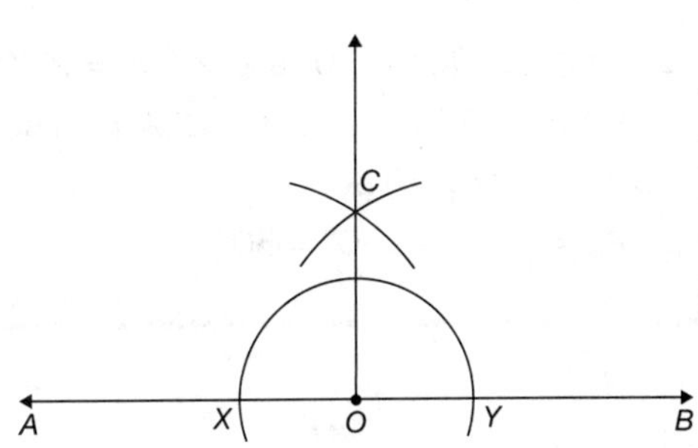

1. Draw a line AB. Mark a point *O* on *AB*.
2. With *O* as centre and a suitable radius draw an arc which cuts the line *AB* at *X* and *Y* respectively.
3. With *X* and *Y* as centres and more than half of *XY* as radius, draw two arcs to meet each other at *C*. Join *OC* to get the ray *OC*. Now the angle *BOC* or angle *AOC* is 90°.

EXAMPLE 8.4

In the given figure, C is a point on the line segment BD. Find the measurements of $\angle ACB$ and $\angle ABC$.

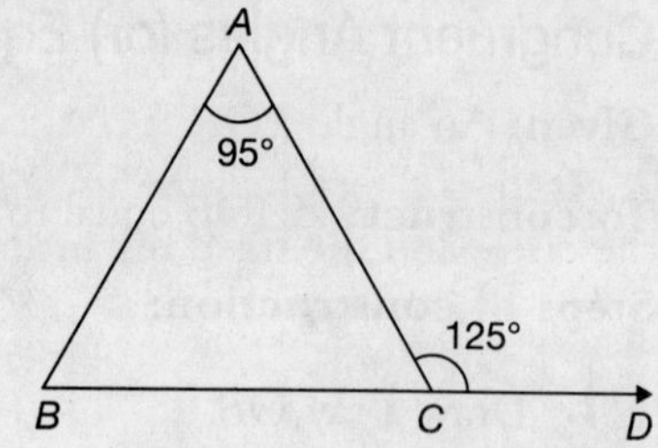

SOLUTION

$(\angle ACB, \angle ACD)$ is a linear pair.

$\Rightarrow \angle ACB + 125° = 180°$

$\angle ACB = 180° - 125° = 55°$

$\angle ABC + \angle CAB = \angle ACD$ (Exterior angle)

$\angle ABC + 95° = 125°$

$\angle ABC = 125° - 95° = 30°$

EXAMPLE 8.5

In the given figure, PTQ, PMR, SMT and QRS are straight lines. Find the angle of $\angle RMS$.

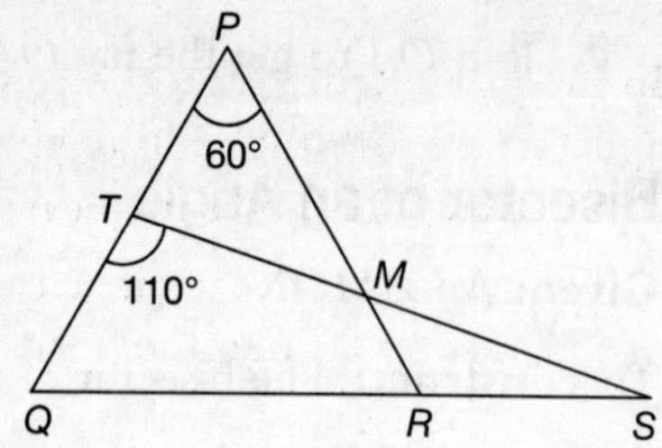

SOLUTION

Since PQ is a straight line and $\angle QTM = 110°$.

$\angle TPM + \angle PMT = \angle QTM$

$60° + \angle PMT = 110°$

$\Rightarrow \angle PMT = 110° - 60° = 50°$

$\Rightarrow \angle PMT = \angle RMS$ (Vertically opposite angles)

$\Rightarrow \angle RMS = 50°$

EXAMPLE 8.6

In the figure, ABD, BCD are two triangles. BD is the bisector of $\angle ABC$ and $\angle ADC$. $\overline{AB} \parallel \overline{CD}$ and $\overline{AD} \parallel \overline{BC}$. If $\angle BCD = 50°$, then find the angle of $\angle BAD$.

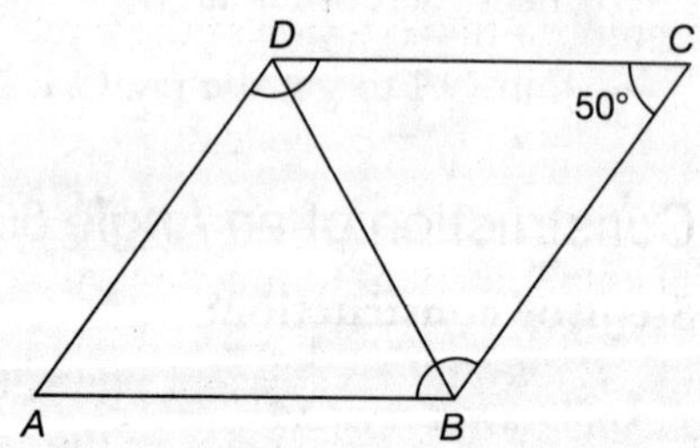

SOLUTION

$\angle BCD = 50°$ and $\overline{BC} \parallel \overline{AD}$.

$\angle CDA + \angle BCD = 180°$ (Co-interior angles)

$\Rightarrow \angle CDA + 50° = 180°$

$\angle CDA = 180° - 50°$

$\angle CDA = 130°$

Similarly, $\angle ABC = 130°$ $(\because \overline{AB} \parallel \overline{CD})$

Since BD is the bisector of $\angle ADC$ and $\angle ABC$,

$\angle ABC = \angle ABD + \angle CBD$ $(\because \angle ABD = \angle CBD)$

$2\angle ABD = 130° \Rightarrow \angle ABD = \angle CBD = \frac{130}{2} = 65°$

$\angle ADB + \angle BDC = 130°$ and $\angle ADB = \angle BDC = \frac{130}{2} = 65°$

In ΔABD, $\angle ABD + \angle ADB + \angle BAD = 180°$

$130° + \angle BAD = 180°$

$\angle BAD = 180° - 130° = 50°$

Circles

A **circle** is a set of all points in a plane which are at a fixed distance from a fixed point. The fixed point is the centre of the circle and the fixed distance is the radius of the circle.

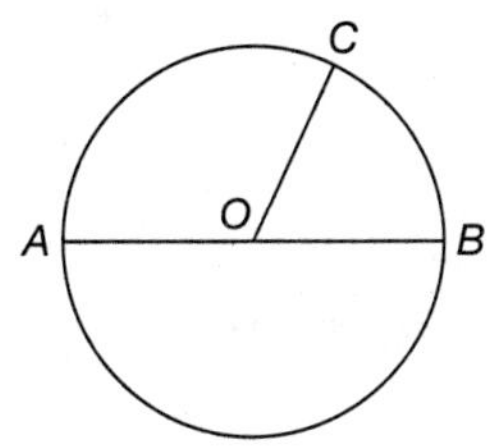

Konnect

For a given area, a circle has the shortest perimeter among all shapes.

In the given figure, O is the centre of the circle and OC is the radius of the circle. AB is the diameter of the circle. OA and OB are also the radii of the circle. The diameter is twice the radius [$d = 2r$]. The centre of the circle is generally denoted by 'O', the diameter is represented as 'd' and radius is specified as 'r'.

The perimeter of the circle is called the **circumference of the circle**. The circumference of the circle is π times the diameter.

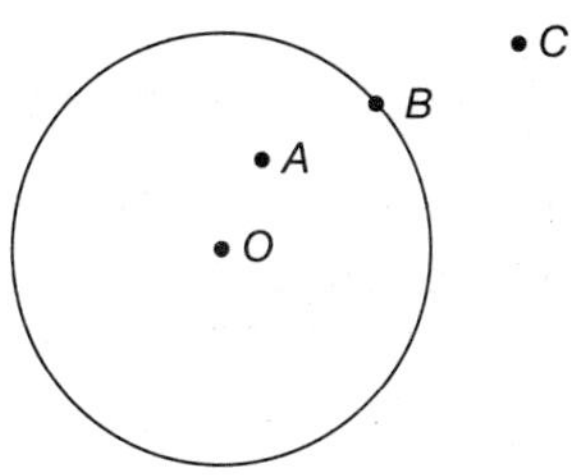

Example: In the given circle with centre O, here, A, B and C are three points in the plane in which the circle lies. We see that $OA < r$, $OB = r$ and $OC > r$. The points O and A are inside the circle. The point B is located on the circle and C is a point outside the circle. The set of all points P in the plane of the circle for which $OP < r$ is called the **interior of the circle** and the set of points Q for which $OQ > r$ is called the **exterior of the circle**. B is a point on the circumference of the circle, $OB = r$. A is a point in the interior of the circle, $OA < r$. As C is a point in the exterior of the circle, $OC > r$.

Chord

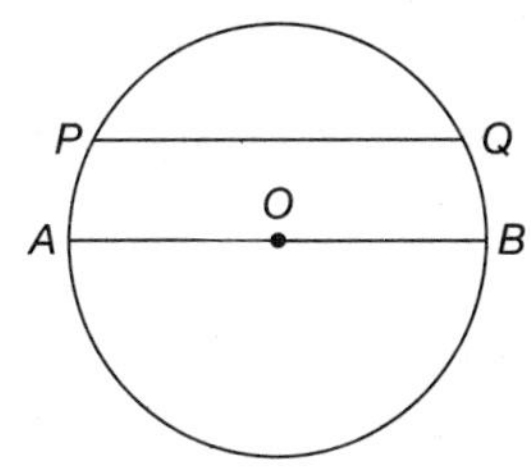

The line segment joining any two points on a circle is called a **chord of the circle**.

Example: In the adjacent figure, both $\overline{PQ}$ and $\overline{AB}$ are chords. AB passes through the centre O. Hence, it is a diameter of the circle. A diameter is the longest chord of the circle. It divides the circle into two equal parts.

Secant

A line which intersects a circle in two distinct points is called **secant of the circle**.

Tangent

A line lying in the plane of the circle that meets the circle in exactly one point is called a **tangent to the circle**. The point at which it meets the circle is the point of tangency or point of contact.

Konnect

If you draw two circles of the same size that touch each other perfectly at one point, the line connecting their centers is called a 'Tangent.'

Arc

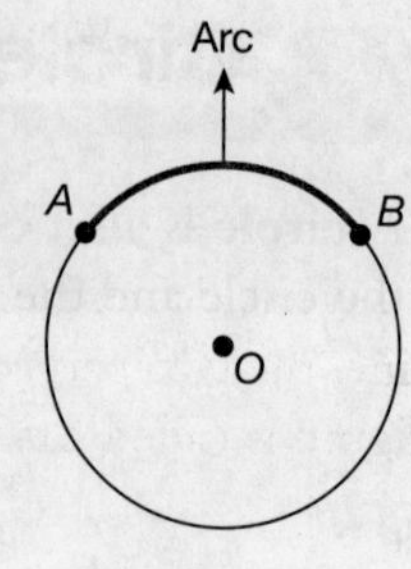

A continuous piece of a circle is called an **arc of the circle**. The end points of a diameter of a circle divide the circle into two equal arcs. Each of these arcs is called **semicircle**. The region enclosed by a semicircle and the diameter together with the semicircle is called a **semi-circular region**. If the length of an arc is less than that of a semicircle, it is a minor arc. If the length is more, then it is a **major arc**.

Circumference

The whole arc of the circle is called its **circumference**.

Circumference of a circle = $2\pi r$, where $\pi = \frac{22}{7}$ and r is the radius of the circle.

Angle Subtended by a Pair of Points

The **angle subtended** by two points A and B at the point P is the angle APB. The angle subtended by an arc or a chord is the angle subtended by the end points of the arc or chord.

Segment of a Circle

The part of a circular region bounded by an arc AB and the chord AB, including the arc and chord is called the **segment of the circle**. If the arc is minor, then the segment is also minor. If the arc is major, then the segment is also major.

Sector of a Circle

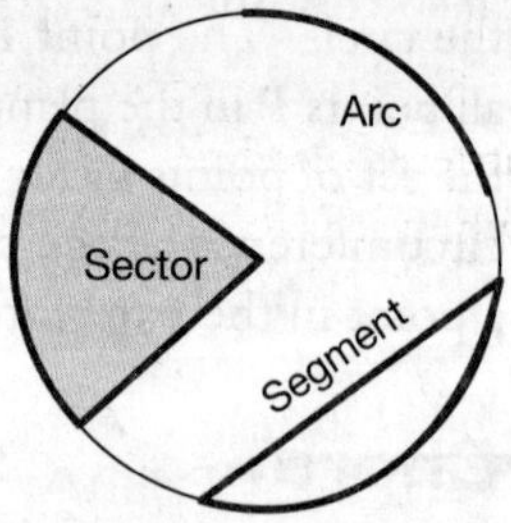

In a circle with centre O, the union of an arc AB and the bounding radii, OA and OB is called the **sector** AOB. If the arc is minor, then the sector is minor. If the arc is major, then the sector is major.

Quadrant

A sector of an angle 90° is called a **quadrant**.

EXAMPLE 8.7 Find the circumference of the circle whose radius is 7 cm.

SOLUTION

Circumference of the circle = $2\pi r$

$$= 2 \times \frac{22}{7} \times 7 = 44 \text{ cm}$$

EXAMPLE 8.8 The circumference of a circle is 22 cm. Find the diameter of the circle.

SOLUTION

Given that: $2\pi r = 22$ cm

$$2 \times \frac{22}{7} \times r = 22 \text{ cm}$$

$$r = 22 \times \frac{7}{2 \times 22} = \frac{7}{2}$$

$\therefore$ Diameter of the circle = $2r = 2 \times \frac{7}{2} = 7$ cm

Symmetry

Let us examine the following figure, drawn on a rectangular piece of paper.

What do you infer? We can observe that when the figure is folded about the dotted line, the two parts on either side of the dotted lines coincide. This property of geometrical figure is called **line symmetry**.

Dumbell shape

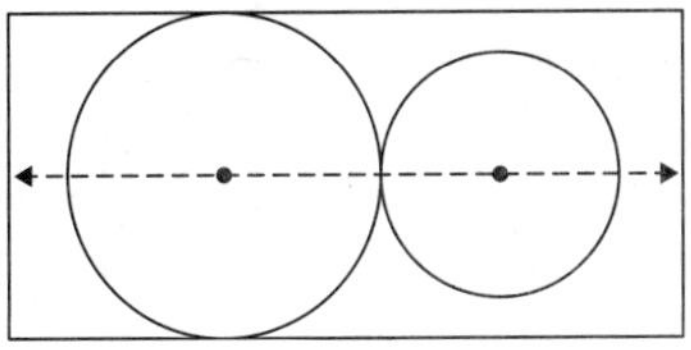

Two circles touching externally

Info Bytes!

Knowledge of geometry was used by the Greeks in making buildings!

Let us see one more example.

Trace a geometrical figure on a rectangular piece of paper as shown below.

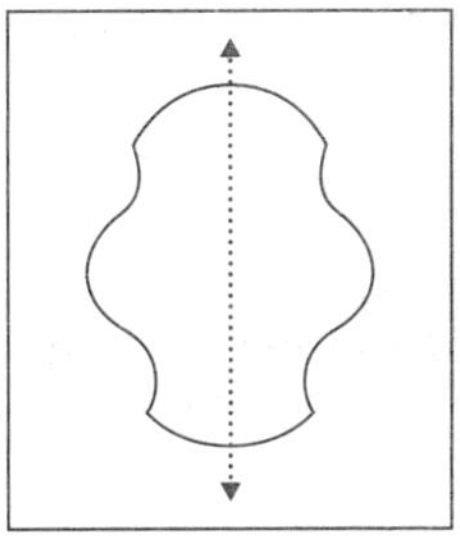

Now fold the paper along the dotted line. You will find that the two parts of the figure on either sides of the line coincide. Thus the line divides the figure into two identical parts. In this case, we say that the figure is symmetrical about the dotted line or line symmetric. Also, the dotted line is called **the line of symmetry** or **the axis of symmetry**.

So, a geometrical figure is said to be line symmetric or symmetrical about a line if there exists at least one line in the figure such that the parts of the figure on either sides of the line coincide when it is folded about the line.

EXAMPLE 8.9 *ABCD* is a rhombus. Draw its lines of symmetry.

SOLUTION

The diagonals of a rhombus are the lines of symmetry of rhombus.

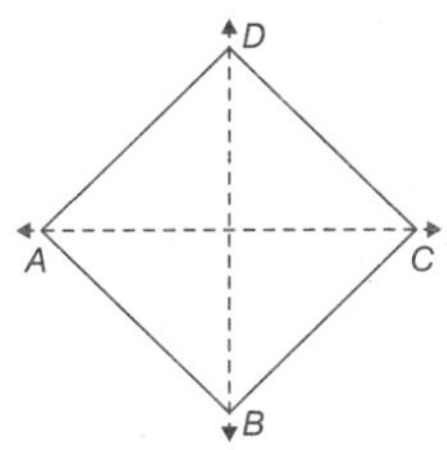

EXAMPLE 8.10 Draw a line of symmetry of an isosceles right triangle.

SOLUTION

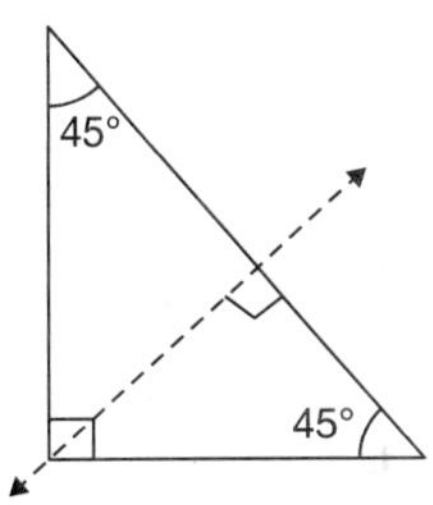

Konnect

The word 'symmetry' comes from the Greek word 'symmetria,' which means 'agreement in dimensions.'

EXAMPLE 8.11 Draw all the lines of symmetry of a square.

SOLUTION

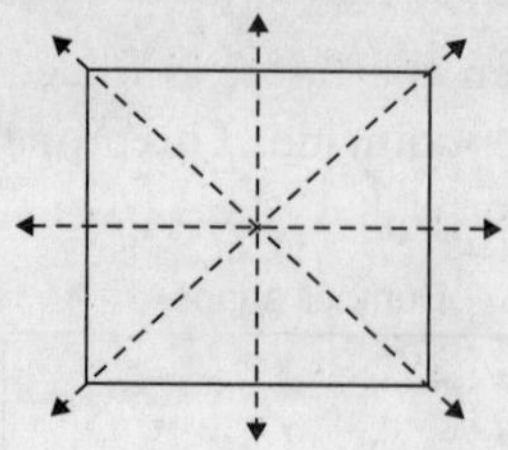

EXAMPLE 8.12 Draw the line(s) of symmetry for the first four words of English alphabet, if exist.

SOLUTION

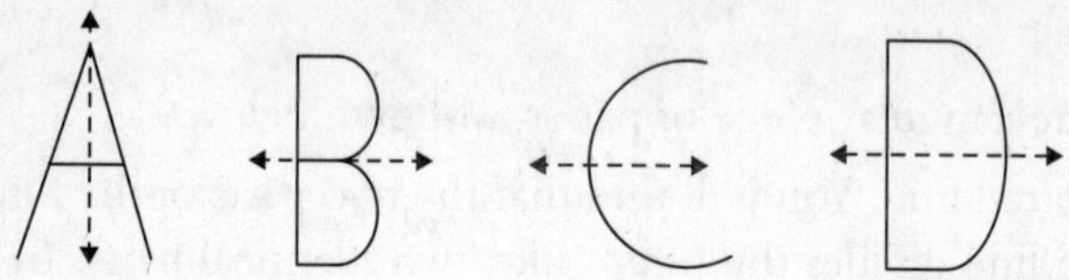

POINTS TO REMEMBER

- ✔ A plane is a surface which extends indefinitely in all directions.
- ✔ A line is a set of infinite points that has no end points and it is infinite in length.
- ✔ A line segment is a part of a line. The line segment has two end points and it has a finite length.
- ✔ Two or more lines lying in a same plane are called coplanar lines.
- ✔ Two lines which meet at a point are called intersecting lines.
- ✔ Two rays which meet at a point are said to form an angle at their meeting point.
- ✔ Two intersecting lines making an angle of 90° with each other are called perpendicular lines.
- ✔ When the sum of two angles is 90°, the two angles are called complementary angles.
- ✔ When the sum of two angles is 180°, the two angles are called supplementary angles.
- ✔ If two angles have a common vertex and a common ray and the other two sides lie on either side of the common ray, then they are said to be adjacent angles.
- ✔ If a pair of angles are adjacent and the non-common rays are opposite to each other, then the angles are said to form a linear pair.
- ✔ Two or more lines in a plane passing through a same point are called concurrent lines.
- ✔ Two coplanar lines that do not meet are called parallel lines.
- ✔ The perimeter of the circle is called the circumference of the circle. The circumference of the circle is π times the diameter.
- ✔ The line segment joining any two points on a circle is called a chord of the circle.
- ✔ A line which intersects a circle in two distinct points is called secant of the circle.
- ✔ A line lying in the plane of the circle that meets the circle in exactly one point is called a tangent to the circle.
- ✔ A continuous piece of a circle is called an arc of the circle.
- ✔ The part of a circular region bounded by an arc AB and the chord AB, including the arc and chord is called the segment of the circle.
- ✔ A sector of an angle 90° is called a quadrant.

PRACTICE QUESTIONS CLASSROOM WING

Very Short Answer Type Questions

Direction for questions from 1 to 5: **Select the correct alternative from the given choices.**

1. Which of the following is a complementary angle to 36°?

(a) 36° (b) 64°
(c) 72° (d) 54°

2. Which of the following is a reflex angle?

(a) 90° (b) 120°
(c) 180° (d) 200°

3. The angle between the hours hand and the minutes hand of a clock at 6'O clock is a/an

(a) right angle
(b) acute angle
(c) straight angle
(d) obtuse angle

4. Which of the following pairs of angles are supplementary?

(a) (0, 180°) (b) (90°, 90°)
(c) (120°, 60°) (d) All the above

5. Two lines $\overleftrightarrow{AB}$ and $\overleftrightarrow{CD}$ intersect at '*P*'. The number of pairs of adjacent angles formed is

(a) 2 (b) 3
(c) 4 (d) 6

Direction for question 6: **Match Column A with Column B.**

6.

Column A (An angle)	Column B (Complimentary angle)	Column C (Supplementary angle)
1. 35°	**a.** 0°	**f.** 180°
2. 0°	**b.** 40°	**g.** 155°
3. 90°	**c.** 45°	**h.** 145°
4. 50°	**d.** 55°	**i.** 130°
	e. 90°	**j.** 90°

Direction for questions from 7 to 11: **Fill in the blanks.**

7. If two of the angles of a triangle are 70° and 80°, then the third angle of the triangle is _______.

8. If two sides of a triangle are 7 cm and 10 cm, then the largest possible integer value of the third side is _______.

9. Two sides of a triangle are equal. If one of its angles is 100°, then one of the remaining angles is _______.

10. In a right-angled isosceles triangle, the measures of the angles are _______.

11. In a ΔABC, $\angle B = 65°$ and $\angle C = 80°$, then the longest side is _______.

Direction for questions from 12 to 16: **Select the correct alternative from the given choices.**

12. Which of the following is true?

(A) A triangle can have utmost two right angles.
(B) A triangle can have two obtuse angles.
(C) A triangle can have three acute angles.

(a) A, B and C (b) Only B and C
(c) Only B (d) Only C

13. Which of the following is false?

(A) The sum of any two sides of a triangle is equal to the third side.
(B) The sum of the exterior angles of a triangle is equal to 360°.

(a) A and B
(b) Only A
(c) Only B
(d) None of these

14. Which of the following is an acute triangle?

(a) Isosceles triangle
(b) Equilateral triangle
(c) Right triangle
(d) None of the above

15. Which of the following is true?

(A) Triangle is a polygon.
(B) An isosceles triangle can be obtuse.
(C) All scalene triangles are acute.

(a) Only A
(b) Only B and C
(c) Only A and B
(d) A, B and C

16. Which of the following is the length of the sides of a triangle?
(a) 3 cm, 7 cm, 10 cm
(b) 2 cm, 5 cm, 7 cm
(c) 6 cm, 12 cm, 19 cm
(d) 7 cm, 24 cm, 25 cm

Direction for question 17: **Match Column A with Column B.**

17.

Column A (Triangle)	Column B (Angles of triangle)
(a) Right triangle	(p) 60°, 20°,100°
(b) Isosceles triangle	(q) 60°, 60°, 60°
(c) Acute triangle	(r) 60°, 30°, 90°
(d) Scalene triangle	(s) 40°, 40°, 100°

Direction for questions from 18 to 27: **Observe the given figure and fill in the blanks.**

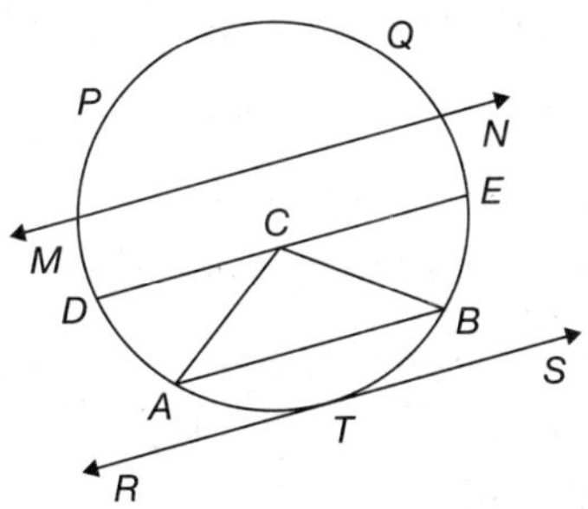

18. If 'C' is the centre of the circle and A is the point on the circle, then AC is called _______ of the circle.

19. If A, B are the points on the circle. The line segment $\overline{AB}$ is called ______ of the circle.

20. P, Q are the points on the circle. The part of the circle, PQ is called ______ of the circle.

21. The region bounded by the line segment AB and the part of the circle ATB is called _______ of the circle.

22. The line RS which touches the circle at T is called ______ to the circle.

23. The line intersecting the circle at M and N is called ______ of the circle.

24. $\overline{DE}$ is passing through the centre, DE is called ______ of the circle.

25. The arc DTE is called ______ of the circle.

26. The region bounded by the two radii CA and CB and the arc AB is called ______.

27. A sector of an angle 90° is called ______.

Direction for questions from 28 to 32: **Select the correct alternative from given choices.**

28. Which of the following is true?
(a) Diameter passes through the centre of the circle.
(b) The longest chord is the diameter.
(c) The diameter is equal to 2 times the radius.
(d) All the above

29. Which of the following is an angle of the major sector?
(a) 60° (b) 100°
(c) 200° (d) 400°

30. Which of the following is false?
(a) Radius is perpendicular to the tangent at the point of contact.
(b) Major segment contains the centre of the circle.
(c) The line segment joining any two points on the circumference is called arc.
(d) None of the above

31. Which of the following is the angle of a quadrant?
(a) 60° (b) 90°
(c) 180° (d) 360°

32. Which of the following can be the angle subtended by a minor arc at the centre?
(a) 100° (b) 220°
(c) 180° (d) 270°

Direction for questions from 33 to 37: **Fill in the blanks.**

33. An isosceles triangle has ______ line (s) of symmetry.

34. A semicircle has ______ line (s) of symmetry.

35. A quadrant of a circle has ______ lines of symmetry.

36. The letter I has ______ lines of symmetry.

37. A letter X has ______ lines of symmetry.

***Direction for questions from 38 to 42:* Select the correct alternative from the given choices.**

38. Which of the following can have infinite lines of symmetry?

(A) Ellipse (B) Semicircle (C) Line segment

(a) A, B (b) A, C

(c) B, C (d) C

39. Which of the following letters of English alphabet has only two lines of symmetry?

(a) *Y* (b) *W*

(c) *H* (d) *E*

40. Which of the following has no line of symmetry?

(a) *P* (b) *Q*

(c) *R* (d) All of these

41. Which of the following have exactly 3 lines of symmetry?

(a) *M* (b) Equilateral triangle

(c) *N* (d) Line segment

42. Which of the following has no line of symmetry?

(a)  (b) 

(c)  (d) 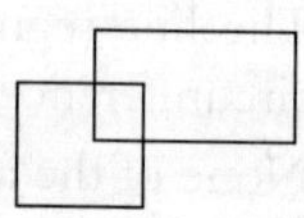

***Direction for question 43:* Match Column A with Column B.**

43.

Column A	Column B
(a) Two lines of symmetry	(p) 
(b) Three lines of symmetry	(q) 
(c) Four lines of symmetry	(r) 
(d) No line of symmetry	(s) 

***Direction for questions 44 and 46:* Draw the following and indicate their lines of symmetry.**

44. Two congruent intersecting circles.

45. A square inscribed in a circles.

46. Complete the following figures to have the specified number line of symmetry and draw their lines of symmetry.

(a) 

(4 lines of symmetry)

(b) 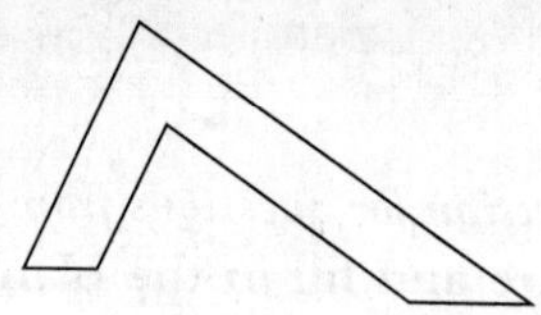

(1 line of symmetry)

Short Answer Type Questions

***Direction for question 47:* These questions are based on the following data.**

47. In the given figure, $l \parallel m$, and n is a transversal of l and m. Also $a = 30°$.

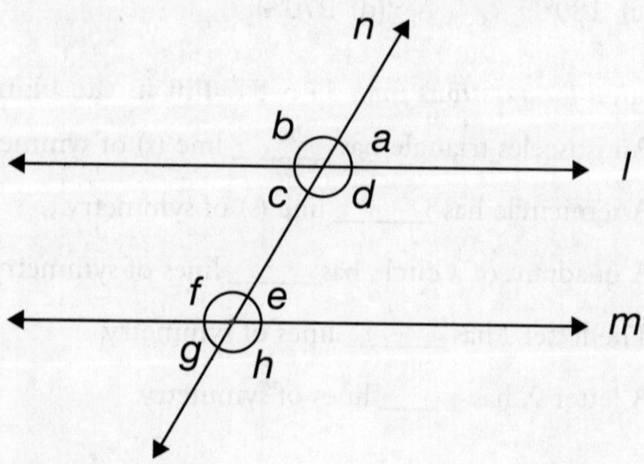

(i) Find the measure of e.

(ii) Find the measure of $f + d$.

(iii) Find the measure of $h - c$.

(iv) Find the measure of $b - g + f$

48. Find the supplement of 50°36′ 52″.

49. In the figure, t intersects two parallel lines p and q. Find the angles of $4x - 15°$ and $3x - 15°$.

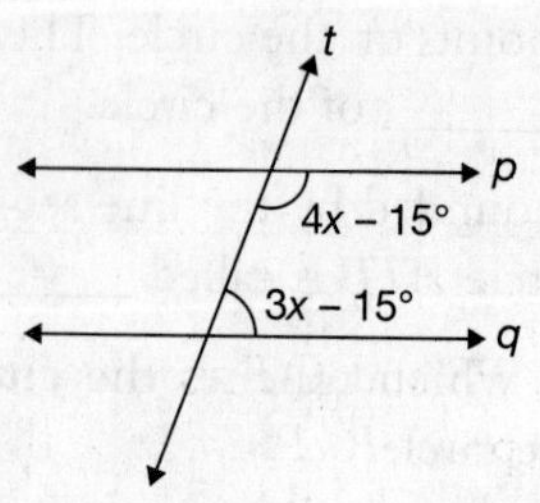

50. In the figure, ℓ || m and $r \parallel t$. They intersect at P, Q, R and S as shown in the figure. Find the angles of $\angle SPQ$ and $\angle PSR$.

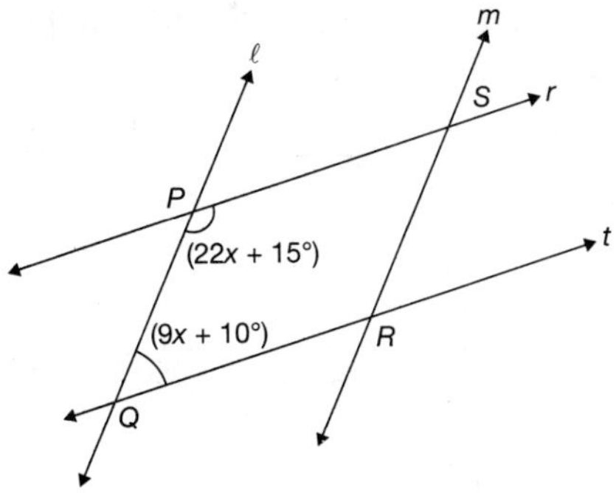

51. In a triangle ABC, if $\angle A = 70°$ and $AB = AC$, then find the measures of $\angle B$ and $\angle C$.

52. List out all the triangles formed in the figure.

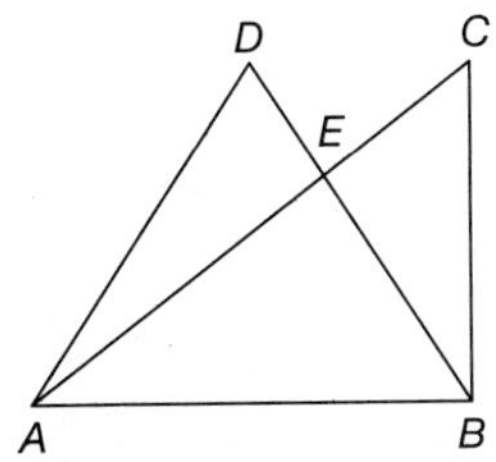

53. In the figure, $\overline{DC} \parallel \overline{AB}$. If $\angle ACB = 40°$ and $\angle CAD = 30°$, AC is the bisector of $\angle DAB$, then find the angle of $\angle ADC$.

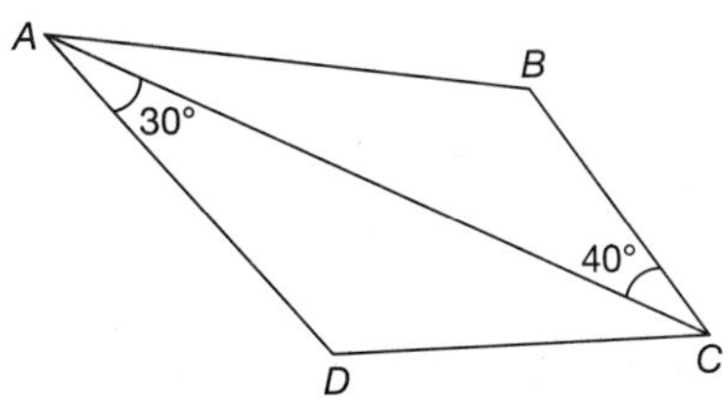

54. In the given figure, $AB = BC$, $\angle BAC = 70°$ and BC is produced to E, $AC = CD$ and $\angle ADE$ is the exterior angle of ΔADC. Find the angle of $\angle ADE$.

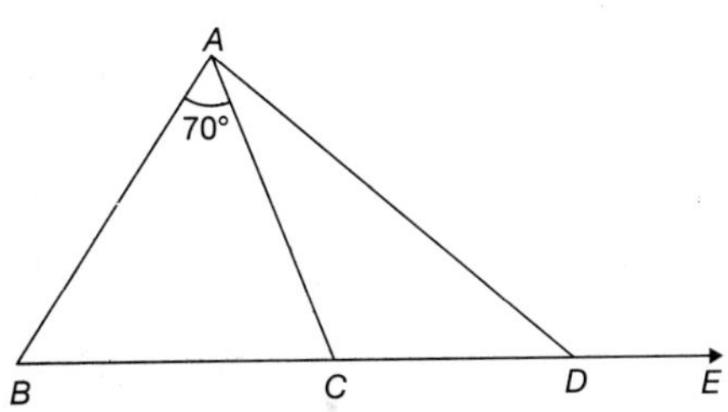

55. In the figure, PS and QT are two straight lines intersecting at the point R. $PR = RQ$. If $\angle PRQ = 98°$ and $\angle TSR = 40°$, then find the angles of $\angle T$ and $\angle Q$.

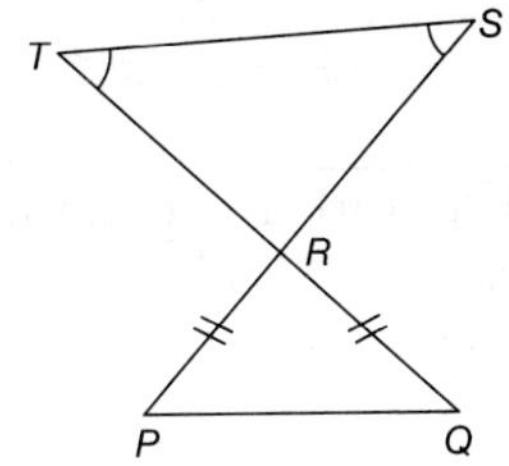

56. The radius of a circle is 10.5 cm. Find its circumference.

57. The circumference of a circle is 132 cm. Find the length of its diameter.

58. Draw a chord of length 6 cm in a circle of radius 4 cm and shade the major segment.

59. Make a sector of angle 90° in a circle of radius 3.5 cm.

60. The circumference of a circle is 220 cm. Find the perimeter of its quadrant.

61. Draw the line of symmetry for the following.

(a) 

(b) 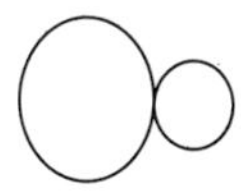

(c) 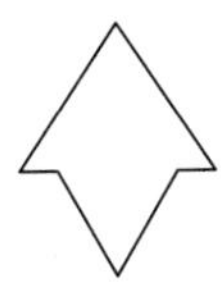

(d) 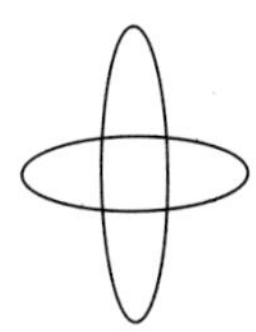

62. Construct an equilateral triangle of side 4 cm and draw all its lines of symmetry.

63. Draw an acute angle POQ and draw its line symmetry.

64. Write all the letters of English alphabet which has exactly two lines of symmetry and draw their lines of symmetry.

65. Identify the shapes on the basis of description.
   (i) A three-sided polygon with all sides equal
   (ii) The longest side of a right-angled triangle.

66. Identify the following pairs of angles as complimentary and supplementary
   (i) 60° and 30°
   (ii) 45° and 135°
   (iii) 60° and 10°
   (iv) 80° and 10°

Essay Type Questions

67. In the figure $\overline{PA} \parallel \overline{QB}$. If AT and BS intersect at 'C', find the measure of $\angle TCS$.

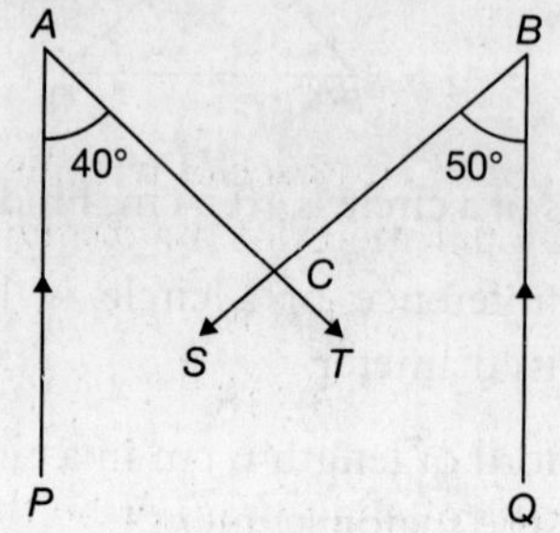

68. In the figure, ABD, BCD are two triangles. BD is the bisector of $\angle ABC$ and $\angle ADC$. If $\angle BCD = 40°$, then find the measure of $\angle BAD$.

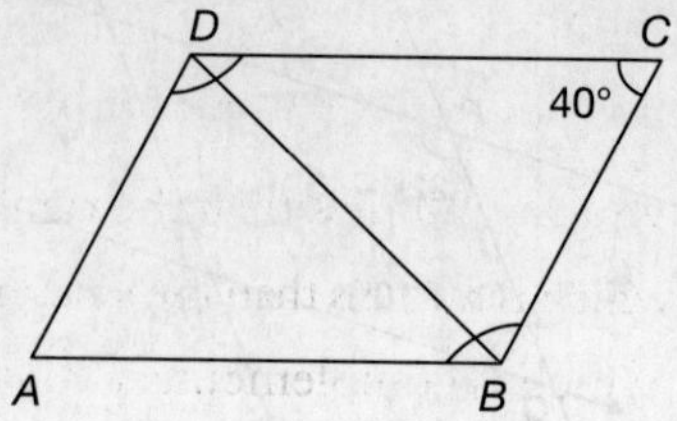

PRACTICE QUESTIONS COMPETITION WING

Level 1: Apply Your Concepts

Direction for questions from 1 to 5: **Fill in the blanks.**

1. An angle which is 30° less than the right angle is ______.
2. An angle which is 50° less than the straight angle is ______.
3. An angle which is complementary to itself is ________.
4. A line which intersects two or more lines at distinct points is called ________.
5. If ℓ is a transversal of p and q, a pair of corresponding angles is equal, then the lines p and q are _______.
6. ABC is an isosceles triangle. If AB = 7 cm and BC = 15 cm, find the perimeter of the triangle ABC.
   (a) 37 cm (b) 15 cm
   (c) 45 cm (d) 30 cm
7. The two sides of an isosceles triangle are 6 cm and 12 cm. Find the perimeter of the triangle (in cm).
   (a) 32 (b) 30
   (c) 24 (d) 18
8. Which of the following cannot be the measures of an isosceles triangle ABC?
   (a) Angle A is 50° and angle B is 80°
   (b) Angle A is 65° and angle B is 50°
   (c) Angle A is 60° and angle B is 70°
   (d) All of these

Level 2: Review Your Concepts

9. In the given figure, $\angle QPR = 50°$, $\angle QRS = 135°$ and $PQ = PR$ and $ST = SR$. Find the angle of $\angle S$.

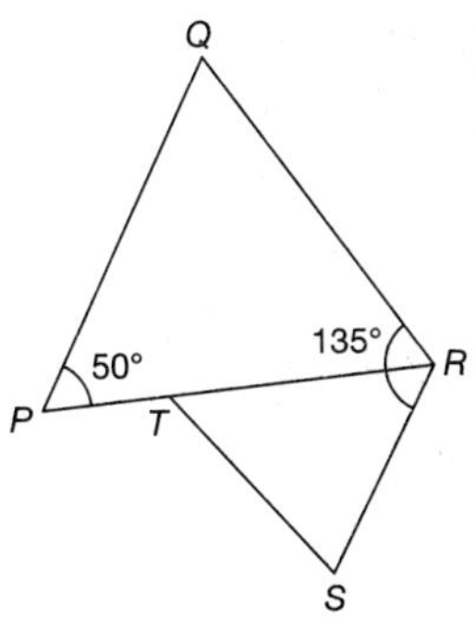

10. The perimeter of the quadrant of a circle is 37.5 cm. Find the area of the circle (in cm^2).
    (a) 346.5 (b) 325.5
    (c) 275.25 (d) 173.25
11. The sides of a scalene triangle are integers in cm. If the perimeter of the triangle is 15 cm, then how many such triangles exist?
    (a) One (b) Two
    (c) Three (d) Infinitely many
12. 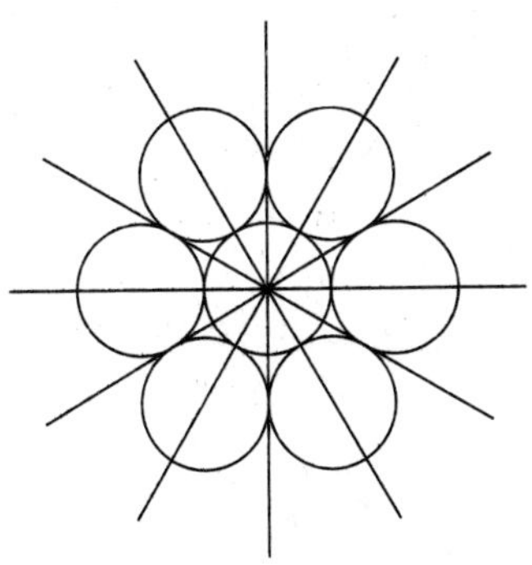

    In the given figure, the radii of the circles are equal. The middle circle is touching all the other circles and each of the other circles is touching exactly three circles as shown in the figure. What is the total number of lines of symmetry that can be drawn for the given figure?
    (a) 3 (b) 6
    (c) 12 (d) Infinitely many

Level 3: Assess Your Concepts

Direction for questions 13–14: **These questions are based on the following data.**

13. In the given figure, $l \parallel m$.

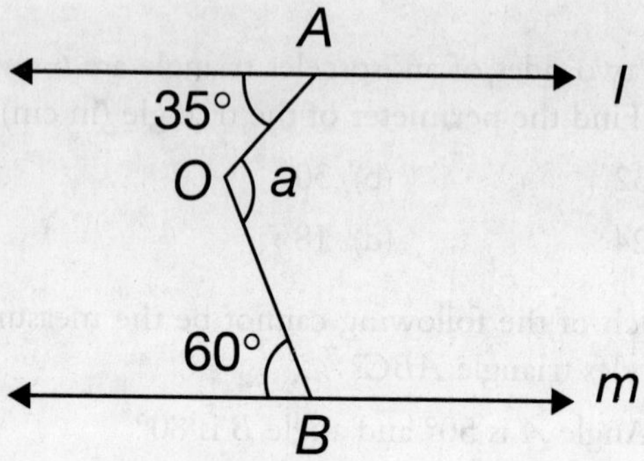

(i) Find the measure of a.

(ii) Find the measure of reflex $\angle AOB$.

(iii) Two sides of an isosceles triangle are 6 cm and 13 cm. Find the measure of the third side of the triangle. Also find the perimeter of the triangle.

14. In the given figure, $\angle BAC = 60°$, $\angle ACD = 120°$, AB = AC, and DE = EC.

If E is the midpoint of BC and CD = 5 cm, find the perimeter of triangle ABC.

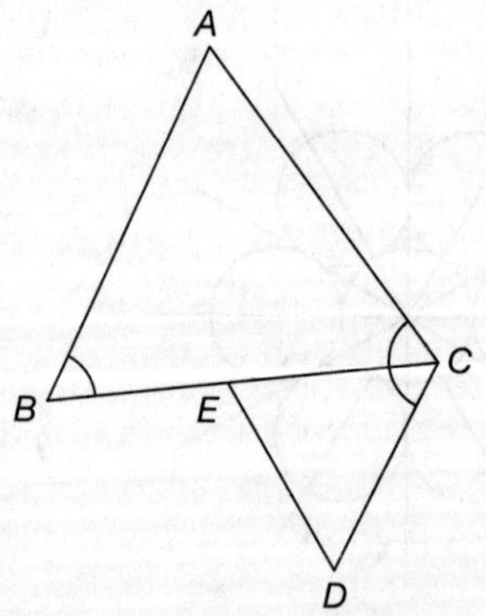

15. Calculate the value of x in the figure given below.

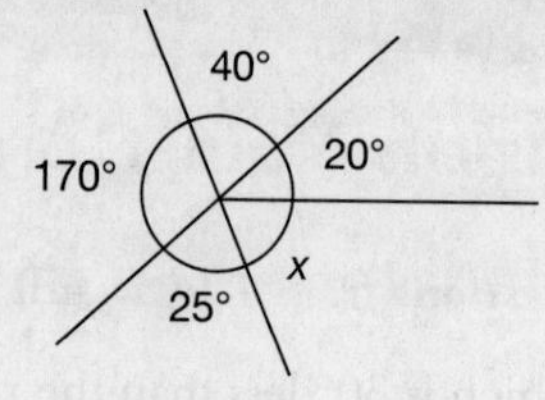

16. If l, m and n are lines parallel to each other, calculate the measures of the angles α and β in the given figure. Given that angle ABC is 100° and angle DBC is 75°. Also, A, E; D, B; and C, F are points on l, m and n respectively.

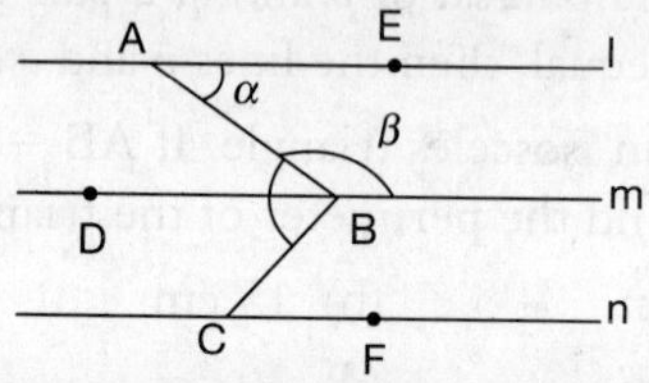

17. How many degrees are there in an angle which is equal to one-fourth of its supplement?

AT

ANSWER KEYS

Crossword

Across

2. Secant 5. Chord 6. Perpendicular 8. Plane 10. Concurrent

Down

1. Intersecting 3. Supplementary 4. Complementary 5. Circumference 7. Tangent
9. Arc

Classroom Wing

Very Short Answer Type Questions

1. (d) 2. (d) 3. (c) 4. (d) 5. (c)
6. 1. (d) → (1) → (h), 2. (e) → (2) → (f), 3. (a) → (3) → (j), 4. (b) → (4) → (i) 7. 30° 8. 16 cm
9. 40° 10. 45°, 45°, 90° 11. *AB* 12. (d) 13. (b) 14. (b) 15. (c) 16. (d)
17. (a) → (r), (b) → (s), (c) → (q), (d) → (p) 18. Circle 19. Chord 20. Arc
21. Segment 22. Tangent 23. Secant 24. Diameter 25. Semicircle
26. Sector 27. Quadrant 28. (d) 29. (c) 30. (c) 31. (b) 32. (a) 33. One
34. One 35. One 36. Two 37. Two 38. (d) 39. (c) 40. (d)
41. (b) 42. (d) 43. (a) → (p), (b) → (q), (c) → (r), (d) → (s)

Short Answer Type Questions

47. (i) 30°, (ii) 300°, (iii) 120°, (iv) 270° 48. $129° 23^{1} 08^{11}$ 49. 75° 50. 125°, 55°
51. 55°, 55° 52. ΔABD, ΔABC, ΔABE, ΔAED and ΔBEC 53. 120°
54. 145° 55. 42°, 41° 56. 66 cm 57. 42 cm 60. 125 cm
65. (i) Equilateral triangle; (ii) Hypotenuse
66. (i) Complementary; (ii) Supplementary; (iii) Neither; (iv) Complementary

Essay Type Questions

67. 90° 68. 40°

Competition Wing

Level 1: Apply Your Concepts

1. 60° 2. 130° 3. 45° 4. Transversal 5. Parallel 6. (a)
7. (b) 8. (c)

Level 2: Review Your Concepts

9. 40° 10. (a) 11. (c) 12. (b)

Level 3: Assess Your Concepts

13. 1. 95°, 2. 265°, 3. 32 cm, 14. 30 cm 15. 105° 16. 155° 17. 36°

Hints and Explanations

CLASSROOM WING

Very Short Answer Type Questions

1. $90° - 36° = 54°$

Hence, the correct option is (d).

2. Reflex angle lies between 180° and 360°.

Hence, the correct option is (d)

3.

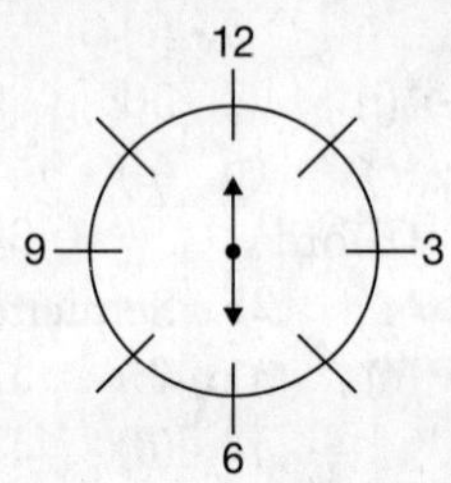

The required angle is a straight angle.

Hence, the correct option is (c).

4. If the sum of two angles is 180°, then the two angles are supplementary.

Hence, the correct option is (d)

5.

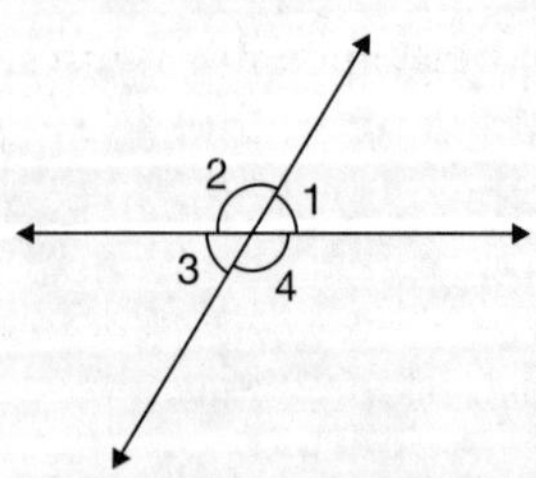

(1, 2), (2, 3), (3, 4), (4, 1)

Hence, the correct option is (c).

6. If the sum of two angles is 90°, then they are said be complimentary.
If the sum of two angles is 180°, then they are said be supplementary.
   (i) The complimentary angle of 35° is $90° - 35° = 55°$.
   The supplementary angle of 35° is $180° - 35° = 145°$. $d \leftrightarrow 1 \leftrightarrow h$
   (ii) The complimentary angle of 0° is $90° - 0° = 90°$.
   The supplementary angle of 0° is $180° - 0° = 180°$. $e \leftrightarrow 2 \leftrightarrow f$
   (iii) The complimentary angle of 90° is $90° - 90° = 0°$.
   The supplementary angle of 90° is $180° - 90° = 90°$. $a \leftrightarrow 3 \leftrightarrow j$
   (iv) The complimentary angle of 50° is $90° - 50° = 40°$.
   The supplementary angle of 50° is $180° - 50° = 130°$. $b \leftrightarrow 4 \leftrightarrow i$

7. Sum of the angles of a triangle is equal to 180°.
Sum of the given two angles
$= 70° + 80° = 150°$
$\therefore$ Third angle $= 180° - 150° = 30°$

8. $10 - 7 < x < 10 + 7$
$\therefore$ 16 cm is the measure of the third side.

9.

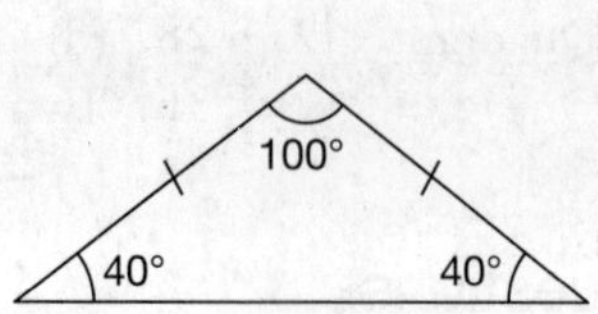

One of the base angles is 40°.

10. In a right-angled isosceles triangle, the angles are 45°, 45° and 90°.

11. $\angle B = 65°$, $\angle C = 80°$
$\Rightarrow \angle A = 35°$
$\Rightarrow$ The side opposite to 80° is the longest side that is AB.

12. A triangle can have three acute angles.
Hence, the correct option is (d).

13. The sum of any two sides of a triangle is equal to the third side.
Hence, the correct option is (b).

14. Equilateral triangle is an acute angled triangle.
Hence, the correct option is (b).

15. All scalene triangles are need not to be acute.
Hence, the correct option is (c).

16. 7, 24, 25 can be the sides of the triangle.
Hence, the correct option is (d).

17. (a) → (r), (b) → (s), (c) → (q), (d) → (p)

18. Radius

19. Chord

20. Arc

21. Segment

22. Tangent

23. Secant

24. Diameter

25. Semicircle

26. Sector

27. Quadrant

28. All statements are true.

Hence, the correct option is (d).

29. An angle of the major sector is 200°.

Hence, the correct option is (c).

30. The line segment joining any two points on the circumference is called arc.

Hence, the correct option is (c).

31. Angle of quadrant is 90°.

Hence, the correct option is (b).

32. The angle subtended by a minor arc at the centre is 100°.

Hence, the correct option is (a).

33. An isosceles triangle has one line of symmetry.

34. A semicircle has one line of symmetry.

35. A quadrant of a circle has one lines of symmetry.

36. The letter I has two lines of symmetry.

37. *X* has two lines of symmetry. 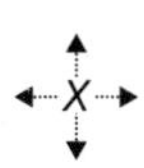

38. A line segment has infinite lines of symmetry.

Hence, the correct option is (d).

39. 

Hence, the correct option is (c).

40. *P*, *Q* and *R* have no lines of symmetry.

Hence, the correct option is (d).

41. Equilateral triangle has 3 lines of symmetry.

Hence, the correct option is (b).

42. Option (d) has no line of symmetry.

Hence, the correct option is (d).

43. (a) → (p), (b) → (q), (c) → (r), (d) → (s)

44.

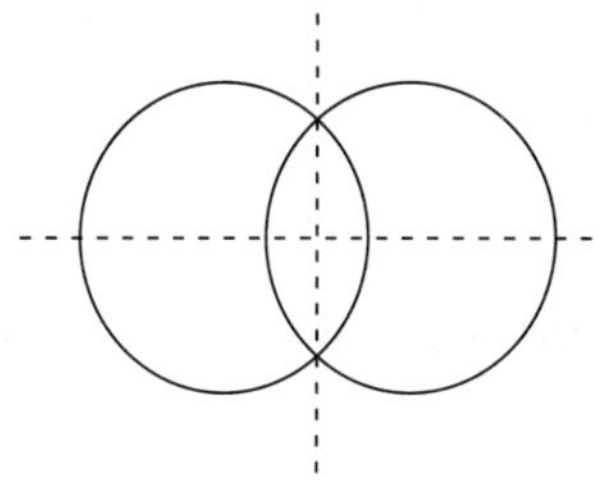

Two lines of symmetry

45.

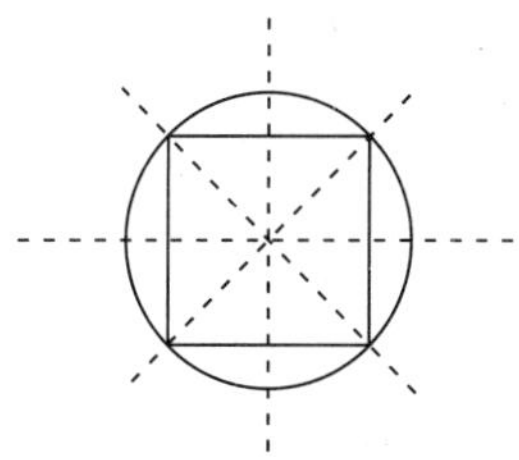

Four lines of symmetry

46. (a)

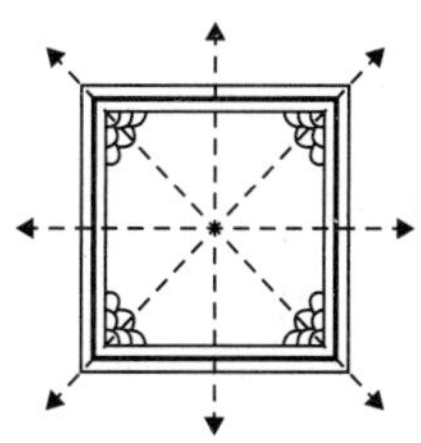

(4 lines of symmetry)

(b) The following is the one of the possible figures.

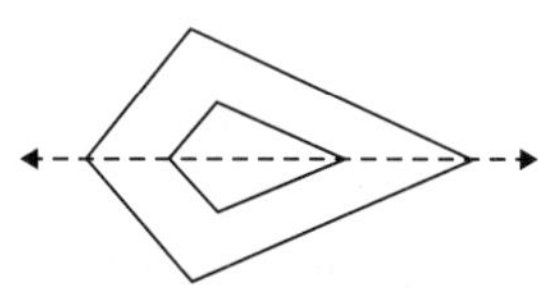

(1 line of symmetry)

Short Answer Type Questions

47. Given that $l \parallel m$, and n is a transversal of l and m. Also $a = 30°$.

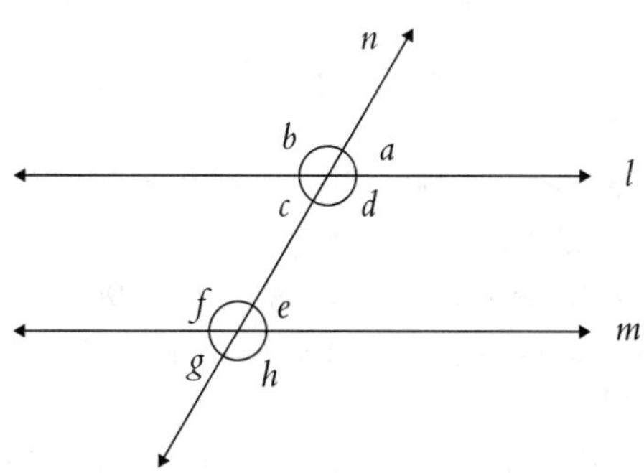

(i) $a = e$

(Since the corresponding angles are equal)

$e = a = 30°$.

(ii) $a + d = 180°$

(Since linear pair angles are supplementary)

$30° + d = 180°$

$d = 180° - 30° = 150°$

$d = f$

(Since the alternate interior angles are equal)

$f = d = 150°$

Hence, $d + f = 150° + 150° = 300°$.

(iii) $a = c$

(Since the vertically opposite angles are equal)

$a = c = 30°$.

$f = h$

(Since the vertically opposite angles are equal)

$h = f = 150°$.

Hence, $h - c = 150° - 30° = 120°$.

(iv) $a + b = 180°$

(Since linear pair angles are supplementary)

$30° + b = 180°$

$b = 180° - 30° = 150°$

$a = g$

(Since the alternate exterior angles are equal)

$g = a = 30°$

Hence, $b - g + f = 150° - 30° + 150° = 270°$.

48. The supplement of $50° \, 36' \, 52'' = 180° - (50° \, 36' \, 52'')$

$= 179° \, 59'60'' - 50° \, 36'52''$

$= 129° \, 23'08''$

$\therefore$ The supplement of $50^0 \, 36' \, 52''$ is $129° \, 23' \, 08''$.

49.

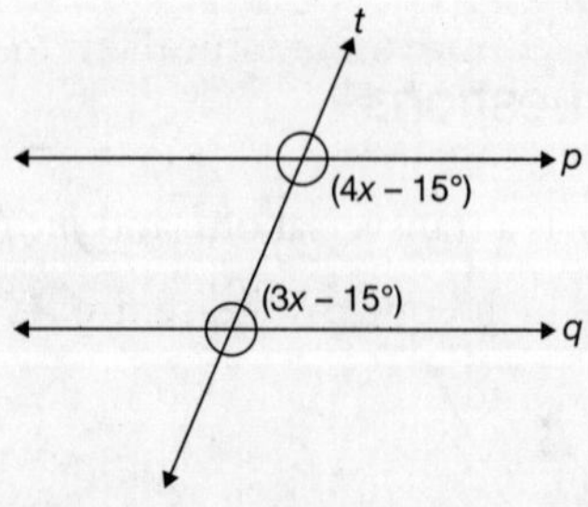

Given p, q are parallel lines and t is a transversal.

Given angles are co-interior angles.

$\Rightarrow 4x - 15° + 3x - 15° = 180°$

$\Rightarrow 7x - 30° = 180°$

$\Rightarrow 7x = 210°$

$x = 30°$

$\therefore 4x - 15° = 4 \times 30° - 15°$

$= 120° - 15°$

$= 105°$

$3x - 15° = 3x - 15°$

$= 3 \times 30° - 15$

$= 90 - 15°$

$= 75°$

50.

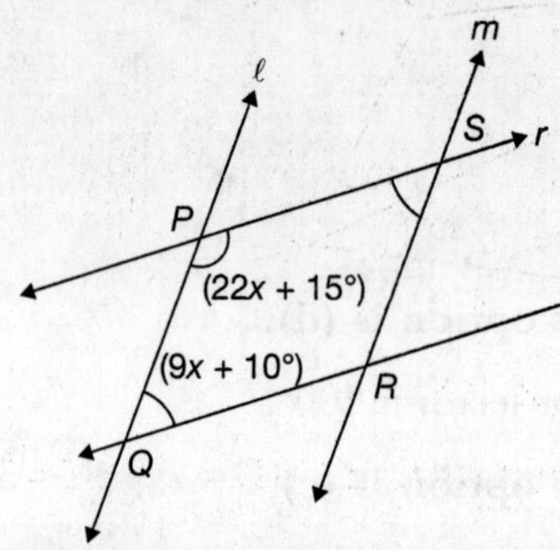

$\angle P + \angle Q = 180°$ (Since they are co-interior angles and $r \parallel t$)

$\Rightarrow 22x + 15 + 9x + 10 = 180°$

$31x = 180° - 25°$

$31x = 155°$

$x = 5°$

$\therefore \angle P = 22x + 15°$

$= 22 \times 5° + 15°$

$= 110° + 15° = 125°$

Given $\ell \parallel m$,

$\angle P + \angle S = 180°$

$125° + \angle S = 180°$

$\angle S = 55°$

51. Given $\angle A = 70°$

$AB = AC$

We know that:

$70° + 2x° = 180°$

$2x° = 180° - 70° = 110°$

$x° = \dfrac{110°}{2} = 55°$

$\Rightarrow \angle B = \angle C = 55°$

52.

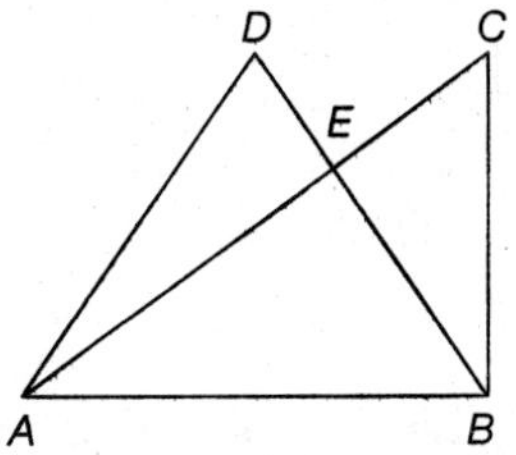

The following are the triangles formed in the figure.

ΔABD, ΔABC, ΔABE, ΔAED and ΔBEC.

53.

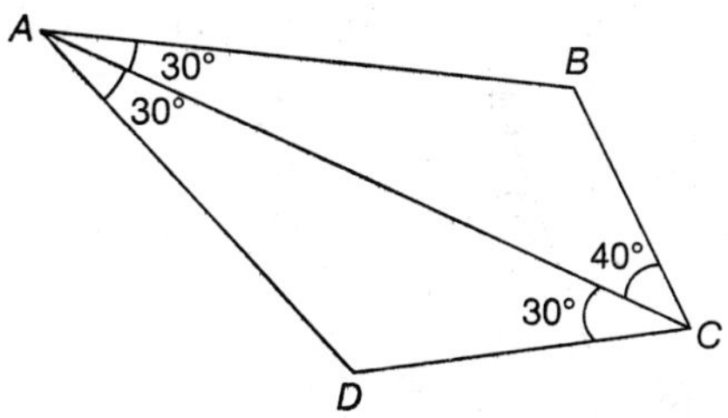

Given $\angle CAD = 30°$, $\angle ACB = 40°$.

As AC is the bisector of $\angle BAD$, $\angle CAD = \angle BAC = 30°$.

Given, $\overline{AB} \parallel \overline{DC}$.

$\therefore \angle ACD = \angle BAC = 30°$

In ΔADC, $\angle ADC = 180° - 30° - 30° = 120°$

54.

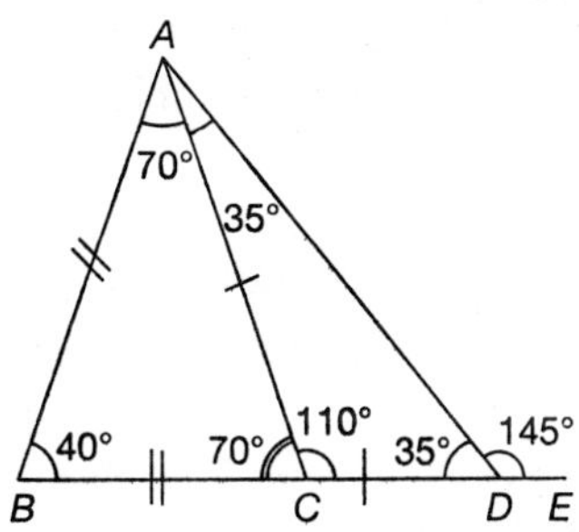

Since $AB = BC$, $\angle BAC = \angle ACB = 70°$

$\therefore \angle ABC = 180° - 70° - 70° = 40°$

$\Rightarrow \angle ACD = 180° - 70° = 110°$

$AC = CD$ (Given)

$\Rightarrow \angle CAD = \angle ADC = \dfrac{180° - 110°}{2} = 35°$

$\therefore \angle ADE = 180° - 35° = 145°$

55.

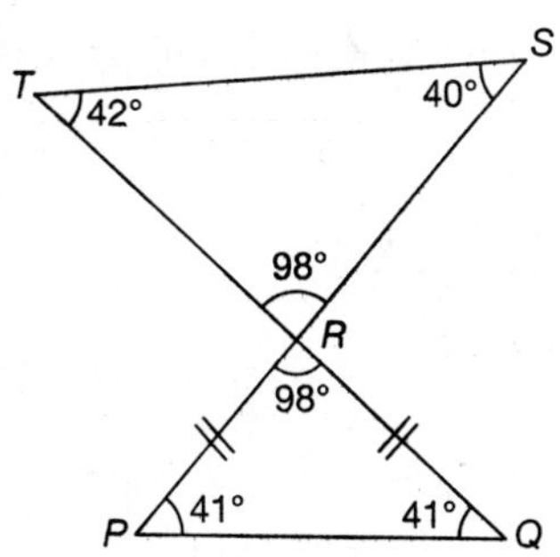

$\angle TRS = \angle PRQ = 98°$ (Vertically opposite angles)

In ΔTRS,

$\angle RTS = 180° - 98° - 40°$

$= 180° - 138°$

$= 42°$

In ΔPRQ, $\angle RPQ = \angle RQP$ (Since $PR = QR$)

$= \dfrac{180° - 98°}{2} = \dfrac{82°}{4} = 41°$

56. Given $r = 10.5$ cm

Circumference $= 2\pi r$

$= 2 \times \dfrac{22}{7} \times 10.5$

$= 44 \times 1.5$

$= 66$ cm

57. Circumference $= 2\pi r = 132$ cm

$2 \times \dfrac{22}{7} \times r = 132$

$r = \dfrac{132 \times 7}{2 \times 22}$; $r = 21$ cm

Diameter $= 2r = 2(21) = 42$ cm

58.

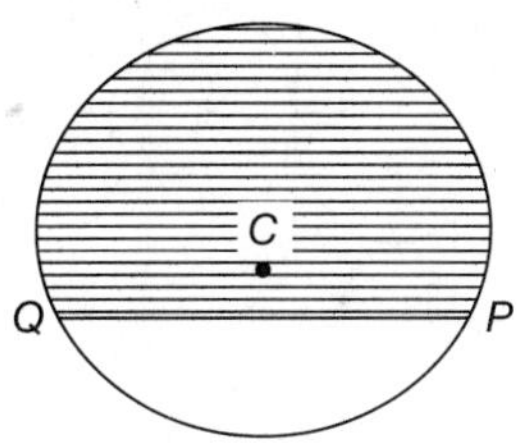

Steps of construction:

1. Draw a circle of radius 4 cm and mark the centre as C.
2. Mark a point P on the circle.
3. Draw an arc with P as centre and radius 6 cm to cut the circle at Q.
4. Join $\overline{PQ}$.
5. Shade the segment which contains the centre 'C'.

59.

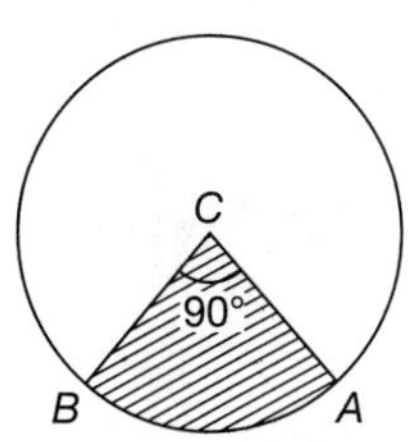

Steps of construction:

1. Draw a circle of radius 3.5 cm.

2. Mark the centre as C.
3. Mark a point A on the circle and join A to C.
4. Mark a point B on the circle such that $\angle ACB = 90°$ with the help of a protractor.
5. Join BC.
6. Shade the region bounded by the radii AC and BC, the arc AB.

60. Circumference of the circle $(2\pi r) = 220$ cm

$2 \times \frac{22}{7} \times r = 220$

$r = 35$ cm

The length of the arc of the quadrant

$= \frac{1}{4}$ of the circumference

$= \frac{1}{4} \times 220 = 55$ cm

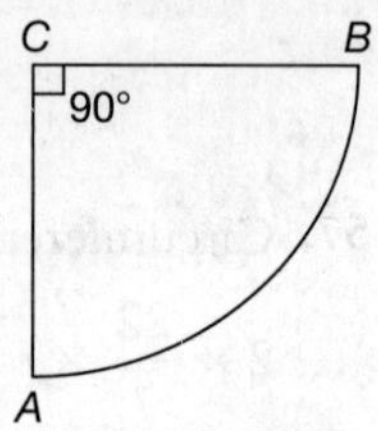

Perimeters of the quadrant

= 2 × Radius + Length of the arc

$= 2 \times 35 + 55$

$= 70 + 55 = 125$ cm

61. (a)

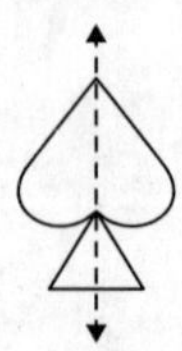

(b)

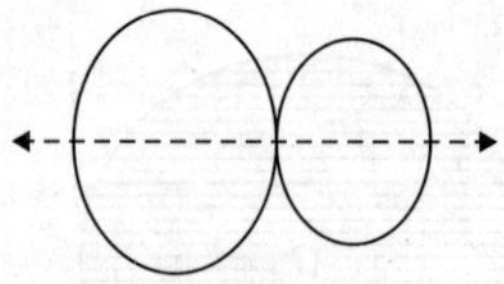

(c)

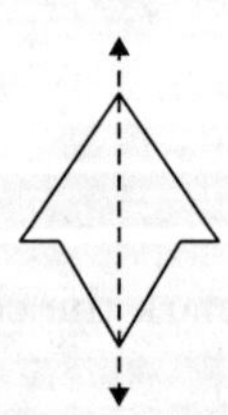

(d)

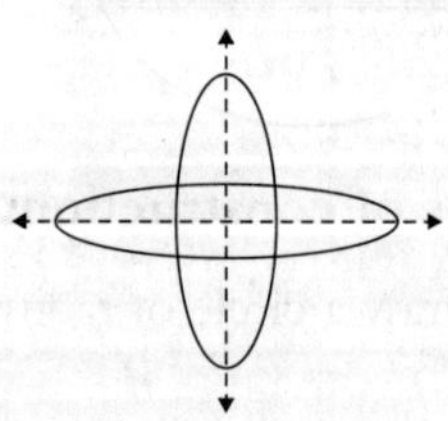

62.

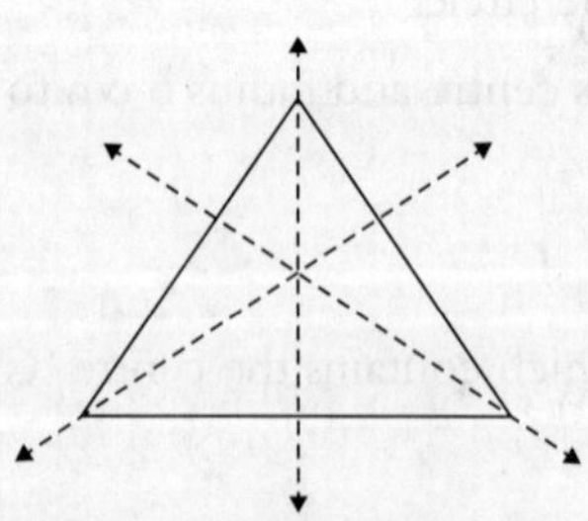

63.

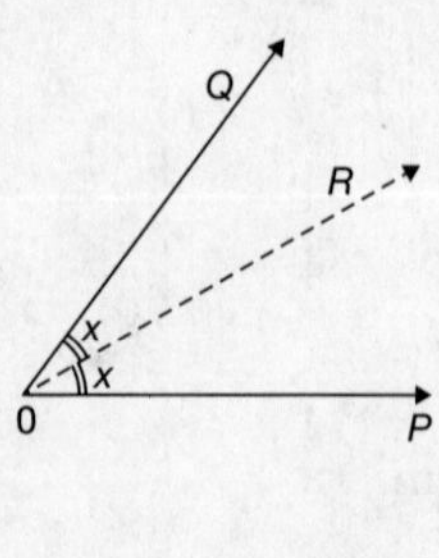

64.

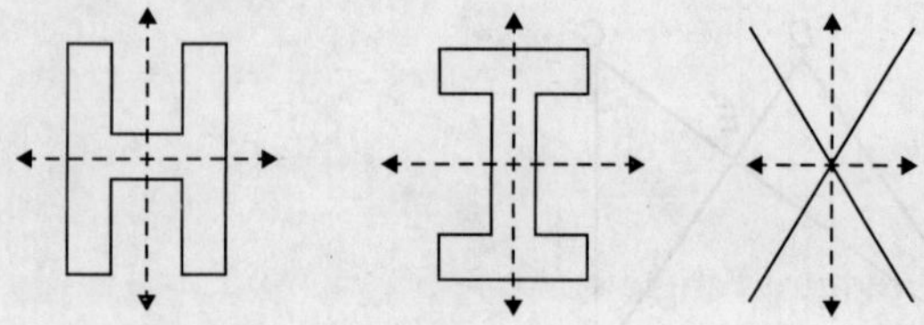

There are three letters of English alphabets which have two lines of symmetry.

65. (i) Equilateral triangle
(ii) Hypotenuse

66. (i) Complementary
(ii) Supplementary
(iii) Neither
(iv) Complementary

Essay Type Questions

67. Given that $\overline{AP} \parallel \overline{BQ}$.

Draw $\overline{MN} \parallel \overline{AP} \parallel \overline{BQ}$.

∠PAC = ∠ACM (Alternate angles)

⇒ ∠ACM = 40°

Similarly, ∠BCM = ∠CBQ = 50°

⇒ ∠ACB = 40° + 50° = 90°

⇒ ∠TCS = ∠ACB (Vertically opposite angles)

= 90°

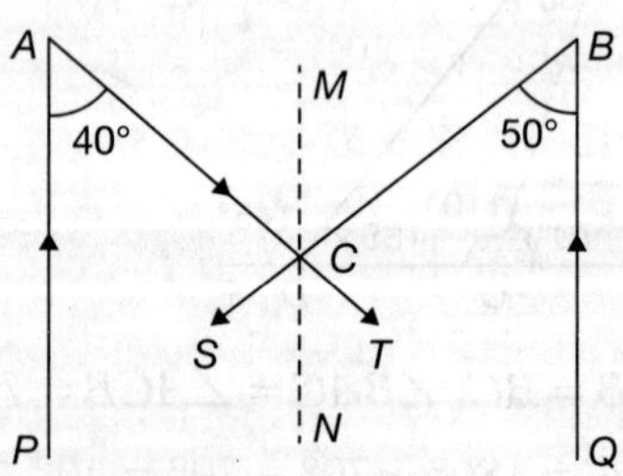

68. ∠BCD = 40°.

BD is the bisector of ∠ABC and ∠ADC.

∠BDC = ∠BDA and ∠CBD = ∠ABD

In ΔBCD,

∠BDC + ∠CBD = 180° ∠BCD = 180° – 40° = 140°

⇒ ∠BDA + ∠ABD = 140° (since ∠BDC = ∠BDA and ∠CBD = ∠ABD)

In ΔABD,

∠BAD = 180° – (∠BDA + ∠ABD).

= 180° – 140° = 40°

COMPETITION WING

Level 1: Apply Your Concepts

1. The required angle = 90° – 30° = 60°
2. The required angle = 180° – 50° =130°
3. 45° + 45° = 90°

   ∴ 45° is the complement of itself.
4. A transversal
5. Parallel
6. Given that ABC is an isosceles triangle, AB = 7 cm and BC = 15 cm.

   As ABC is an isosceles triangle, two of its sides must be equal.

   From the given information, AB BC.

   AB = AC or BC = AC

   Case-1: If AB = AC = 7 cm, AB + AC = 14 cm is not greater than the third side BC (= 15 cm).

   AB AC.

   Case-2: If BC = AC = 15 cm, BC + AC = 30 cm is greater than the third side BC (= 15 cm).

   Also, BC – AC = 0 cm is less than the third side BC (= 15 cm).

   BC = AC = 15 cm.

   The perimeter of the triangle ABC = AB + BC + AC

   = (7 + 15 + 15) = 37 cm.
7. Given that the two sides of an isosceles triangle are 6 cm and 12 cm.

   The third side can be of length 6 cm or 12 cm.

   If the length of the third side is 6 cm, then triangle cannot be formed with the measurements 6 cm, 6 cm and 12 cm, since 6 cm + 6 cm is not greater than 12 cm.

   If the length of the third side is 12 cm, then a triangle will be formed with the measurements 6 cm, 12 cm and 12 cm.

   Moreover, it is an isosceles triangle.

   Hence, the perimeter of the triangle is 6 cm + 12 cm + 12 cm = 30 cm.

   Hence, the correct option is (b).
8. If any two angles of a triangle are equal, then the triangle is isosceles.

   The sum of all the angles of a triangle is 180°.

   Choice (a): Angle A is 50° and angle B is 80°.

   Angle $C = 180° - 50° - 80° = 50°$. ⇒ ABC is an isosceles triangle.

   Choice (b): Angle A is 65° and angle B is 50°.

   Angle $C = 180° - 65° - 50° = 65°$. ⇒ ABC is an isosceles triangle.

   Choice (c) Angle A is 60° and angle B is 70°.

   Angle $C = 180° - 60° - 70° = 50°$ ⇒ ABC is not an isosceles triangle.

   Hence, choice (c) follows.

   Hence, the correct option is (c).

Level 2: Review Your Concepts

9. In the figure, PQR and TRS are triangles.

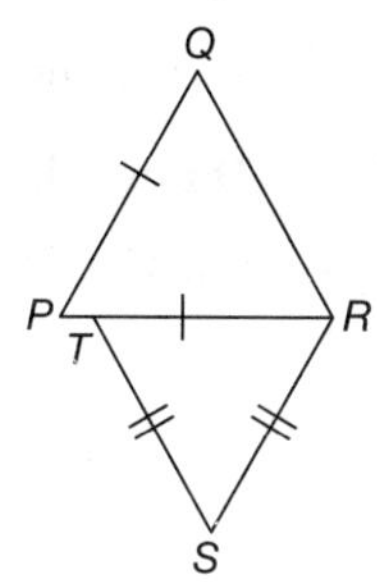

   In ΔPQR, $PQ = PR$

   $\Rightarrow \angle Q = \angle R$

   $\angle P + \angle Q + \angle R = 180°$

   $50° + \angle R + \angle R = 180°$

   $2\angle R = 130°$

   $\angle R = 65°$

   $\therefore \angle Q = \angle R = 65°$

   In ΔTRS, $\angle TRS = 135° - 65°$

   $\angle TRS = 70°$

   In ΔTRS, $TS = SR$

   $\Rightarrow \angle STR = \angle TRS = 70°$

   $\Rightarrow \angle S = 180° - (70° + 70°)$

   $\angle S = 40°$
10. Given that the perimeter of the quadrant of a circle is 37.5 cm.

   $\Rightarrow (2\pi r/4) + 2r = 37.5$

   $\Rightarrow (11r/7) + 2r = 37.5$

   $\Rightarrow (11/7 + 2)r = 37.5$

$\Rightarrow (25/7)r = 37.5$

$\Rightarrow r = 10.5$

The area of the circle (in cm²) = πr^2.

= (22/7)(10.5)2

= (22)(1.5)(10.5)

= (33)(10.5)

= 346.5

Hence, the correct option is (a).

11. Given that the sides of the scalene triangle are integers in cm and the perimeter of the triangle is 15 cm.

We know that, no two sides are equal in a scalene triangle.

Also, in a triangle, the sum of any two sides is greater than the third side and the difference of any two sides is less than the third side.

As the perimeter of a scalene triangle is 15 cm, the measures of the sides can be (2 cm, 6 cm, 7 cm), (3 cm, 5 cm, 7 cm) and (4 cm, 5 cm, 6 cm).

Hence, choice (c) follows.

Hence, the correct option is (c).

12. The lines of symmetry are shown in the figure. The number of lines of symmetry is 6.

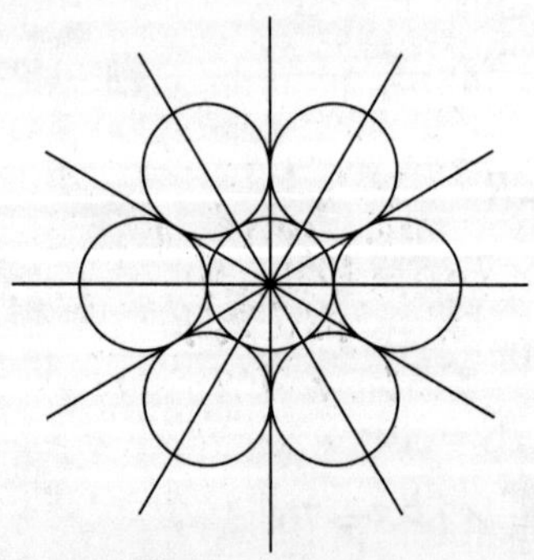

Hence, the correct option is (b).

Level 3: Assess Your Concepts

13. Given that $l \parallel m$.

Let us draw a parallel line to l passing through the point O.

$\Rightarrow l \parallel m \parallel n$.

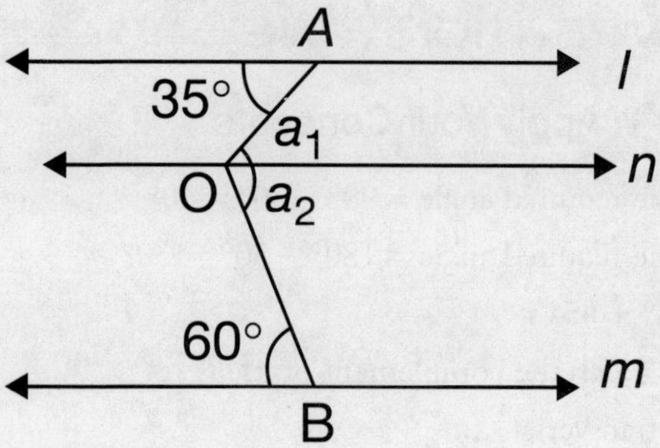

(i) Let $a = a_1 + a_2$

As $l \parallel n$ and a_1, 35° are alternate interior angles.

$a_1 = 35°$

As $m \parallel n$ and a_2, 60° are alternate interior angles.

$a_2 = 60°$

Now $a = a_1 + a_2 = 35° + 60° = 95°$.

(ii) The reflex ∠AOB = 360° – a

= 360° – 95° = 265°.

(iii) Given that two sides of an isosceles triangle are 6 cm and 13 cm.

As two sides of an isosceles triangle are equal, the third side is either 6 cm or 13 cm.

In a triangle, the sum of any two sides is greater than the third side.

If the third side is taken as 6 cm, 6 cm + 6 cm $\not>$ 13 cm.

Hence, 6 cm cannot be the measure of the third side.

Therefore, the measure of the third side is **13 cm**.

Perimeter of the triangle = 6 cm + 13 cm + 13 cm = **32 cm**.

14. Given that ∠BAC = 60°, ∠ACD = 120°, AB = AC, and DE = EC.

Also, BE = EC and CD = 5 cm.

In ΔABC, AB = AC.

⇒ ∠ABC = ∠ACB

In ΔABC, ∠ABC + ∠ACB + ∠BAC = 180° (angle sum property)

∠ABC + ∠ACB = 180° – 60° = 120°

∠ABC = ∠ACB = $\frac{120°}{2}$ = 60°.

⇒ ABC is an equilateral triangle.

Now, $\angle ECD = \angle ACD - \angle ACB = 120° - 60° = 60°$.

In ΔDCE, DE = EC.

$\Rightarrow \angle ECD = \angle EDC = 60°$.

$\Rightarrow \angle DEC = 180° - 60° - 60° = 60°$.

$\Rightarrow$ DEC is also an equilateral triangle.

$\Rightarrow$ EC = CD = 5 cm.

$\Rightarrow$ BC = 2(5) = 10 cm.

The perimeter of triangle ABC = 3 (10 cm) = 30 cm.

15. The angles at a point add up to 360°.

Hence $(20° + 40° + 25° + 170°) + x = 360°$

$\therefore x = 360° - 255° = 105°$

16. As $\angle DBC = 75°$

$\angle DBA = 100° - \angle DBC = 100° - 75° = 25°$

$\alpha = \angle DBA = 25°$

(As α and DBA are alternate angles, they are equal)

As interior angles on the same side of the transversal are supplementary,

$\alpha + \beta = 180° \Rightarrow \therefore \beta = 180° - 25 = 155°$

17. Let the angle be x. Then its supplement is $180° - x$.

Given, $x = \frac{1}{4}(180° - x)$

$\Rightarrow 5x = 180°$

$\Rightarrow x = 36°$.

[illegible] 16. [illegible] $\angle DBC$ [illegible]

[illegible] $\angle BDA$ [illegible]

[illegible] [illegible]

[illegible] ... and ... are alternate angles, they are equal) [illegible]

[illegible] ... are the angles on the same side of the transversal [illegible]

... are supplementary [illegible]

[illegible] $180°$ [illegible]

[illegible] 17. [illegible] supplement [illegible] $180°$ [illegible]

18. [illegible]

[illegible] $= 180°$ [illegible]

CHAPTER

9

Mensuration

Remember

Before beginning this chapter, you should be able to:

- Recall different units of lengths
- Understand the meaning of area and volume

Key Ideas

After completing this chapter, you should be able to:

- Determine areas of rectangles and squares
- Calculate surface areas and volumes of cubes and cuboids

Scientific Crypt

A Tribute to Aryabhata (476-550 CE)

Aryabhata (476–550 CE), a luminary in the field of mathematics and astronomy, stands as a foundational figure in the classical age of Indian intellectual thought. Born in Kusumapura, present-day Patna, Bihar, India, Aryabhata's life was marked by insatiable curiosity and a relentless pursuit of knowledge.

Little is known about his early life, but his impact on mathematics and astronomy is profound. He authored the Āryabhaṭīya and Arya-siddhanta. In his magnum opus, the Āryabhaṭīya, Aryabhata unveiled the secrets of arithmetic, algebra, and trigonometry. His ingenious approximation of π as 3.1416 showcased not only his mathematical prowess but also his courage to challenge conventional wisdom. The concept of the sine, originating as the "half-chord," set the stage for the birth of trigonometry, a legacy that still guides explorations of angles and shapes.

Aryabhata's quest extended to the realm of equations, where he fearlessly unraveled the mysteries of Diophantine problems, pioneering the kuṭṭaka method that laid the foundation for algebraic reasoning. His intellectual courage knew no bounds as he ventured to explore the cosmos, developing a geocentric model, and offering profound explanations for eclipses that revealed his innate understanding of shadow and light.

FUN TIME

CROSSWORD

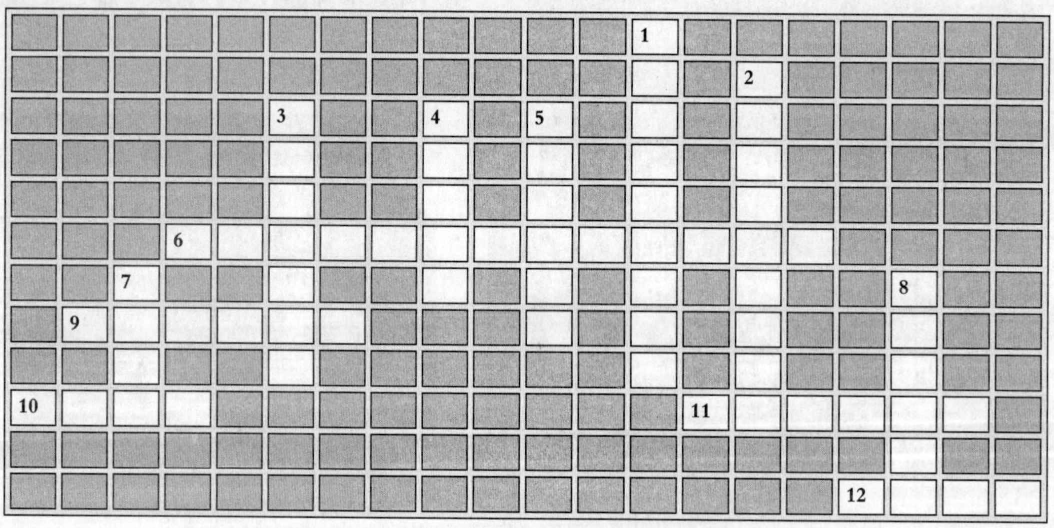

Across

6. A four-sided figure where the sum of all its interior angles is 360°.
9. A solid bounded by six rectangular faces where opposite faces are congruent.
10. The magnitude of a plane region.
11. A measurement of a line segment's one dimension.
12. The line joining the centres of the two parallel polygons of a prism.

Down

1. The total length of the line segments enclosing a closed planar figure.
2. A quadrilateral with opposite sides of equal length and all angles right angles, but not necessarily all sides of the same length.
3. A solid figure obtained by joining the vertices of a polygon to a point in space using straight lines.
4. Any object that occupies space and has a definite shape.
5. A rectangle where all sides have the same length.
7. A solid where the length, breadth, and height of a cuboid are all equal.
8. The fixed point in space where all triangles of a pyramid (lateral faces) meet.

INTRODUCTION

The branch of Mathematics that deals with the computation of geometric magnitudes, such as the length of a line segment, the area of a surface and the volume of a solid is called **Mensuration**. We will discuss the computation of areas and perimeters of plane figures (rectangle and square), surface areas and volumes of cube and cuboid in this chapter.

Plane Figures

A figure lying on a plane is called a **plane figure**. Triangles, rectangles and circles are some examples of plane figures. A plane figure is a closed figure if it has no free end. It is called a **simple closed figure** if it does not cross itself. A plane figure is made up of lines or curves or both. The part of the plane which is enclosed by a simple closed figure is called a **plane region**. The magnitude of a plane region is called its **area**.

Info Bytes!

A characteristic feature of quadrilateral is that, the sum of all inetrior angles is 360°.

A line segment has one dimension, such as length. Hence, its size is measured in terms of its length.

A planar region has two dimensions, such as length and breadth. Hence, its size is measured in terms of its area.

The **perimeter** of a closed planar figure is the total length of the line segments enclosing the figure.

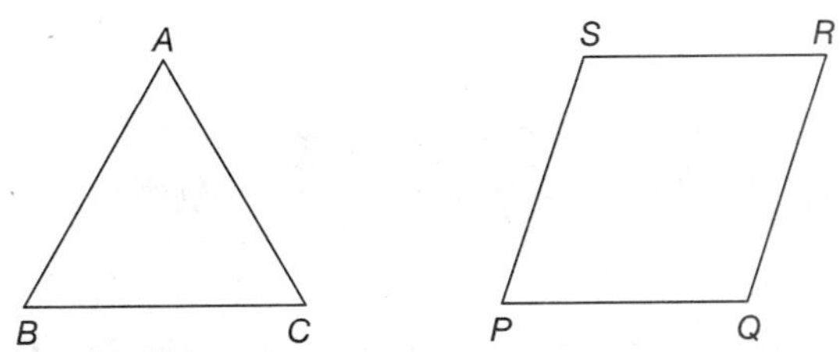

Figure 9.1 A Triangle and a quadrilateral

In the figure 9.1, ABC is a triangle and $PQRS$ is a quadrilateral.

The perimeter of the $\Delta ABC = AB + BC + CA$.

The perimeter of the quadrilateral $PQRS = PQ + QR + RS + SP$.

Konnect

An 'acre' was originally the amount of land a team of oxen could plough in a single day.

Units of Measurement

The length of a line segment is measured in units such as centimetres, inches, metres, feet, etc.

Area is measured in units such as square centimetres, square inches, square meters, square feet, etc.

Table 9.1 Basic unit conversions

Length	Volume	Weight
1 km = 1000 m	1 kL = 1000 L	1 kg = 1000 g
1 m = 0.001 km	1 L = 0.001 L	1 g = 0.001 kg
1 m = 1000 mm	1 L = 1000 mL	1 g = 1000 mg
1 mm = 0.001 m	1 mL = 0.001 L	1 mg = 0.001 g

Rectangle

A rectangle is a closed figure having four sides, in which the opposite sides are equal and each angle measures 90°.

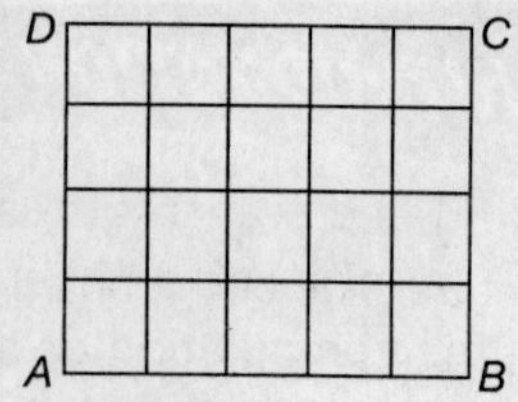

Figure 9.2 A rectangle

Example: In the given rectangle *ABCD*, $AB = 5$ cm and $BC = 4$ cm. Each of the small squares in the rectangle *ABCD* measures 1 cm by 1 cm and the area occupied by each small square is 1 sq. cm. There are 4 rows, each row consisting of 5 unit squares.

∴ The area occupied by the rectangle = (4) × (5) = 20 sq. cm

The number of unit squares in the rectangle *ABCD* is equal to the product of the number of unit squares along the length and the number of unit squares along the breadth.

Thus, we see that the area of a rectangle = (Length) × (Breadth)

$$\text{Perimeter of a rectangle} = 2\,(\text{Length} + \text{Breadth})$$

Square

A square is a rectangle in which all the sides are equal.

$$\text{Area of a rectangle} = (\text{Length}) \times (\text{Breadth})$$

In a square,

$$\text{Length} = \text{Breadth (Side)}$$

∴

$$\text{Area of a square} = (\text{Side})^2$$

$$\text{Perimeter of a square} = 4\,(\text{Side})$$

Info Bytes!

All squares are rectangles but all rectangles are not sqaures!
The area of a rectangle can be thought of as how many one-by-one squares can fit inside it.

Konnect

Area of a right isosceles triangle = $\frac{a^2}{2}$, where *a* is the length of each sides of the triangle which is equal.

EXAMPLE 9.1 The side of a square is 7 m and the perimeter of a rectangle is equal to the perimeter of the square. If the length of the rectangle is 10 m, then find the ratio of the areas of the square and the rectangle.

SOLUTION

The side of a square = 7 m

The length of a rectangle = 10 m

Let the breadth of a rectangle be '*b*' m.

Since the perimeter of the rectangle is equal to the perimeter of the square,

$2(10 + b) = 4 \times 7$

$10 + b = 14$

$b = 4$ m

The ratio of the areas of the square and the rectangle = $7^2 : 10 \times 4 = 49 : 40$

EXAMPLE 9.2 A sign board indicating "PARKING AREA" is in the form of an equilateral triangle with perimeter 180 cm. Find the length of the side of the equilateral triangle.

SOLUTION

Let the side of the board be 'a' cm.

Since the board is in the shape of an equilateral triangle,

Perimeter = $3a$

$\therefore$ $3a = 180$

$a = \dfrac{180}{3} = 60$ cm

$\therefore$ The length of the side of the board = 60 cm

EXAMPLE 9.3 If the three sides of a triangle are the distinct prime factors of 231 cm, then find the perimeter of the triangle.

SOLUTION

The prime factors of 231 are 3, 7 and 11.

Perimeter of a triangle = 3 + 7 + 11 = 21 cm

Solids

A plane figure may have one dimension or two dimensions. A circle is said to be unidimensional. Triangles and quadrilaterals have two dimensions. For two-dimensional figures, the dimensions are length, breadth, depth or height. But many objects with a definite shape such as a brick, a matchbox, a pencil, a marble, a tank, an ice cream cone, etc., have a third dimension. These objects are known as solids.

Thus, a solid is a three-dimensional object. In general, any object that occupies space and has a definite shape is called a **solid**. Solids like cubes, cuboids, etc., have plane or flat surfaces.

Info Bytes!

A prism takes its name from the shape of its base.

Prism

Prism is a solid figure in which two identical and parallel polygons form the top and the bottom faces. The lateral faces are parallelograms.

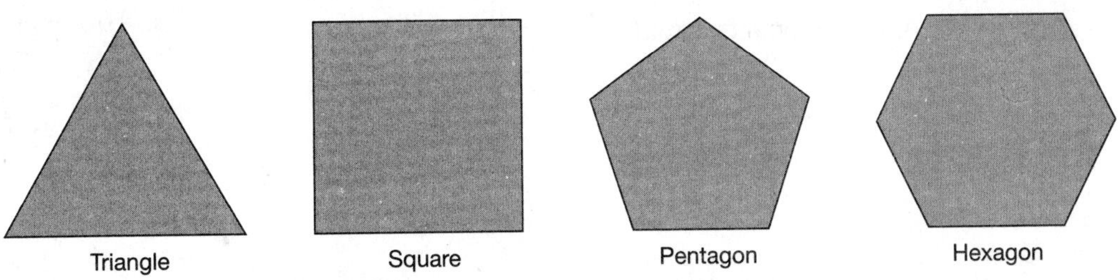

Figure 9.3 Various shapes of the base of prism

The line joining the centres of the two parallel polygons is called the **axis of the prism** and the length of the axis is referred to as the **height of the prism.**

If the two parallel and identical polygons are regular, and if the axis is perpendicular to the base, then the prism is called a **right prism**. The lateral surfaces of a right prism are rectangles.

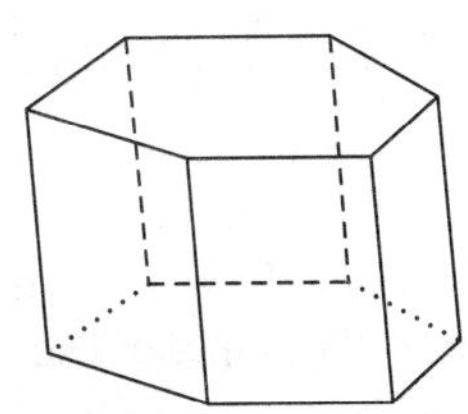

Figure 9.4 A Hexagonal prism

Example: Consider two congruent and parallel triangular planes ABC and PQR. If we join the corresponding vertices of both the planes, i.e., A to P, B to Q and C to R, then the resultant solid formed is a triangular prism.

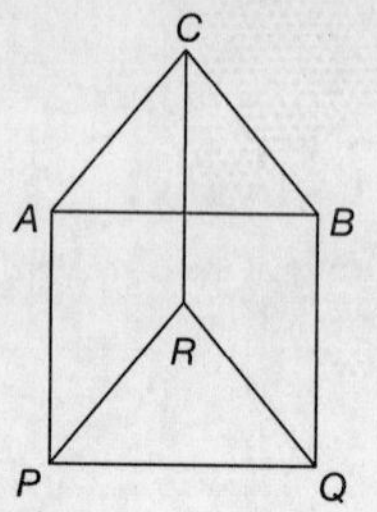

Figure 9.5 A triangular prism

Konnect

For all prisms, the following points remain true:

1. The number of faces = The number of sides of the base + 2
2. The number of vertices = Number of sides of the base × 2
3. The number of edges of a prism = Number of sides of the base × 3

Pyramid

A **pyramid** is a solid figure obtained by joining the vertices of a polygon to a point in the space by straight lines. The base of the solid obtained is the polygon and the lateral faces are triangles. The fixed point in space where all the triangles (i.e., lateral faces) meet is called its **vertex**.

In the figure 9.6, the base $ABCD$ is a quadrilateral. All the vertices of the base are joined to a fixed point O in space by straight lines. The resultant solid obtained is called a **pyramid**.

A straight line joining the vertex and the centre of the base is called the **axis of the pyramid**. If the axis is not perpendicular to the base, then it is an oblique pyramid.

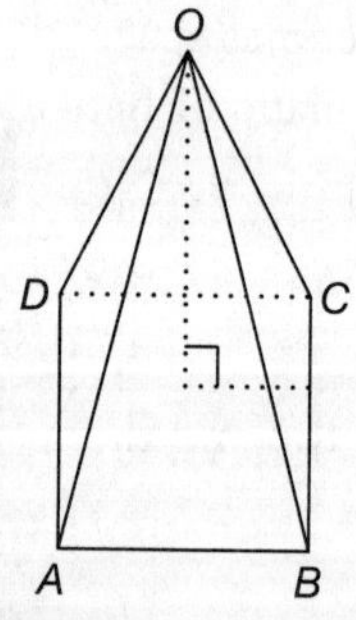

Figure 9.6 A geometrical pyramid

Konnect

For all pyramids, the following points remain true:

1. The number of faces = The number of sides of the base + 1
2. The number of vertices = The number of sides of the base + 1
3. The number of edges = 2 × (The number of sides of the base)

Cuboid

A **cuboid** is a solid bounded by six rectangular faces and the opposite faces are congruent.

In the given figure 9.7, faces $ABFE$ and $DCGH$ are congruent. Similarly, faces $BCGF$ and $ADHE$ are congruent and faces $ABCD$ and $EFGH$ are congruent. Each face is a rectangle. The line segments like AB, BC and BF are called **edges**. A cuboid has 6 faces and 12 edges.

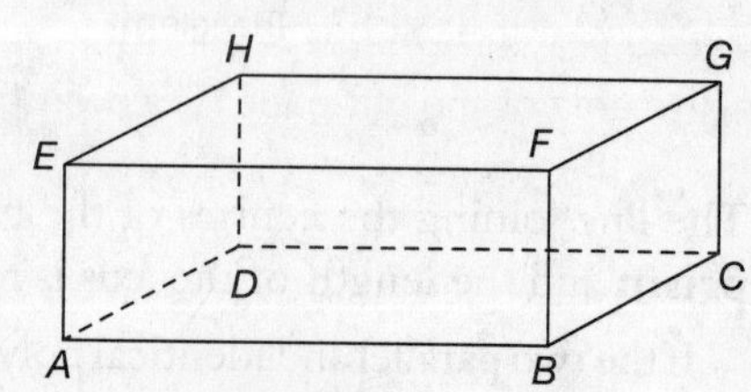

Figure 9.7 A Cuboid

A matchbox, a brick, a room, etc., are in the shape of a cuboid. The three dimensions of the cuboid, length (ℓ), breadth (b) and height (h) are generally denoted by $\ell \times b \times h$.

1. The lateral surface area(LSA) of a cuboid = $ph = 2(\ell + b)h$ sq. units, where p is the perimeter of the base.
2. The total surface area of a cuboid = LSA + 2(base area) = $2(\ell + b)h + 2\ell b = 2(\ell b + bh + \ell h)$ sq. units.
3. The volume of a cuboid = $Ah = (\ell b)h = \ell bh$ cubic units, where A is the area of the base.

Konnect

If a box made of wood of thickness t has inner dimensions ℓ, b and h, then the outer length = $\ell + 2t$, the outer breadth = $b + 2t$ and the outer height = $h + 2t$.

Cube

If all the dimensions of a cuboid, i.e., its length, breadth and height are equal, then the solid is called a **cube**.

All the edges of a cube are equal in length and each edge is called the **side of the cube**. Thus, the size of a cube is completely determined by its sides.

If the edge of cube is a unit, then:

1. The LSA of the cube = $4a^2$ sq. units.
2. The total surface area of the cube = LSA + 2(area of base) = $4a^2 + 2a^2 = 6a^2$ sq. units.
3. The volume of the cube = a^3 cubic units.

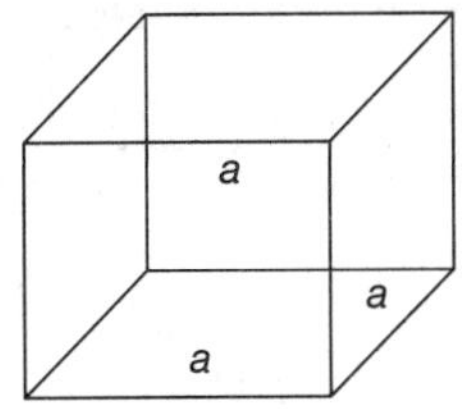

Figure 9.8 A cube

Info Bytes!

Dice are perfect examples of cubes. When you roll a die, you're rolling a cube.

EXAMPLE 9.4 Write the number of vertices, edges and faces of a pentagonal prism?

SOLUTION

The number of vertices = $2 \times 5 = 10$

Number of sides of the base = 5

The number of edges = $3 \times 5 = 15$

The number of faces = $5 + 2 = 7$

EXAMPLE 9.5 The dimensions of a gift box are 1.8 cm × 1.5 cm × 0.8 cm. Find how much gift paper is required to cover it? (Ignore the overlaps)

SOLUTION

Length of the gift box = 1.8 cm

Breadth of the gift box = 1.5 cm

Height of the gift box = 0.8 cm

The area of the gift paper to cover the gift box = Total surface area of the box

$$= 2(\ell b + bh + h\ell)$$
$$= 2(1.8 \times 1.5 + 1.5 \times 0.8 + 0.8 \times 1.8)$$
$$= 2(2.7 + 1.2 + 1.44)$$
$$= 2(5.34) = 10.68 \text{ sq. cm}$$

EXAMPLE 9.6 If the lateral surface area of a cube is 72 sq. cm, then find the total surface area of the cube.

SOLUTION

Let the edge of the cube be 'a' cm.

Lateral surface area of the cube $4a^2 = 72 \Rightarrow a^2 = \frac{72}{4} = 18$

The total surface area of a cube $= 6a^2 = 6 \times 18 = 108$ sq. cm

EXAMPLE 9.7 The inner dimensions of a shoebox are 30 cm × 20 cm × 10 cm. How many small toy blocks of length 5 cm, breadth 2 cm, and height 4 cm can be placed in the shoebox?

SOLUTION

Number of erasers that can be placed into the shoe box.

$$= \frac{\text{Volume of the shoe box}}{\text{Volume of each toy block}}$$

$$= \frac{(30 \times 20 \times 10)}{(5 \times 2 \times 4)} = \frac{6000}{40} = 150$$

POINTS TO REMEMBER

- ✔ The part of the plane which is enclosed by a simple closed figure is called a plane region.
- ✔ The magnitude of a plane region is called its area.
- ✔ Any object that occupies space and has a definite shape is called a solid.
- ✔ The line joining the centres of the two parallel polygons is called the axis of the prism and the length of the axis is referred to as the height of the prism.
- ✔ A pyramid is a solid figure obtained by joining the vertices of a polygon to a point in the space by straight lines.
- ✔ A cuboid is a solid bounded by six rectangular faces and the opposite faces are congruent.
- ✔ If all the dimensions of a cuboid, i.e., its length, breadth and height are equal, then the solid is called a cube.

DW

PRACTICE QUESTIONS CLASSROOM WING

Very Short Answer Type Questions

Direction for questions from 1 to 5: **Select the correct alternative from the given choices.**

1. If the angles of a triangle are in the ratio 1 : 1 : 1, then the ratio of their sides is
   (a) 1 : 1 : 1 (b) 1 : 2 : 3
   (c) $1 : \sqrt{3} : 2$ (d) $1 : 1 : \sqrt{2}$

2. If the side of a square is doubled, then the area of the square
   (a) remains same (b) becomes double
   (c) becomes triple (d) becomes 4 times

3. If the area of a square is 25 m^2, then the side of the square is _______ m.
   (a) 125 (b) 625
   (c) $\frac{1}{25}$ (d) 5

4. The area and perimeter of a square are numerically equal, then the numerical value of the side of the square is
   (a) 3 (b) 4 (c) 5 (d) 6

5. The length and breadth of a rectangle are in the ratio 3 : 2. The perimeter of the rectangle is 10 cm, then its length is _______ cm.
   (a) 2 (b) 5 (c) 3 (d) 4

Direction for questions from 6 to 10: **Fill in the blanks.**

6. The total surface area of a cube of an edge 10 cm is _______.

7. The volume of a cuboidal box is 24 cm^3 and base area is 12 sq. cm, then the height of the box is _______.

8. The perimeter of a base of a cuboid is 16 cm and the height of the cuboid is 2 cm, then the lateral surface area of the cuboid is _______.

9. The sum of the lengths of all the edges of a cube is 60 cm, then the length of the edge of the cube is _______.

10. The edge of a cube is increased by 100%, then the lateral surface area of the cube is increased by _______%.

Direction for questions from 11 to 15: **Select the correct alternative from the given choices.**

11. The ratio of the lateral surface area and the total surface area of a cube is
    (a) 1 : 2 (b) 2 : 3 (c) 3 : 2 (d) 1 : 4

12. The lateral surface area of a matchbox which is 6 cm long, 2 cm wide and 1.5 cm thick is _______ sq. cm.
    (a) 30 (b) 34 (c) 42 (d) 24

13. The total surface area of a cuboid which is 2.5 m long, 2 m wide and 1.4 m high is _______ sq. cm.
    (a) 11.3 (b) 22.6 (c) 12.6 (d) 7

14. A cube is to be coloured in such a way that no two opposite faces have the same colour, then the minimum number of colours required is
    (a) 6 (b) 2 (c) 3 (d) 4

15. If the edge of a cube is doubled, then the volume of the cube is _______ that of the initial cube.
    (a) 4 times (b) 8 times (c) 12 times (d) 6 times

Direction for question 16: **Match Column A with Column B and Column C.**

16. P is a cube of edge 4 cm and Q is another cube of edge 5 cm.

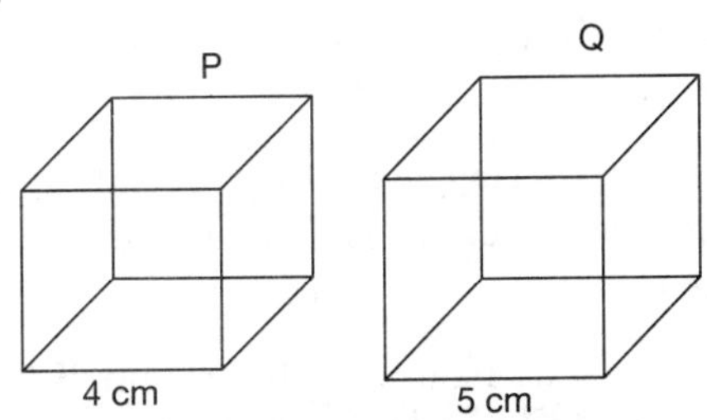

Column A	Column B (Cube-P) (In cm/sq cm/ cu cm)	Column C (Cube-Q) (In cm/sq cm/ cu cm)
1. Total length of the edges	a. 36	f. 150
2. LSA	b. 48	g. 125
3. TSA	c. 64	h. 100
4. Volume	d. 72	i. 90
	e. 96	j. 60

Directions for questions 17 and 18. ***Solve the following.***

17. Find the perimeter of an equilateral triangle with side 8 cm.

18. The perimeter of a 40 cm wide rectangle is 160 cm. Find its area.

Short Answer Type Questions

19. The perimeter of a rectangular field is 20 m. The measurements of the field are integers in metres. If the length of the field is more than that of the breadth, find the largest possible area of the field.

20. In a rectangular field with a length of 120 m and a breadth of 80 m, two paths of width 5 m are laid. One path is parallel to the length, and the other is parallel to the breadth. The remaining portion of the field is left for growing green grass. Find the area of the field left for growing grass.

21. A rectangular sheet is cut along its length into five equal squares as shown in the figure. The area of a square is 16 cm^2. Find the perimeter of the rectangle.

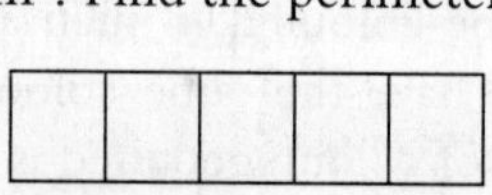

22. From a square sheet of side 8 cm, a piece of a paper width 2 cm is removed along the border. Then find the area of the removed piece of paper.

23. A hall in the shape of rectangle is 16 feet long and 12 feet wide. How many tiles with 2 feet × 1 feet are required to cover the floor of the hall?

24. Two persons *A* and *B* took a wire of equal length. '*A*' bent it in the form of a rectangle with perimeter 12 cm. *B* bent it in the form of a square, then find the area of the square formed.

25. If the area of a rectangle is 24 sq. cm and the length and breadth are integers in cm, then find the maximum possible perimeter of the rectangle.

26. Two sides of a triangle are 2016 cm and 2017 cm, then find the minimum possible perimeter of the triangle which is an integer in cm.

27. A Rubik's cube of edge 3 cm is formed with 27 identical cubes. Find the edge of each identical cube.

28.

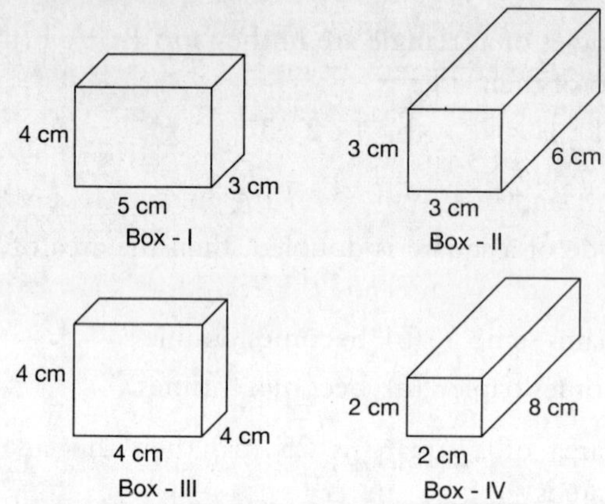

Tarun made 4 types of boxes as shown in the figure. Arrange them in the descending order of their volumes.

29. The dimensions of a room are 20 ft × 15 ft × 12 ft. Find the cost of painting the walls of the room at ₹20 per sq. ft.

30. The dimensions of a trench are 6 m × 3 m × 4.5 m. Find the cost incurred in digging it at ₹250 per cubic metre.

31. A cubical container of edge 30 cm is full of water. The water is to be poured into cuboidal containers of 6 cm long, 5 cm wide and 4 cm high. How many such containers are required?

32. Border of a square-shaped frame which is 16-m long needs to be painted. If the cost of painting 1 m of border is ₹4, how much would it cost to paint the entire border of the frame?

33. A 10-m long hall has a floor area of 100 m^2. Find its perimeter.

34. A cube-shaped oil tank which is 1.5-m long is full of oil. If 500 L of oil spills out from the tank, how much oil remains in it?

Essay Type Questions

Direction for question 35: **These questions are based on the following data.**

35. Four identical square pieces of side 1 cm are removed from the four corners of a square sheet of side 10 cm. The remaining paper is folded to form a cuboidal box without lid. Find the outer surface area of the box. Also, find the volume of the container formed.

36. A cubical container of edge 60 cm is full of water. If it is leaking at the bottom of the container at the rate of 30 millilitre per second, how long will it take to empty the container?

PRACTICE QUESTIONS COMPETITION WING

Level 1: Apply Your Concepts

Direction for questions from 1 to 5: **Fill in the blanks.**

1. If the length of a rectangle is equal to the breadth of the rectangle, then the rectangle becomes a ________.
2. The side of an equilateral triangle is 672 cm long, then the perimeter of the triangle is ________.
3. The lengths of two sides of an isosceles triangle are 2016 cm and 2017 cm, then the maximum possible perimeter of a triangle is ________.
4. If the sum of the length and the breadth of a rectangle is 1009 cm, then the perimeter of the rectangle is ________.
5. A square of the perimeter is p units, then its area is ________ sq. units.
6. The volume of a cuboid is 120 cu cm. If the dimen sions of the cuboid are consecutive integers in cm, which of the following is the sum of the dimensions of the cuboid?

   (a) 13 cm (b) 14 cm
   (c) 15 cm (d) 16 cm

7. The area of a right triangle is 36 sq cm. Which of the following are the measures of the perpendicular sides of the triangle?

   (a) 6 cm and 3 cm (b) 6 cm and 6 cm
   (c) 9 cm and 4 cm (d) 12 cm and 6 cm

8. The perimeter of a rectangle is 30 cm. The length and breadth of the rectangle are integers in cm. Find the number of possible pairs of length and breadth in cm.

   (a) 1 (b) 6
   (c) 7 (d) 8

9. The inner dimensions of a rectangular box are 45 cm × 30 cm × 20 cm. How many match boxes of length 6 cm, breadth 3 cm and height 2 cm can be placed in the rectangular box?

   (a) 500 (b) 650
   (c) 750 (d) 1500

Level 2: Review Your Concepts

Direction for question 10: **Match the Column – A with the Column – B.**

10. The edge of a cube is an integer in cm. The Column B consists of numbers which are possible values for the components given in the Column A.

Column A (A cube)	Column B (In cm/sq cm/cu cm)
1. Total length of the edges	**a.** 150
2. LSA	**b.** 1331
3. TSA	**c.** 942
4. Volume	**d.** 108
	e. 196

11. Four identical strips in the form of right isosceles triangles are removed from the four corners of a square sheet of side 8 cm. Find the area of the remaining sheet, if the length of each equal sides of the triangles is 4 cm.
12. In the given figure, $ABCD$ is a rectangle. I, II and III are squares. Find the area of the shaded region.

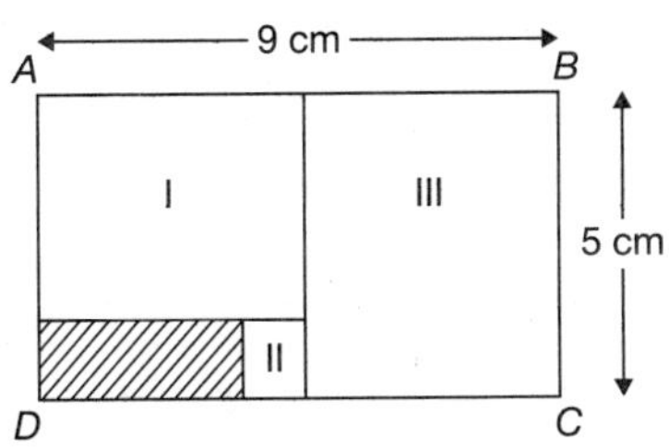

13. Four identical square pieces of side 2 cm are removed from the four corners of a square sheet of side 6 cm. The remaining paper is folded to form a cuboidal box without lid. Find the outer surface area of the box.
14. Four dice of edge each 1 cm are stacked so as to form a cuboid. Find the total surface area of the cuboid (in square centimetres).

   (a) 4 (b) 8
   (c) 9 (d) 18

15. Two sides of a triangle are 2018 cm and 2019 cm, then find the minimum possible perimeter of the triangle which is an integer in cm.

   (a) 4037 (b) 4038
   (c) 4039 (d) 8069

Level 3: Assess Your Concepts

16. The LSA of a cuboid is 450 sq cm and the sum of its length and breadth is 25 cm.

(i) What is the height of the cuboid?

(ii) If the length and breadth of the cuboid are consecutive integers, what is the volume of the cuboid?

17. Two sides of a triangle are 2022 cm and 2024 cm, then find the maximum possible perimeter of the triangle which is an integer in cm.

18. A large square tile is divided into a small square-tiles surrounded by four congruent rectangular tiles as shown. Find the area of the large square if the perimeter of each of the congruent rectangles is 96?

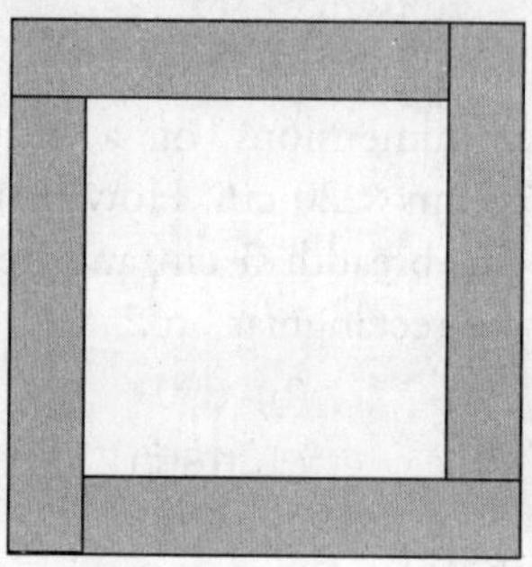

19. The adjacent sides of the decagon shown meet at right angles. What is its perimeter?

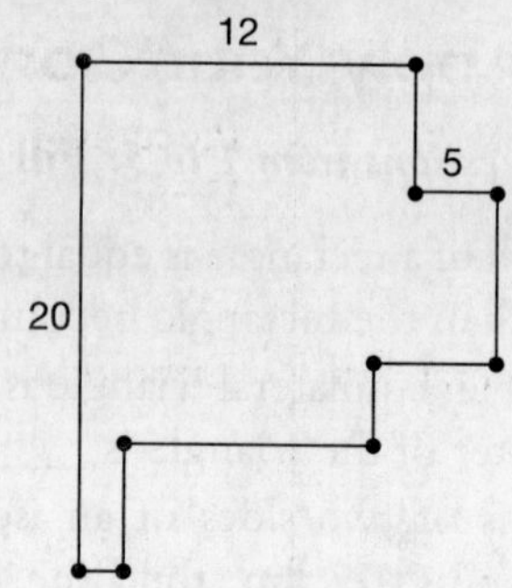

20. There are two goats and both of them are tied separately to two adjacent corners of a square plot of side 28 m with ropes 14 m long. Find the area of the plot over which the goats cannot graze.

ANSWER KEYS

Crossword

Across

1. Perimeter 2. Rectangle 3. Pyramid 4. Solid 5. Square
7. Cube 8. Vertex

Down

6. Quadrilateral 9. Cuboid 10. Area 11. Length 12. Axis

Classroom Wing

Very Short Answer Type Questions

1. (a) 2. (d) 3. (d) 4. (b) 5. (c)
6. 600 cm^2 7. 2 cm 8. 32 sq. cm 9. 5 cm 10. 300%
11. (b) 12. (d) 13. (b) 14. (b) 15. (b)
16. 1. (b) → (1) → (j); 2. (c) → (2) → (h); 3. (e) → (3) → (f); 4. (c) → (4) → (g); 17. 24 cm
18. 1600 cm^2

Short Answer Type Questions

19. 24 sq m 20. 8625 sq m 21. 48 cm 22. 48 sq. cm 23. 96 24. 9 cm^2
25. 50 cm 26. 4035 cm 27. 1 cm 28. III, I, II, IV 29. ₹16800
30. ₹20250 31. 225 32. ₹256 33. 40 m 34. 2875 L

Essay Type Questions

35. 64 cm 36. 12 min

Competition Wing

Level 1: Apply Your Concepts

1. Square 2. 2016 cm 3. 6050 cm 4. 2018 cm 5. $\frac{p^2}{16}$ 6. (c)
7. (d) 8. (c) 9. (c)

Level 2: Review Your Concepts

10. 1. → (d); 2. → (e); 3. → (a); 4. → (b) 11. 32 sq. cm 12. 3 sq. cm
13. 20 sq. cm 14. (d) 15. (c)

Level 3: Assess Your Concepts

16. 1. 9 cm; 2. 1404 cu cm 17. 8091 cm 18. 576 19. 74
20. 476 cm^2

Hints and Explanations

CLASSROOM WING

Very Short Answer Type Questions

1. Since the angles of a triangle are in the ratio 1 : 1 : 1, the triangle is an equilateral triangle.

   ∴ The ratio of the sides = 1 : 1 : 1

   Hence, the correct option is (a).

2. Let the side of a square be a.

   Since the side of a square is doubled.

   ⇒ New side = $2a$

   Area of the square = $(2a)^2 = 4a^2$.

   ∴ Area of the square becomes 4 times.

   Hence, the correct option is (d).

3. Let the side of a square be a.

   Area of square $a^2 = 25$

   $a = \sqrt{25} = 5$ m

   Hence, the correct option is (d).

4. Let the side of the square be a.

   Since area and perimeter of a square are numerically equal,

   $a^2 = 4a$

   ∴ $a = 4$

   Hence, the correct option is (b).

5. Given $\ell : b = 3 : 2$

   Let $\ell = 3x$, b = $2x$

   Perimeter of the rectangle = $2(3x + 2x) = 10x$

   ∴ $10x = 10$

   $x = 1$

   ∴ Length = $3x = 3 \times 1 = 3$ cm

   Hence, the correct option is (c).

6. The edge of a cube $a = 10$ cm

   Total surface area of the cube = $6a^2 = 6(10)^2$

   $= 600 \text{ cm}^2$

7. The volume of the cuboidal box = 24 cm^3

   Base area of the cuboidal box = 12 sq. cm

   Height of the cuboidal box = $\dfrac{\text{Volume}}{\text{Base area}}$

   $= \dfrac{24}{12} = 2$ cm

8. The perimeter of the base of the cuboid = 16 cm

   Height of the cuboid = 2 cm

   Lateral surface area of the cuboid

   = Perimeter of the base × Height

   = 16 × 2 = 32 sq. cm

9. Let the edge of the cube be a cm.

   Number of edges of the cube = 12

   Sum of the lengths of all the edges of the cube = 60 cm

   ∴ $12a = 60$

   $a = \dfrac{60}{12} = 5$

   ∴ Edge of the cube = 5 cm

10. Let the edge of the cube be a units.

    Lateral surface area of the cube = $4a^2$ sq. units.

    If edge of the cube is increased by 100%, then new edge = $2a$.

    The lateral surface area of the new cube

    $= 4(2a)^2 = 16a^2$ sq. units

    Increase in area = $16a^2 - 4a^2 = 12a^2$

    % increase in area = $\dfrac{12a^2 \times 100\%}{4a^2} = 300\%$

11. Let the edge of the cube be 'a'.

    Lateral surface area : Total surface area

    $= 4a^2 : 6a^2 = 2 : 3$

    Hence, the correct option is (b).

12. Lateral surface area of the match box $= 2(\ell + b)h$

$= 2(6 + 2)(1.5) = 2(8)(1.5) = 24$ sq. cm

Hence, the correct option is (d).

13. Total surface area of the cuboid $= 2(\ell b + bh + h\ell)$

$= 2(2.5 \times 2 + 2 \times 1.4 + 1.4 \times 2.5)$

$= 2(5 + 2.8 + 3.5) = 2(11.3)$

$= 22.6$ sq. cm

Hence, the correct option is (b).

14. Number of faces of the cube = 6

∴ Minimum number of colours required = 2

Hence, the correct option is (b).

15. Let the edge of the cube be a.

Volume of the cube $= a^3$

If edge of the cube is doubled, then new edge $= 2a$.

New volume $= (2a)^3 = 8a^3$

∴ Volume of the cube is 8 times that of the initial cube.

Hence, the correct option is (b).

16. P is a cube of edge 4 cm and Q is another cube of edge 5 cm.

Total length of the edges = 12 × Edge of the cube

$\text{LSA} = 4 \times (\text{Edge})^2$

$\text{TSA} = 6 \times (\text{Edge})^2$

$\text{Volume} = (\text{Edge})^3$

1. Total length of the edges of the cube P (in cm) $= 12 \times 4 = 48$.

   Total length of the edges of the cube Q (in cm) $= 12 \times 5 = 60$.

   $b \leftrightarrow 1 \leftrightarrow j$

2. LSA of the cube P (in sq cm) $= 4 \times (4)^2 = 64$.

   LSA of the cube Q (in sq cm) $= 4 \times (5)^2 = 100$.

   $c \leftrightarrow 2 \leftrightarrow h$

3. TSA of the cube P (in sq cm) $= 6 \times (4)^2 = 96$.

   TSA of the cube Q (in sq cm) $= 6 \times (5)^2 = 150$.

   $e \leftrightarrow 3 \leftrightarrow f$

4. Volume of the cube P (in cu cm) $= (4)^3 = 64$.

   Volume of the cube Q (in cu cm) $= (5)^3 = 125$.

   $c \leftrightarrow 4 \leftrightarrow g$

17. Perimeter = 8 + 8 + 8

= 24 cm

18. Perimeter $= 2(l + b)$

$160 = 2(l + 40)$

$l = 40$ cm

Area $= l \times b$

Area $= 1600 \text{ cm}^2$

Short Answer Type Questions

19. Given that the perimeter of a rectangular field is 20 m.

$2(l + b) = 20$

$l + b = 10$, where l and b are positive integers and $l > b$.

$\therefore (l, b) = (9, 1), (8, 2), (7, 3)$ and $(6, 4)$.

(l, b)	$(9, 1)$	$(8, 2)$	$(7, 3)$	$(6, 4)$.
Area (in sq m) $= l \times b$	9	16	21	24

∴ The largest possible area of the field = **24 sq m.**

20. 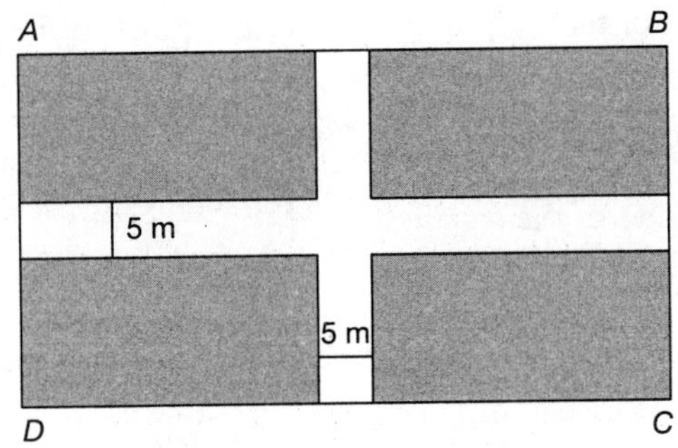

Length of the field $(l) = 120$ m.

Breadth of the field $(b) = 80$ m.

Width of the field = 5 m.

Let us assume these paths are laid in the middle of the field.

Hence, the area of the green field

$= 4 \times \left(\frac{120 - 5}{2}\right) \times \left(\frac{80 - 5}{2}\right)$

$= 115 \times 75 = 8625$ **sq m**.

21. The area of the square $= 16 \text{ cm}^2$

$\therefore a^2 = 16$

$a = 4$ cm

Length of the rectangle = 4(5) = 20 cm

Breadth of the rectangle = 4 cm

Perimeter of the rectangle = 2(20 + 4)

= 2(24) = 48 cm

22. Side of an outer square sheet = 8 cm

Area of an outer square = $8^2 = 64$ sq. cm

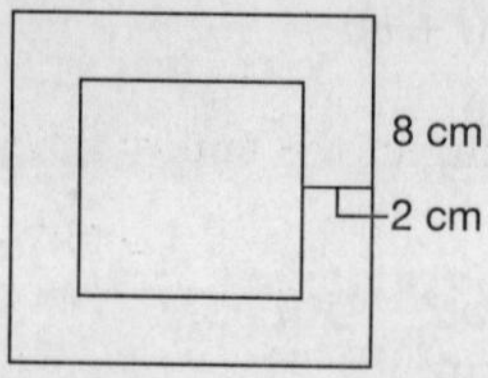

Width of a removed piece of paper = 2 cm

Side of the inner square = 8 − 2(2) = 8 − 4 = 4 cm

Area of the inner square = $4^2 = 16$ sq. cm

Area of the removed paper = Area of the outer square − Area of the inner square

= 64 − 16 = 48 sq. cm

23. Length of the rectangular hall = 16 ft

Breadth of the rectangular hall = 12 ft

Length of the tile = 2 ft

Breadth of the tile = 1 ft

Number of tiles required to cover the floor of the hall

$= \frac{\text{Area of the rectangle}}{\text{Area of the tile}} = \frac{16 \times 12}{2 \times 1} = 96$

24. Let the side of the square be a.

Since A and B took an equal length of the wire.

∴ Perimeter of the square = Perimeter of the rectangle

$4a = 12$

$a = 3$ cm

Area of the square = $a^2 = 3^2 = 9$ cm^2

25. Let ℓ and b be the length and breadth of the rectangle respectively (in cm).

Area of the rectangle = $\ell b = 24$ sq. cm

The possible values of (ℓ, b) = (24, 1), (12, 2), (8, 3), (6, 4)

∴ The maximum possible perimeter of the rectangle, $2(\ell + b) = 2(24 + 1)$ cm = 50 cm.

26. The two sides of a triangle are 2016 cm and 2017 cm. We know that the sum of any two sides of a triangle is greater than the third side.

Let the third side of the triangle be a cm.

$2016 + 2017 > a$

$4033 > a$ (i)

The difference of any two sides of the triangle is less than the third side.

$2017 - 2016 < a$

$1 < a$ (ii)

From (i) and (ii), we get:

To get the minimum perimeter (in integral measure) of a triangle, a should be minimum, i.e., $a = 2$.

∴ The minimum possible perimeter of the triangle

= 2016 + 2017 + 2

= 4035 cm

27. Edge of the Rubik's cube = 3 cm

Volume of Rubik's cube = 3^3 cu. cm = 27 cu. cm

Let the edge of each identical cube be 'a' cm.

Number of identical cubes = 27

Volume of each identical cube = a^3

$= \frac{\text{Volume of Rubik's cube}}{\text{Number of identical cubes}} = \frac{27}{27} = 1$

$a^3 = 1^3 \Rightarrow a = 1$

∴ Edge of each identical cube = 1 cm

28. Volume of the box I = $\ell \times b \times h$

= 5 × 3 × 4 = 60 cu. cm

Volume of the box II = 6 × 3 × 3

= 54 cu. cm

Volume of the box III = 4 × 4 × 4

= 64 cu. cm

Volume of the box IV = 8 × 2 × 2

= 32 cu. cm

Descending order of their volumes: III, I, II, IV.

29. Length of a room = 20 ft

Breadth of a room = 15 ft

Height of a room = 12 ft

Area of the 4 walls of the room = Lateral surface area of the room = $2(\ell + b)h$

= 2(20 + 15)12

= 24(35) = 840 sq. ft

The cost of painting the walls of the room at ₹20 per sq. ft

= 840 × ₹20 = ₹16800

30. Length of the trench = 6 m

Breadth of the trench = 3 m

Depth of the trench = 4.5 cm

The volume of the trench = 6 × 3 × 4.5 = 81 cu. m

The cost incurred in digging it at ₹250 per cu m

= 81 × ₹250 = ₹20250

31. Edge of the cubical container (a) = 30 cm

Volume of the cubical container = a^3 = = 30^3 = 30 × 30 × 30

Length of the cuboidal container (l) = 6 cm

Breadth of the cuboidal container (b) = 5 cm

Height of the cuboidal container (h) = 4 cm

Volume of each cuboidal container = $l \times b \times h$ = 6 × 5 × 4

The required number of cubical containers

$$= \frac{\text{Volume of the cubical container}}{\text{Volume of each cuboidal container}}$$

$$= \frac{30 \times 30 \times 30}{6 \times 5 \times 4}$$

= 15 × 15

= 225

32. Perimeter of the frame = 4 × 16 = 64 m

Painting cost for 1 m = ₹4

Painting cost for 64 m = ₹4 × 64 = ₹256

33. Area of hall = $l \times b$

100 = 10 × b

b = 100/10

b = 10 m

Perimeter = 2(10 + 10)

= 40 m

34. Length of the tank = 150 cm

Volume of the tank = 150 × 150 × 150

= 3,375,000 cc = 3375 L

Water remaining in the tank = 3375 – 500

= 2875 L

Essay Type Questions

35. Side of a square sheet = 10 cm.

Side of each square piece = 1 cm.

Out surface area of the cuboidal box = Area of the sheet – 4(Area of each piece)

= 10 × 10 – 4 (1 × 1)

= 100 – 4

= 96 sq. cm.

Length of the cuboidal box (l) = 10 – 2 × 1 = 8 cm.

Breadth of the cuboidal box (b) = 10 – 2 × 1 = 8 cm.

Height of the cuboidal box (h) = Side of the square piece = 1 cm.

Volume of the cuboidal box = $l \times b \times h$ = 8 × 8 × 1

= 64 cu. cm.

36. Edge of the cubical container (a) = 60 cm

Volume of water = Volume of the cubical container = a^3 == 60^3 == 216000 cu.cm

= 216000 millilitre (since 1 cu.cm = 1 millilitre)

Time taken to empty the container

$$= \frac{\text{Volume of water}}{\text{Rate}} = \frac{216000}{30}$$

= 720 seconds

$$= \frac{720}{60} \text{ minutes}$$

= 12 minutes

COMPETITION WING

Level 1: Apply Your Concepts

1. If the length of a rectangle is equal to the breadth of the rectangle, then the rectangle is called square.
2. The side of an equilateral triangle (a) = 672 cm

   ∴ Perimeter of the equilateral triangle

   $= 3a = 3(672) = 2016$ cm
3. The two sides of an isosceles triangle are 2016 cm and 2017 cm.

   Since the given triangle is an isosceles triangle. So, the third side is either 2016 cm or 2017 cm.

   The maximum possible perimeter of the triangle = 2016 + 2017 + 2017 = 6050 cm
4. $\ell + b = 1009$ cm

   Perimeter of the rectangle $= 2(\ell + b) = 2 \times 1009$

   $= 2018$ cm
5. Let the side of a square be 'a'.

   $4a = p$

   $a = \frac{p}{4}$

   Area of the square $= a^2 = \left(\frac{p}{4}\right)^2 = \frac{p^2}{16}$ sq. units.
6. Given that the volume of a cuboid is 120 cu cm, where the dimensions of the cuboid are consecutive integers in cm.

   $l \times b \times h = 120 = 6 \times 5 \times 4$

   $\therefore l + b + h = 6 + 5 + 4 = 15$ cm.

   Hence, the correct option is (c).
7. The area of a right triangle is 36 sq cm.

   $\Rightarrow \frac{a \times b}{2} = 36$

   $a \times b = 72$

   Going by the options choice (4) follows.

   Hence, the correct option is (d).
8. Given, $2(l + b) = 30$ cm

   $(l + b) = 15$ cm

   The possible pairs are (14, 1), (13, 2), (12, 3), (11, 4), (10, 5), (9, 6), (8, 7).

   Hence, the correct option is (c).
9. Number of match boxes that can be placed in the rectangular box.

   $= \frac{45 \times 30 \times 20}{6 \times 3 \times 2}$

   $= 750$

   Hence, the correct option is (c).

Level 2: Review Your Concepts

10. Given that the edge of cube is an integer in cm.

    1. Total length of the edges = 12× Edge of the cube, which is a multiple of 12.

       Among the numbers given in the column B, 108 is a multiple of 12 i.e., $108 = 12 \times 9$.

       Hence, the total length of the edges of a cube can be 108 cm. $1 \leftrightarrow \boldsymbol{d}$
    2. LSA $= 4 \times (\text{Edge})^2$, which is 4 times a perfect square number.

       Among the numbers given in the column B, 196 is 4 times a perfect square number i.e., $196 = 4 \times 7^2$.

       Hence, the LSA of a cube can be 196 sq cm. $2 \leftrightarrow \boldsymbol{e}$
    3. TSA $= 6 \times (\text{Edge})^2$, which is 6 times a perfect square number.

       Among the numbers given in the column B, 150 is 6 times a perfect square number i.e., $150 = 6 \times 5^2$.

       Hence, the TSA of a cube can be 150 sq cm. $3 \leftrightarrow \boldsymbol{a}$
    4. Volume $= (\text{Edge})^3$, which is a perfect cube.

       Among the numbers given in the column B, 1331 is a perfect cube i.e., $1331 = 11^3$.

       Hence, the volume of the cube can be 196 cu cm. $4 \leftrightarrow \boldsymbol{b}$
11. Side of the square sheet = 8 cm

    Area of the square $= 8^2 = 64$ sq. cm

    Side of the isosceles triangle, $a = 4$ cm

    Area of the isosceles triangle $= \frac{1}{2}a^2$

    $= \frac{1}{2} \times 4 \times 4$

    $= 8$ sq. cm

    Area of the remaining paper

    = Area of the square − 4 × Area of the isosceles triangle

    $= 64 - 4(8) = 64 - 32$

    $= 32$ sq. cm

12. Length of the rectangle $ABCD = 9$ cm

Breadth of the rectangle = 5 cm

Side of the square III = 5 cm

Side of the square I = 9 – 5 = 4 cm

Side of the square II = 5 – 4 = 1 cm

Length of the shaded region = 4 – 1 = 3 cm

Breadth of the shaded region = 1 cm

Area of the shaded region = 3 × 1 = 3 sq. cm

13. Side of a square paper = 6 cm

Side of each square piece = 2 cm

Total surface area of a box = Area of the sheet – 4(Area of each piece)

= 6 × 6 – 4 (2 × 2)

= 36 – 16 = 20 sq. cm

14. The dimensions of a cuboid are 4 cm × 1 cm × 1 cm.

The total surface area of a cuboid

= 2 ($lb + bh + hl$) sq. cm

The total surface area of a cuboid formed

= 2 (4 × 1 + 1 × 1 + 1 × 4)

= 2 × 9 = 18 sq. cm

Hence, the correct option is (d).

15. The given sides are 2018 cm and 2019 cm.

The sum of the sides is 4037 cm and the difference between the sides is 1 cm.

The length of the third side must lie between 1 cm and 4037 cm.

The smallest integer after 1 is 2, therefore the length of the third side is 2 cm.

The minimum possible perimeter of the triangle

= 2 + 2018 + 2019 = 4039 cm.

Hence, the correct option is (c).

Level 3: Assess Your Concepts

16. Given that the LSA of a cuboid is 450 sq cm and the sum of its length and breadth is 25 cm.

(i) LSA of the cuboid $= 2h(l+b) = 450$ ...(1)

$l + b = 25$ ...(2)

From the equations (1) and (2), $2h(25) = 450$.

$h(50) = 450$

$h = \frac{450}{50} = 9$ cm.

Height of the cuboid $(h) = 9$ **cm**.

(ii) $h = 9$ cm.

$l + b = 25$.

Also, given that the length and the breadth of the cuboid are consecutive integers.

$l = 13$ cm and $b = 12$ cm.

Volume of a cuboid $= l \times b \times h$.

$= 13 \times 12 \times 9$

$= 1404$ **cu cm**.

17. The two sides of a triangle are 2022 cm and 2024 cm.

We know that sum of any two sides of a triangle is greater than the third side.

Let third side of the triangle be 'x cm.

$2022 + 2024 > x$.

$4046 > x$ (1)

Also, the difference of any two sides of the triangle is less than the third side.

$2024 - 2022 < x$

$2 < x$ (2)

From (1) & (2), we get $2 < x < 4046$

To get the maximum perimeter (in integer measure) of a triangle, 'x' should be maximum, i.e., $x = 4045$.

∴ The maximum possible perimeter of the triangle

= 2022 + 2024 + 4045

= 8091 cm.

18. As shown below, let us take the two sides of the tile as: x (longer side); and y (shorter side).

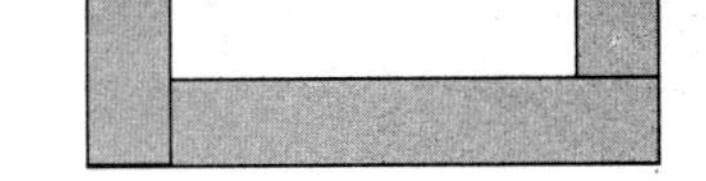

We know that, the perimeter of the tiles is 14, so $2x + 2y = 96$, which means $x + y = 24$.

However, we can observe that $(x + y)$ is also the length of the larger square.

Therefore, the area of the larger square will be $(x + y)^2 = (24)^2 = 576$.

19. Let us label all the unlabelled sides as:

a, b, c and d (for all vertical unlabelled-sides), and x, y, and z (for all horizontal unlabelled-sides)

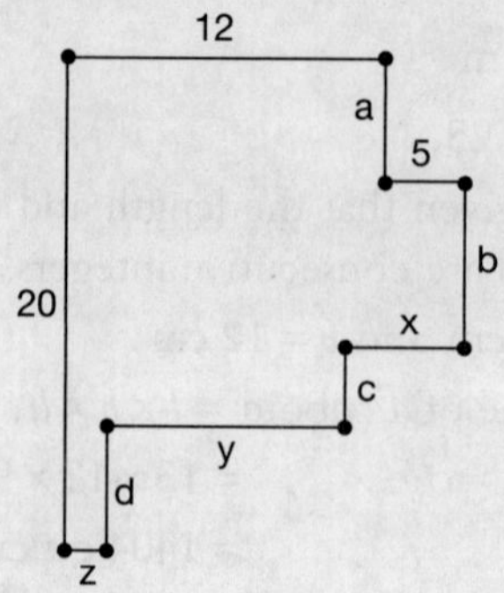

We, can observe that $(a + b + c + d) = 20$, and $(x + y + z) = 12 + 5 = 17$.

So, the perimeter of the figure is $= 20 + 12 + a + 5 + b + x + c + y + d + z$

$= 20 + 12 + 5 + (a + b + c + d) + (x + y + z) = 2) + 12 + 5 + 20 + 17 = 74$

20.

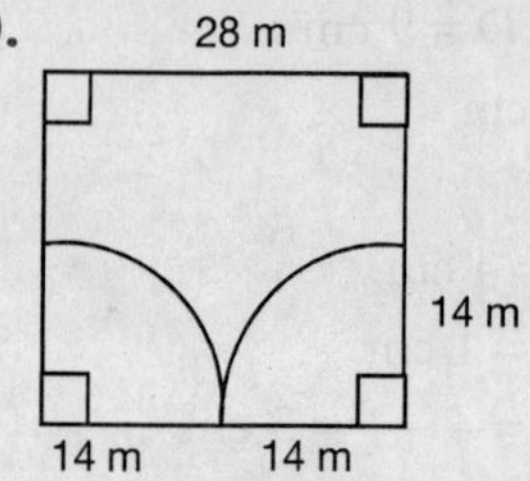

Area of the square $= (28)\ (28)\ m^2 = 784\ m^2$.

Area over which the goats can graze

$= 2\left(\frac{90°}{360°}\right)\left(\frac{22}{7}\right)(14)(14)\ m^2 = 308\ m^2$

Area over which the goats cannot graze

$= (784 - 308)\ m^2$

$= 476\ m^2$.

CHAPTER

10

Statistics

Remember

Before beginning this chapter, you should be able to:

- Understand the data in a tabular form
- Understand pictures

Key Ideas

After completing this chapter, you should be able to:

- Present data in charts, graphs, etc.
- Understand statistical graphs: Bar graphs and pie graphs

Scientific Crypt

A Tribute to Prasanta Chandra Mahalanobis (1893-1972)

Prasanta Chandra Mahalanobis, often referred to as the "Father of Statistics in India," was a distinguished Indian scientist and statistician. He played a crucial role in the development and promotion of statistics as a scientific discipline in India.

Born on June 29, 1893, in Calcutta (now Kolkata), India, he came from a family with strong academic and intellectual roots. He earned his Bachelor of Science degree with honors in physics in 1912 and later studied at King's College, Cambridge, where he had the opportunity to meet and interact with the brilliant mathematician Srinivasa Ramanujan. His exposure to advanced statistical methods and their applications in various fields influenced his decision to focus on statistics as a career.

Upon returning to India, Mahalanobis recognized the need for statistical methods to inform policy decisions and contribute to the country's development. He established the Indian Statistical Institute (ISI) in Baranagar, Kolkata, West Bengal, in 1931, with the aim of promoting research, training, and the application of statistical techniques in various fields. He played a significant role in designing large-scale sample surveys. Among his many contributions, Mahalanobis is best known for developing the Mahalanobis distance, a statistical measure used to quantify the distance between data points in a multidimensional space. This concept found applications in numerous fields.

FUN TIME

CROSSWORD

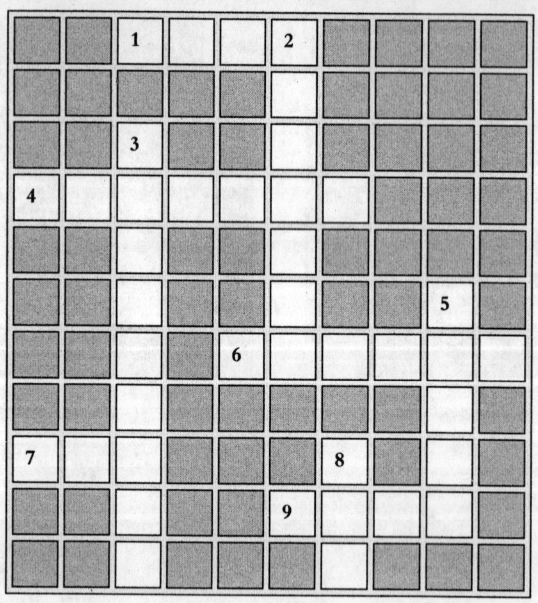

Across

1. Information which is contained in the form of numerical figures or a set of given facts.
4. When the data is collected directly from the source and is original, it is referred to as ________ data.
6. The central value of a group of data that has been arranged in ascending or descending order.
7. A graphical arrangement of data using bars of different heights is known as _______ graph.
9. By plotting the obtained points on a graph paper and joining the given points by means of lines, we can obtain a ________ graph.

Down

2. A number representing the central value of a collection of data.
3. Similar to bar graphs, but this groups numbers into ranges.
5. The difference between the highest and the lowest values of the data.
8. In _________ graph, a circle is divided into various sectors, in proportion to the various component parts of the total.

INTRODUCTION

Political states and countries gather information about their citizens to facilitate governance and to plan development and policies. Then in due course of time, statistics evolved as a branch of Mathematics which deals with the collection, classification and analysis of numerical data. The word '*statistics*' is derived from the Latin word '*status*' or the Italian word '*stata*' or the Greek word '*Statistik*' which means political state. We will learn about statistical graphs and their measures of central tendency in this chapter.

Data

Information which is contained in the form of numerical figures or a set of given facts is called **data**.

Example: The percentage of marks scored by 10 pupils of a class in a test is given as

72, 84, 82, 96, 94, 98, 99, 67, 92 and 93

The set of these figures is the data related to the marks scored by 10 pupils in a class test.

Info Bytes!

Tally marks is a fast method recording information about numbers in groups of five. Each of the first four numbers are presented by one vertical line and a diagonal line across them represents the fifth number.

Konnect

1. The data obtained from direct observation is called **raw data**. The marks obtained by 10 students in a monthly test is an example of raw data or ungrouped data.
2. The difference between the highest and the lowest values of the data is called '**range**'. ***Example:*** The range of the data of the first 25 natural numbers is 25 – 1 = 24.

Some Basic Definitions

Before getting into the details of tabular representation of data, let us review some basic definitions.

1. **Observation:** Each numerical figure in a data is called an observation.
2. **Frequency:** The number of times a particular observation occurs is called its frequency.

Table 10.1 Tally chart

<table>
<tr><th>Number</th><th>Tallies</th></tr>
<tr><td>One</td><td>|</td></tr>
<tr><td>Two</td><td>||</td></tr>
<tr><td>Three</td><td>|||</td></tr>
<tr><td>Four</td><td>||||</td></tr>
</table>

Tabulation or Presentation of Data

A systematic arrangement of data in a tabular form is called **tabulation or presentation of the data**. This grouping results in a table called the **frequency table** which indicates the number of scores within each group. Many conclusions about the characteristics of the data, the behaviour of variables, etc., can be drawn from this table.

Figure 10.1 Tally number 5

The quantitative data that is to be analysed statistically can be represented as individual series or discrete series.

1. **Individual series:** Any raw data which is collected wholly forms an individual series.

Examples: **(i)** The weight of 8 students: 35, 40, 36, 42, 32, 30, 50 and 46 (in kg).

(ii) The marks scored by 12 students in a test in Mathematics is as follows.

45, 72, 76, 57, 49, 64, 75, 88, 92, 90, 60 and 55

2. **Discrete series:** A discrete series is formulated from raw data by taking the frequency of the observations into consideration.

Example:

x	5	10	15	20	25
$f(x)$	2	1	2	3	2

Info Bytes!

'Numerical Data' is data that deals with numbers. For example, the number of pages in your textbook or the number of days in a month.

Types of Data

There are two types of data.

Primary Data: When the data is collected directly from the source and is original, it is called **primary data**.

Example: Surveys, experimental observations, etc.

Secondary Data: The secondary data means the information that has already been collected by any other person and is readily available for future study.

Example: Data collected from a book, internet, etc.

EXAMPLE 10.1 Given below is the data showing the number of children in a family, in a locality of 15 families. 1, 3, 5, 4, 3, 2, 1, 1, 3, 2, 2, 1, 4, 2 and 1. Draw the frequency table to represent the data.

SOLUTION

Arranging the data in ascending order we have: 1, 1, 1, 1, 1, 2, 2, 2, 2, 3, 3, 3, 4, 4, 5. To count, we can use tally marks. We record tally marks in bunches of five, the fifth one crossing the others diagonally, i.e., ~~IIII~~.

Thus, we may prepare a frequency table as shown below:

Number of Children	Tally Marks	Number of Families (Frequency)
1	~~IIII~~	5
2	IIII	4
3	III	3
4	II	2
5	I	1

Statistical Graphs

The information provided by a numerical frequency distribution is easily understood when represented by diagrams or graphs. The diagrams act as visual aids and they create a lasting impression in the viewer's mind. This enables the investigator to make quick conclusions about the distribution.

There are different types of graphs or diagrams to represent statistical data. Some of them are listed below:

1. Bar graph
2. Pie chart
3. Line graph

Bar Graph

A **Bar Graph** is a graphical arrangement of data using bars of different heights.

The important features of bar graphs are given below.

(i) Bar graphs are used to represent unclassified frequency distributions.

(ii) The frequency of a value of a variable is represented by a bar (rectangle) whose length (i.e., height) is equal (or proportional) to the frequency.

(iii) The breadth of the bar is arbitrary and the breadth of all the bars is equal.

(iv) Uniform spaces should be left between any two consecutive bars.

(v) All the bars should rest on the same line called base line.

Info Bytes!

Histograms are similar to bar graphs, but a histogram groups numbers into ranges.

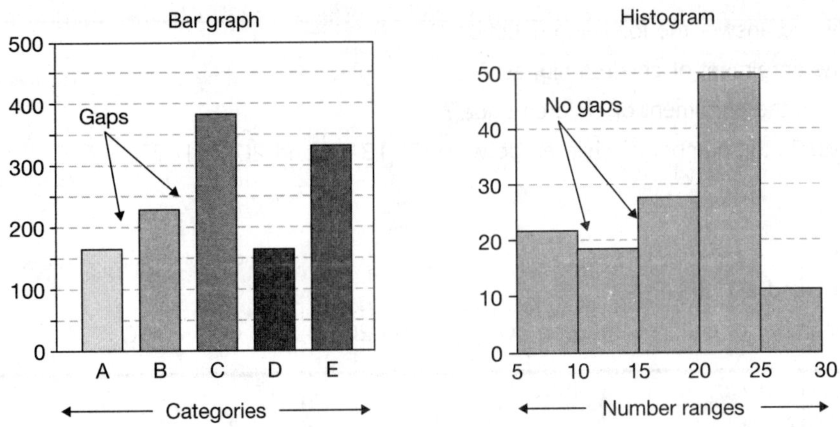

Figure 10.2 Bar graph vs Histogram

EXAMPLE 10.2

The number of different flavours of ice creams sold by a shop keeper during a particular day is given below.

Ice creams	Vanilla	Chocolate	Butterscotch	Strawberry
Number of ice creams	25	17	14	22

Draw a histogram to represent the given data.

SOLUTION

To draw a histogram, take ice cream flavours along the *X*-axis and the number of ice creams along the *Y*-axis.

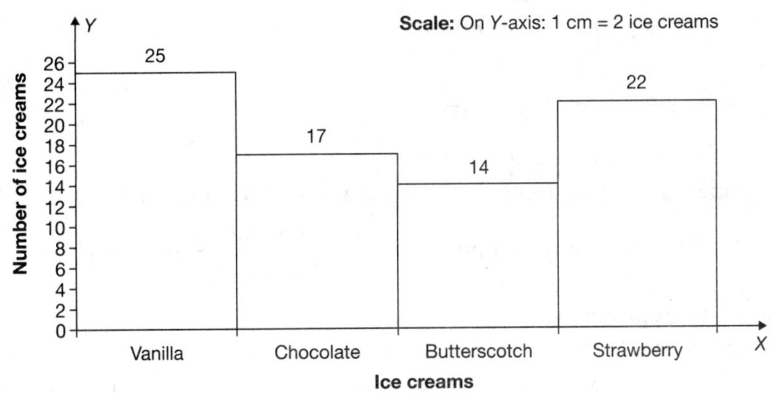

EXAMPLE 10.3

The graph given below shows the number of enrolments of nursery children over a period of 6 years.

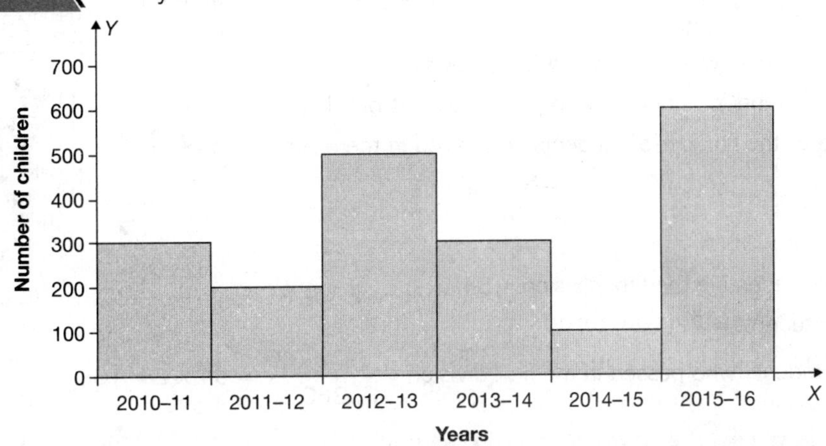

Study the graph carefully and answer the following questions.

(I) In which year was the enrolment of children highest?

(II) In which two years was the enrolment of children equal?

(III) What was the increase in the number of children between 2013-14 and 2015-16?

SOLUTION

(I) In the year 2015-16.

(II) In the years 2010-11 and 2013-14.

(III) The increase in the number of children between 2013-14 and 2015-16 = 600 – 300 = 300.

Pie Graph or Pie Chart

In the pie graph, a circle is divided into various sectors, in proportion to the various component parts of the total. Statistical data can also be presented in the form of a pie graph.

Example: The adjoining figure shows the result of 7th class students.

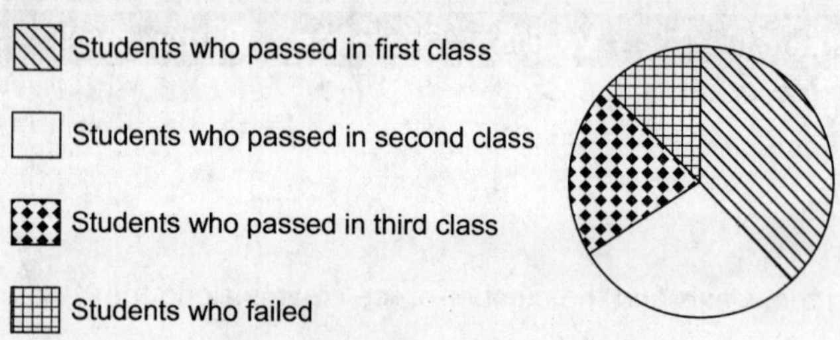

Figure 10.3 A pie chart

Info Bytes!

Pi could be written up to hundred decimal places as 3.14159265 3589793238462643 3832795028841971 6939937510582097 4944592307816406 2862089986280348 253421170679

Steps for the Construction of a Pie Diagram

Step 1: Take the total value of all the items equal to 360°.

Step 2: Convert each component of the data into degrees using the following formula.

$$\text{Degree of any component} = \frac{\text{Component value}}{\text{Total value}} \times 360^\circ$$

Step 3: Draw a circle with an appropriate radius.

Step 4: Mark the angles at the centre of the circle, and draw the sectors.

EXAMPLE 10.4 The performance of 720 students in an examination for the academic year 2015–16 is shown in a pie chart. Study the pie chart carefully and answer the following questions.

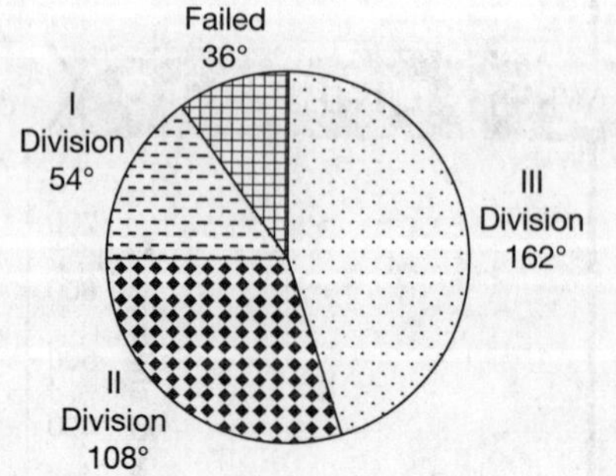

(I) Find the number of students who passed in the first division.

(II) Find the ratio of the number of students who passed to that of failed.

(III) Find the percentage of the number of students who failed in the examination.

SOLUTION

(I) The angle at the centre = 360°

Angle of sector representing the first division = 54°

Total number of students = 720

The number of students who passed in the first division = $\frac{54^\circ \times 720}{360^\circ}$ = 54 × 2 = 108

(II) Angle of sector representing the students who passed in the exam = 324°

Angle of sector representing failed students = 36°

The ratio of the number of students who passed to that of failed = 324 : 36 = 9 : 1

(III) The percentage of students who failed in the examination = $\dfrac{36 \times 100\%}{360} = 10\%$

EXAMPLE 10.5 The following table shows various sports played by students in a school. Draw a pie chart to represent the given data.

Sports	Chess	Cricket	Carroms	Football
Number of students	35	70	42	63

SOLUTION

Total number of students = 210

Pie chart for the given data can be drawn using the following steps.

(1) Draw a circle with suitable radius.

(2) Mark the angles at the centre of the circle and draw the sectors.

Sports	Number of Students	Angle of Sector
Chess	35	$\frac{35}{210} \times 360° = 60°$
Cricket	70	$\frac{70}{210} \times 360° = 120°$
Carroms	42	$\frac{42}{210} \times 360° = 72°$
Football	63	$\frac{63}{210} \times 360° = 108°$

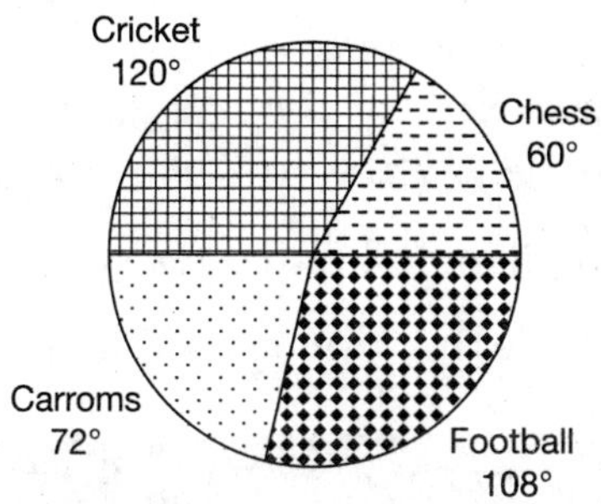

Line Graph

When a table related to two variables x and y is given, take every x value and the corresponding y value as different points. By plotting the obtained points on a graph paper and joining these points by means of lines, the graph obtained is called a **line graph**.

EXAMPLE 10.6 The number of runs given by a bowler in a one-day match in 10 overs is given below. Draw the line graph for the given data.

Overs	1	2	3	4	5	6	7	8	9	10
Number of runs	2	8	5	10	4	7	20	12	7	11

SOLUTION

To draw a line graph, mark overs along the *X*-axis and the number of runs along the *Y*-axis.

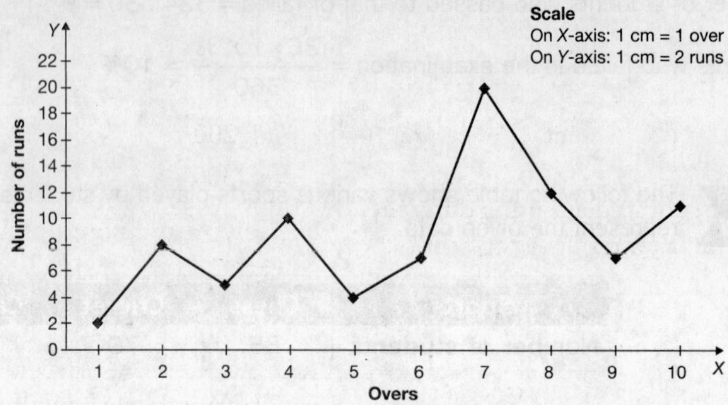

Some Important Terms Related to Data Collection and Record

1. **Average:** A number representing the central value of a collection of data is called the **average**.
   Example: 60 is the average mark in the Mathematics test in a class. It means that 60 lies somewhere between the maximum and minimum marks obtained by the students.
2. **Mean:** It is the central calculated value of a group of numbers. It is calculated by dividing sum of all the observations by number of observations.
   Example: if marks obtained by a class of four students in Mathematics test are: 70, 80, 90 and 100, then mean would be $(70 + 80 + 90 + 100)/4 = 85$
3. **Median:** It is the central value of a group of data that has been arranged in ascending or descending order.
4. **Mode:** It is that number in a group of data which occurs most frequently.

POINTS TO REMEMBER

- ✔ Information which is contained in the form of numerical figures or a set of given facts is called data.
- ✔ The data obtained from direct observation is called raw data.
- ✔ The difference between the highest and the lowest values of the data is called 'range'.
- ✔ When the data is collected directly from the source and is original, it is called primary data.
- ✔ A bar graph is a graphical arrangement of data using bars of different heights.
- ✔ In the pie graph, a circle is divided into various sectors, in proportion to the various component parts of the total.
- ✔ By plotting the obtained points on a graph paper and joining the given points by means of lines, such graph obtained is called a line graph.
- ✔ A number representing the central value of a collection of data is called the average.

PRACTICE QUESTIONS CLASSROOM WING

Very Short Answer Type Questions

Direction for questions from 1 to 5: **Select the correct alternative from given choices.**

The histogram shows the number of students using different modes of transport to commute from residence to school.

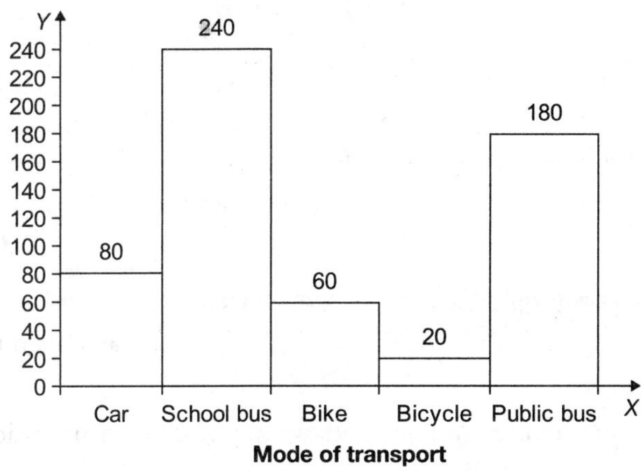

From the bar graph, answer the following questions:

1. What is the total number of pupils who travel by school bus and by bike?

   (a) 200 (b) 320

   (c) 300 (d) 100

2. How many more pupils travel by public bus than by car?

   (a) 100 (b) 120

   (c) 160 (d) 220

3. The number of pupils who travel by bike is 3 times than that of the number of pupils who travel by

   (a) Bicycle (b) Public bus

   (c) Car (d) School bus

4. If 6 girls travel to school by bicycle, then how many boys travel by bicycle?

   (a) 20 (b) 16

   (c) 14 (d) 6

5. The ratio of the number of pupils who travel by school bus and who travel by public bus is

   (a) 3 : 4 (b) 1 : 1

   (c) 4 : 3 (d) 1 : 2

Short Answer Type Questions

6. A bar graph is drawn to the scale of 1 cm = k units. The length of the bar representing 260 units is 5.2 cm. Find the value of k.

7. In a pie chart, a component is represented as a sector with sector angle 108°, then find the percentage of the value of the component totally.

8. Mr. Anand distributes his annual income, after paying income tax, towards the following.

   Food: ₹150000

   Clothes: ₹25000

   Health: ₹25000

   Education: ₹50000

   Miscellaneous: ₹50000

   Savings: ₹600000

   If the above data is represented in a pie chart:

   (i) What is the angle of the sector that represents the savings?

   (ii) What is the sum of the angles of the sectors that represent health and education?

   (iii) What is the difference between the angles of the sectors that represent food and miscellaneous?

   (iv) What is the angle of the sector that represents the clothes?

9. The line graph given below shows the number of text messages received by Keerthi during a week. Study the graph carefully and answer the questions that follow.

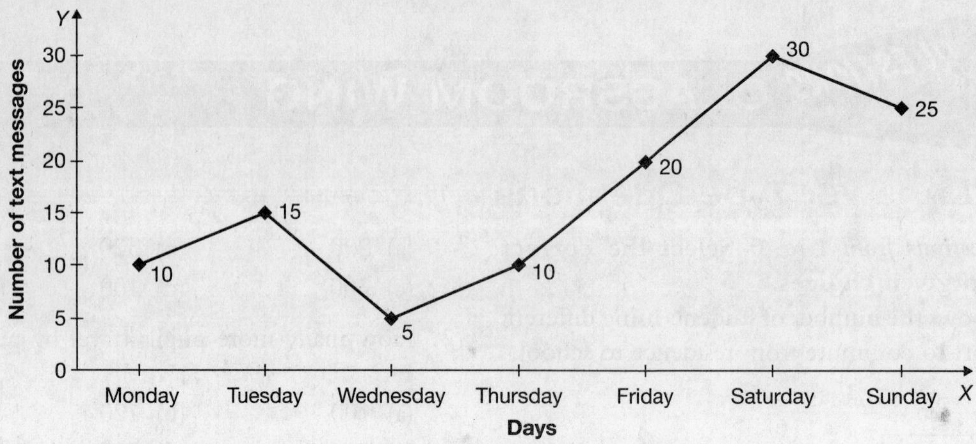

(i) On which day did Keerthi receive the lowest number of text messages?
(ii) On which day did Keerthi receive exactly 20 text messages?
(iii) Find the total number of text messages received by Keerthi in the week.

10. The following table shows the marks scored by a student in an annual examination in various subjects. Draw a histogram to represent the given data.

Subject	Telugu	Hindi	English	Maths	Science	Social Studies
Marks	80	74	82	94	90	88

11. The following table shows the household expenditure of a family on different items. Draw a pie chart to represent the given data.

Item	Rent	Food	Clothing	Education	Others
Expenditure	25%	30%	10%	15%	20%

12. The following table shows the number of toys sold by a mart during a week. Draw a line graph to represent the given data.

Week	Mon	Tue	Wed	Thurs	Fri	Sat	Sun
Number of Toys	21	10	17	24	10	16	20

13. The line graph shows the attendance of 70 students over a week.
(a) On which day of the week were more number of students present?
(b) If 18 boys were present on Thursday, then how many girls were present on the same day?

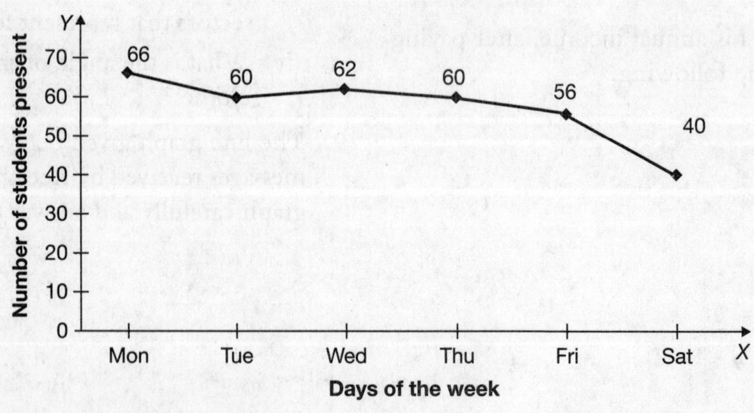

14. In a pie chart, a component value is represented as a sector with sector angle 108°, then find the percentage of the value of the component in the total.

Essay Type Questions

15. The bar graph given below shows the number of cell phones sold by four companies A, B, C and D. Study the graph carefully and answer the questions that follow.

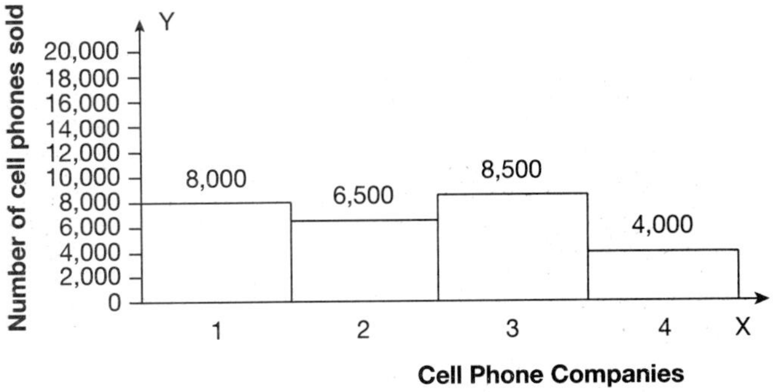

(i) What is the difference between the number of cell phones sold by companies A and C?

(ii) How many cell phones did the company B sell less compared to the highest selling company?

(iii) How many more cell phones are to be sold by company D to reach the target of selling 9000 cell phones in a month?

16. The given pie chart shows the amount of area in a playground allotted to various sports. Study the pie chart carefully and answer the following questions.

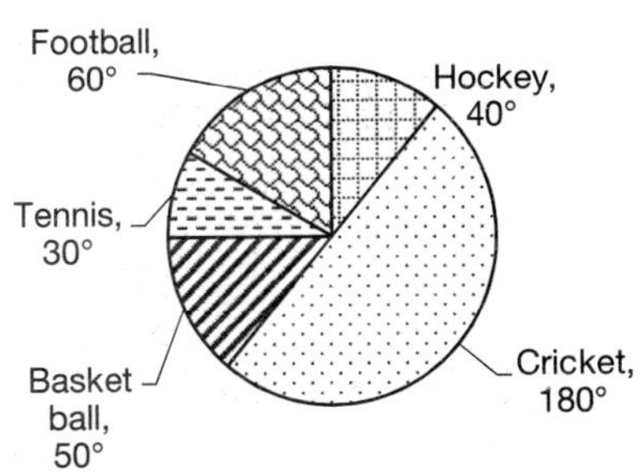

(i) If the area allocated for cricket is 810 sq. ft, then find the total area of the playground.

(ii) Find the area allocated to basketball in the playground.

Direction for question 17: **Match Column A with Column B.**

17. For a given data, Diya drew a bar graph and Jaya drew a pie chart. By reading both diagrams, they understood that 4 cm is equivalent to 28°. Column A consists of the lengths of four bars out of six of the bar graph. Column B consists of sector angles which represent the components of the pie chart.

Column A		Column B	
(a)	3 cm	(p)	42°
(b)	5 cm	(q)	84°
(c)	6 cm	(r)	21°
(d)	2 cm	(s)	56°
		(t)	35°
		(u)	14°

PRACTICE QUESTIONS COMPETITION WING

Level 1: Apply Your Concepts

Direction for questions from 1 to 5: **Fill in the blanks.**

1. In a bar graph, if a bar of height 4 cm represents 28 units, then the height of a bar representing 350 units is ______.

2. In a pie chart, the sum of the angles of all its components is ______.

3. In a pie chart, the central angle of the component 120, when the total value is 360 is ______.

4. In a bar graph, a bar of length 3.2 cm represents 96 units, then the number of units represented by a bar graph of length 2.1 cm is ______.

5. In a pie chart, if the central angle of a component is 108° and its value is 24, then the total value of all the components of the data is ______.

6. The following table shows various sports played by students of a school.

Sport	Football	Volleyball	Badminton	Chess
Number of students	68	34	56	42

If we represent these values in the form of a bar graph, then the height of the bar corresponding to football is 13.6 cm. Find the difference between the heights of the bars corresponding to volley ball and badminton.

(a) 4.4 cm (b) 6.8 cm (c) 8.8 cm (d) 7.7 cm

Direction for question 7: **Match the Column A with Column B.**

7. These questions are based on the following data.

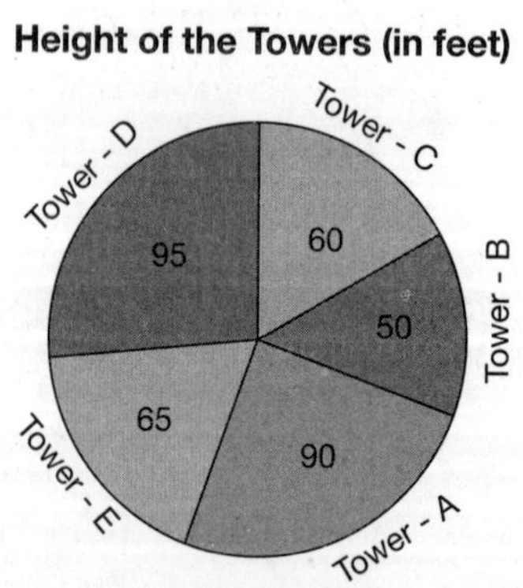

Column A	Column B
(i) What percentage of the height of the tower-B is the height of the tower-E?	a. 20%
(ii) What is the equivalent percentage to the ratio of the height of the tower-C and the sum of the heights of the remaining towers?	b. 30%
(iii) By what percentage is the height of the tower-A more than that of the tower-C?	c. 40%
(iv) By what percentage is the difference of the heights of the towers-D and E less than that of the tower-B?	d. 50%
	e. 60%
	f. 130%

Level 2: Review Your Concepts

Direction for question 8: **Match Column A with Column B.**

8. For a given data, Rithik drew a bar graph and Krithik drew a pie chart. By reading both diagrams, they understood that 3 cm is equivalent to 36°. Column A consists of the lengths of four bars out of six of the bar graph. Column B consists of sector angles which represent the components of the pie chart.

Column A		Column B	
(a)	4 cm	(p)	36°
(b)	6.5 cm	(q)	102°
(c)	7 cm	(r)	12°
(d)	8.5 cm	(s)	84°
		(t)	78°
		(u)	48°

9. The given pie chart shows the amount of money spent by a school on various sports in the year 2015.

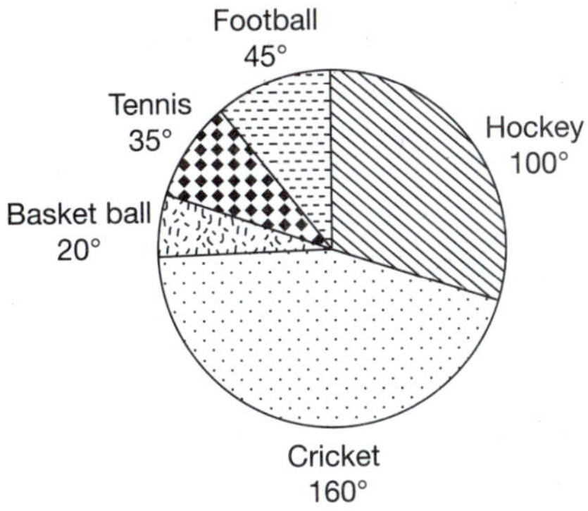

Study the pie chart carefully and answer the following questions.

(i) If the amount spent on football was ₹9000, then how much more money was spent on hockey than on football?

(ii) If the amount spent on football was ₹9000, then what was the total amount spent on all sports?

10. The following table shows the number of marks secured by the students of a class in a 50 marks exam.

Score	Number of students
Less than or equal to 10 marks	2
More than 10 marks and less than or equal to 20 marks	5
More than 20 marks and less than or equal to 30 marks	9
More than 30 marks and less than or equal to 40 marks	14
More than 40 marks and less than or equal to 50 marks	10

How many students secured less than or equal to 30 marks in that exam?

(a) 9 (b) 14

(c) 23 (d) 16

11. Find the sum of the mean and the mode of the following data:

12, 11, 13, 10, 9, 8, 14, 6, and 7

12. Find the difference of the mode and the frequency of the mode of the following data.

1, 1, 1, 1, 2, 2, 2, 3, 3, 3, 3, 3

Level 3: Assess Your Concepts

13. If the mean of a, b, c, d, and e is x, then what is the mean of $(a+10)$, $(b+10)$, $(c+10)$, $(d+10)$, and $(e+10)$?

14. If a bar graph is drawn to the scale of 3 cm = 7 units, what is the length of the bar that represents 259 units.

15. Find the arithmetic mean and the median of the first seven natural numbers.

AT

ANSWER KEYS

Crossword

Across

1. Data 4. Primary 6. Median 7. Bar 9. Line

Down

2. Average 3. Histogram 5. Range 8. Pie

Classroom Wing

Very Short Answer Type Questions

1. (c) 2. (a) 3. (a) 4. (c) 5. (c)

Short Answer Type Questions

6. 50 7. 30% 8. (i) 240°; (ii) 30°; (iii) 40°; (iv) 10°
9. (i) Wednesday; (ii) Friday; (iii) 115 13. (i) Monday; (ii) 42 14. 30%

Essay Type Questions

15. (i) 500; (ii) 2000; (iii) 9000 16. (i) 1620 sq.ft; (ii) 225 sq. ft
17. (a) → *r*; (b) → *t*; (c) → *p*; (d) → *u*

Competition Wing

Level 1: Apply Your Concepts

1. 50 cm 2. 360° 3. 120° 4. 63 5. 80 6. (a)
7. (i) → (f); (ii) → (a); (iii) → (d); (iv) → (c);

Level 2: Review Your Concepts

8. (a) → (u); (b) → (t); (c) → (s); (d) → (q) 9. (i) ₹11000; (ii) ₹72000 10. (d)
11. 20 12. 2

Level 3: Assess Your Concepts

13. $x + 10$ 14. 111 cm 15. AM: 4; Median: 4

Hints and Explanations

CLASSROOM WING

Very Short Answer Type Questions

1. The number of pupils who travel by school bus and by bike = 240 + 60 = 300.

   Hence, the correct option is (c).

2. The number of pupils who travel by public bus = 180

   The number of pupils who travel by car = 80

   ∴ The required difference = 180 – 80 = 100

   Hence, the correct option is (a).

3. The number of pupils who travel by bike = 60

   The number of pupils who travel by bicycle = 20

   The number of pupils who travel by bike is 3 times that of the number of pupils who travel by bicycle.

   Hence, the correct option is (a).

4. The number of girls travelling to school by bicycle = 6.

   The number of boys who travel to school by bicycle = 20 – 6 = 14

   Hence, the correct option is (c).

5. The number of pupils who travel by school bus = 240

   The number of pupils who travel by public bus = 180

   The ratio of pupils who travel by school bus and who travel by public bus = 240 : 180 = 4 : 3

   Hence, the correct option is (c).

Short Answer Type Questions

6. The length of the bar representing 260 units is 5.2 cm.

   The number of units represented by a bar of length 1 cm = $\frac{260}{5.2}$ = 50 units

   ∴ $k = 50$

7. The central angle of the component = 108°

   The sum of the angles of all components = 360°

   The percentage of the component value

   $= \frac{108° \times 100\%}{360°} = 30\%$

8.

Details	Amount (in ₹)	Sector angle
Food	150000	$\frac{150000}{900000} \times 360° = 60°$
Clothes	25000	$\frac{25000}{900000} \times 360° = 10°$
Health	25000	$\frac{25000}{900000} \times 360° = 10°$
Education	50000	$\frac{50000}{900000} \times 360° = 20°$
Miscellaneous	50000	$\frac{50000}{900000} \times 360° = 20°$
Savings	600000	$\frac{600000}{900000} \times 360° = 240°$
Total	**900000**	**360°**

(i) The sector angle that represents the savings = **240°**.

(ii) The sum of the sector angles that represent health and education = 10° + 20° = **30°**.

(iii) The difference between the sector angles that represent food and miscellaneous = 60° – 20° = **40°**.

(iv) The sector angle which represents the clothes = **10°**.

9. (i) Wednesday

   (ii) Friday

   (iii) The total number of text messages received by Keerthi

   = 10 + 15 + 5 + 10 + 20 + 30 + 25 = 115

10. To draw histogram, take subjects along the X-axis and marks along the Y-axis.

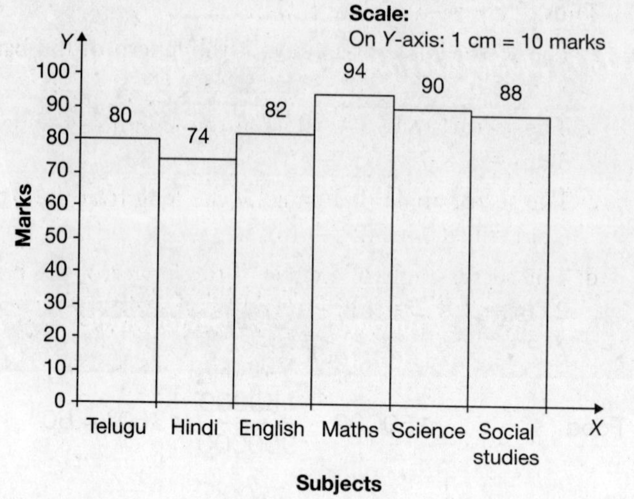

11. Steps:

(1) Draw a circle with suitable radius.

(2) Mark the angles at the centre of the circle and draw the sectors.

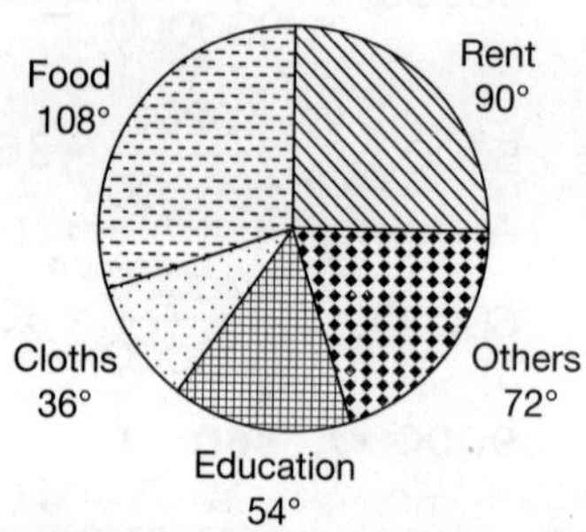

Item	Expenditure	Angle of sector
Rent	25%	$\frac{25}{100}\times 360° = 90°$
Food	30%	$\frac{30}{100}\times 360° = 108°$
Clothing	10%	$\frac{10}{100}\times 360° = 36°$
Education	15%	$\frac{15}{100}\times 360° = 54°$
Others	20%	$\frac{20}{100}\times 360° = 72°$

12. To draw line graph, take days of a week on X-axis and the number of toys sold on Y-axis.

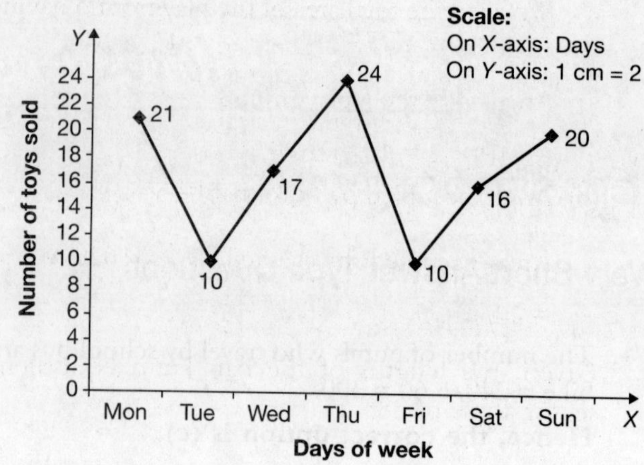

13. (a) Monday.

(b) The number of students present on Thursday = 60.
The number of boys present on Thursday = 18.
The number of girls present on Thursday = 60 – 18 = 42.

14. For a pie chart,

Percentage of the value of the component

$$= \frac{\text{Angle ofthe component}}{\text{Total angle}} \times 100\%$$

$$= \frac{108}{360} \times 100\% = 30\ \%$$

Essay Type Questions

15. From the graph, number of cell phones sold by companies A, B, C and D are 8,000, 6,500, 8,500 and 4,000, respectively.

(a) Difference between number of cell phones sold by companies A and C = 8,500 – 8,000 = 500.

(b) The highest selling company is C which sold 8,500 cell phones. The company B sold (8,500 – 6,500 = 2,000) cell phones less than the highest selling company.

(c) Company B has sold 4,000 cell phones. It needs to sell (9,000 – 4,000) = 5,000 cell phones to reach its target of selling 9,000 cell phones.

16. For a pie chart, Degree of any component

$$= \frac{\text{Component value}}{\text{Total value}} \times 360°$$

(a) The angle occupied by cricket = 180°.
Area occupied by cricket = 810 sq. ft.

We need the total area of the playground having an angle 360°.

Area of the playground $= 810 \times \dfrac{360°}{180°}$

$= 810 \times 2 = 1620$ sq. ft

(b) Angle occupied by basketball = 50°.

Area occupied by basketball $= 1620 \times \dfrac{50°}{360°}$

= 225 sq. ft.

17. Given, the lengths of the bar 4 cm equivalent to sector angle of 28°.

Thus, 1 cm is equivalent to 7°.

a: The sector angle of a circle, if the length of the bar 3 cm = 3 × 7°= 21° → (r)

b: The sector angle of a circle, if the length of the bar 5 cm = 5 × 7°= 35° → (t)

c: The sector angle of a circle, if the length of the bar 6 cm = 6 × 7°= 42° → (p)

d: The sector angle of a circle, if the length of the bar 2 cm = 2 × 7°= 14° → (u)

COMPETITION WING

Level 1: Apply Your Concepts

1. The height of a bar representing 28 units is 4 cm.

The height of the bar representing 350 units

$= \frac{350 \times 4}{28} = 50$ cm

2. The sum of the angles = 360

3. The sum of the angles of all components = 360°

Total value = 360

The central angle of the component 120

$= \frac{120 \times 360°}{360} = 120°$

4. The length of a bar representing 96 units is 3.2 cm.

The number of units represented by a bar graph of length 2.1 cm $= \frac{2.1 \times 96}{3.2} = 63$ units

5. The central angle of the component 24 = 108°

The sum of the angles of all components = 360°

The total value of all the components

$= \frac{24 \times 360°}{108°} = 80$

6. Given, the height of the bar corresponding to football is 13.6 cm.

Then, the height of the bar corresponding to volleyball

$= \frac{34}{68} \times 13.6 = 6.8$ cm

The height of the bar corresponding to badminton

$= \frac{56}{68} \times 13.6 = 11.2$ cm

Therefore, the required difference = 11.2 – 6.8 = 4.4 cm

Hence, the correct option is (a).

7. The height of the tower-A = 90 feet.

The height of the tower-B = 50 feet.

The height of the tower-C = 60 feet.

The height of the tower-D = 95 feet.

The height of the tower-E = 65 feet.

(i) The height of the tower-B = 50 feet.

The height of the tower-E = 65 feet.

The required percentage $= \frac{65}{50} \times 100\%$

$= 65 \times 2\% = 130\%$ (i) $\leftrightarrow$ ***f***

(ii) The height of the tower-C = 60 feet.

The sum of the heights of the remaining towers $= 90 + 50 + 95 + 65 = 300$ feet.

The required ratio = 60 : 300 = 1 : 5.

The equivalent % of 1 : 5 is $= \left(\frac{1}{5}\right) \times 100\% = 20\%$.

(ii) $\leftrightarrow$ ***a***

(iii) The height of the tower-A = 90 feet.

The height of the tower-C = 60 feet.

The height of the tower-A is 30 feet more than that of the tower-C.

The required percentage $= \frac{30}{60} \times 100\%$

$= \frac{1}{2} \times 100\% = 50\%$. (iii) $\leftrightarrow$ ***d***

(iv) The height of the tower-B = 50 feet.

The height of the tower-D = 95 feet.

The height of the tower-E = 65 feet.

The difference of the heights of the towers-D and E $= 95 - 65 = 30$ feet.

The above difference is 20 feet less than the height of the tower-B.

The required percentage $= \frac{20}{50} \times 100\%$

$= 20 \times 2\% = 40\%$. (iv) $\leftrightarrow$ ***c***

Level 2: Review Your Concepts

8. Given, the lengths of the bar 3 cm equivalent to sector angle of 36°.

(a) The sector angle of a circle, if the length of the bar 4 cm $= \frac{4 \times 36°}{3} = 48° \rightarrow$ (u)

(b) The sector angle of a circle, if the length of the bar 6.5 cm $= \frac{6.5 \times 36°}{3} = 78° \rightarrow$ (t)

(c) The sector angle of a circle, if the length of the bar 7 cm $= \frac{7 \times 36°}{3} = 84° \rightarrow$ (s)

(d) The sector angle of a circle, if the length of the bar 8.5 cm $= \frac{8.5 \times 36°}{3} = 102° \rightarrow$ (q)

Therefore, the correct match is as follows:

(a) → (u); (b) → (t); (c) → (s); (d) → (q)

9. (a) The amount spent on football = ₹9000

The central angle of the component football = 45°

The central angle of the component hockey = 100°

$$\text{Amount spent on hockey} = \frac{100° \times 9000}{45°}$$

$$= ₹20000$$

∴ The required difference ₹20000 – ₹9000 = ₹11000

(b) The amount spent on football = ₹9000

Central angle of the component football = 45°

$$\text{Total amount spent on all sports} = \frac{360° \times 9000}{45°}$$

$$= ₹72000$$

10. From the table, we can say that 2 + 5 + 9, i.e., 16 students have secured less than or equal to 30 marks in that test.

Hence, the correct option is (d).

11. Given data: 12, 11, 13, 10, 9, 8, 14, 6, and 7.

$$\text{Mean} = \frac{12+11+13+10+9+8+14+6+7}{9}$$

$$= \frac{90}{9} = 10.$$

Given data in the ascending order: 6, 7, 8, 9, 10, 11, 12, 13, and 14.

As there are 9 observations, the median is 5th observation.

Median $= 10$.

The required sum $= 10 + 10 = 20$.

12. Given data: 1, 1, 1, 1, 2, 2, 2, 3, 3, 3, 3, and 3.

Observation	Frequency
1	4
2	3
3	5

As the observation 3 has the highest frequency (5), the mode of the data is 3.

The required difference $= 5 - 3 = 2$.

Level 3: Assess Your Concepts

13. Given that the mean of a, b, c, d, and e is x.

$$\Rightarrow \frac{a+b+c+d+e}{5} = x.$$

The mean of

$(a+10), (b+10), (c+10), (d+10)$, and $(e+10)$

$$= \frac{(a+10)+(b+10)+(c+10)+(d+10)+(e+10)}{5}$$

$$= \frac{(a+b+c+d+e)+50}{5}$$

$$= \frac{a+b+c+d+e}{5} + \frac{50}{5}$$

$$= x + 10.$$

Hence, the required mean $= \boldsymbol{x} + 10$.

14. Given that the scale of the bar graph: 3 cm = 7 units.

$\Rightarrow$ 7 units = 3 cm

$\Rightarrow$ 1 unit $= \frac{3}{7}$ cm

$\Rightarrow$ 259 units $= \left(\frac{3}{7}\right) \times 259$ cm

$= 3 \times 37 = 111$ cm

Hence, the length of the bar $= 111$ **cm**.

15. The numbers are 1, 2, 3, 4, 5, 6, 7.

As the numbers are in an A.P. the arithmetic mean is the average of first and last terms, i.e., 4.

Since the middle term is 4, the value of the median is also equal to 4.

We can compare ... for the highest ... [illegible] ... of the data.

[illegible]

(a) → (ii), (b) → (i), (c) → (iv), (d) → (iii)

= ₹20000

= ₹72000

[illegible]

CHAPTER

11

Sets

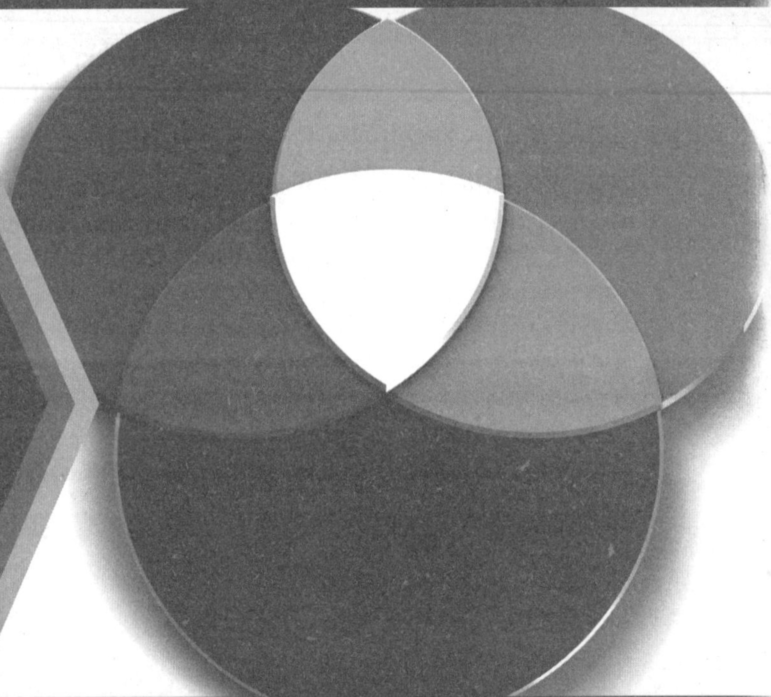

Remember

Before beginning this chapter, you should be able to:

- Name different types of collections
- Recall different types of numbers and number systems

Key Ideas

After completing this chapter, you should be able to:

- Define sets, elements of a set, representation of sets, empty set, singleton set, disjoint sets and subset
- Understand operation on sets
- Understand Venn diagrams
- Learn some formulae on cardinality of sets

Scientific Crypt

A Tribute to Narendra Krishna Karmarkar (1956)

Narendra Krishna Karmarkar is an accomplished Indian mathematician who has made significant contributions to the fields of linear programming, algorithms, and supercomputing. Born in 1956, Gwalior, Madhya Pradesh, India. He is renowned for developing Karmarkar's algorithm, a groundbreaking advancement in linear programming.

In 1984, while at Bell Laboratories, Karmarkar introduced his groundbreaking achievement: Karmarkar's algorithm. This innovative method transformed linear programming by swiftly solving optimization problems with linear constraints. Replacing conventional high-dimensional traversal, his approach efficiently cut through complexity, yielding faster, impactful solutions. Its practical applications spanned business, policy, and beyond, substantially reducing solution times.

FUN TIME

CROSSWORD

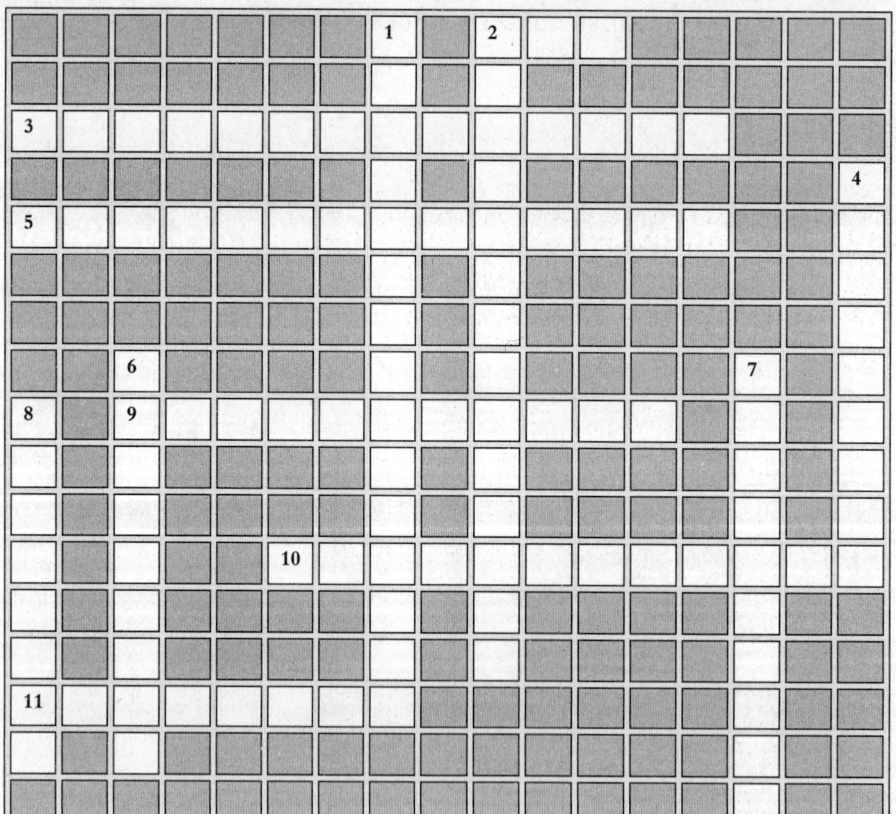

Across

2. A specific collection
3. The set of vowels and the set of first five natural numbers (2 words)
5. How many elements are there in the set? (2 words)
9. You can not count the elements of this set (2 words)
10. The set of vowels and the set of consonants (2 words)
11. the members of the set

Down

1. These are not disjoint (2 words)
2. Not in the roster form (no space between the words) (3 words)
4. The set of whole numbers and the set of non-negative integers (2 words)
6. You can find its cardinal number (2 words)
7. Represent a set (no space between the words) (2 words)
8. You can not find an element in this (2 words)

INTRODUCTION

In Mathematics, the collections of objects is known as 'sets'. The objects are referred to as the elements of the sets. In our daily life we, come across different collections of objects such as a cluster of stars, a flock of sheep, a posse of policemen, etc.

Figure 11.1 Cluster of stars, a flock of sheep and a school of fish

Set

A **set** is a well-defined collection of objects. Let us understand what we mean by a well-defined collection of objects.

We say that a collection of objects is well-defined, if there is some reason or rule by which we can say whether a given object of the universe belongs to or does not belong to the collection. We usually denote the sets by capital letters A, B, C or X, Y, Z, etc.

Examples:

i. Let us consider the collection of even natural numbers less than equal to 10. In this example, we can definitely say what the collection represents. The collection comprises the sequence of even numbers such as 2, 4, 6, 8 and 10.

ii. Let us consider the collection of intelligent girls in a class. In this example, we cannot say precisely which girls of the class belong to our collection. So, this collection is not well-defined.

Hence, the first collection is a set whereas the second collection is not a set. From the above example, the set of the first 5 even natural numbers can be represented as $A = \{2, 4, 6, 8, 10\}$

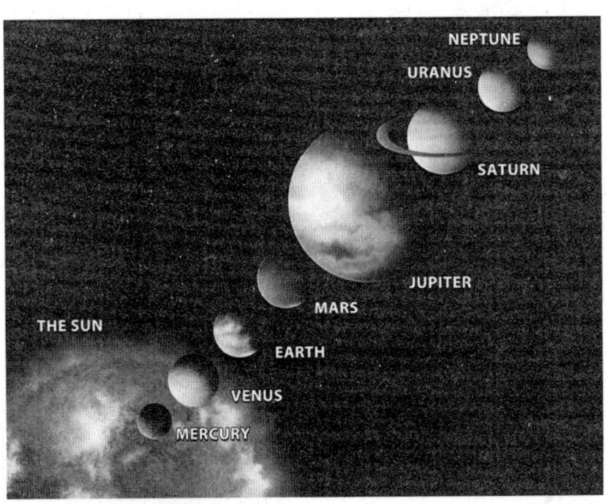

Figure 11.2 Universal set of planets

Info Bytes!

Universal set is a set that is collection of all objects/items of a group in consideration. All sets under this collection are subsets of the universal set. For example, all 8 planets are part of universal set of all planets in the universe.

Elements of a Set

The objects in a set are called its **elements** or **members**. Let us consider a set denoted by A. If a is an element of a set A, then we say that a belongs to A and we write, $a \in A$. If a is not an element of A, then we say that a does not belong to A and we write, $a \notin A$.

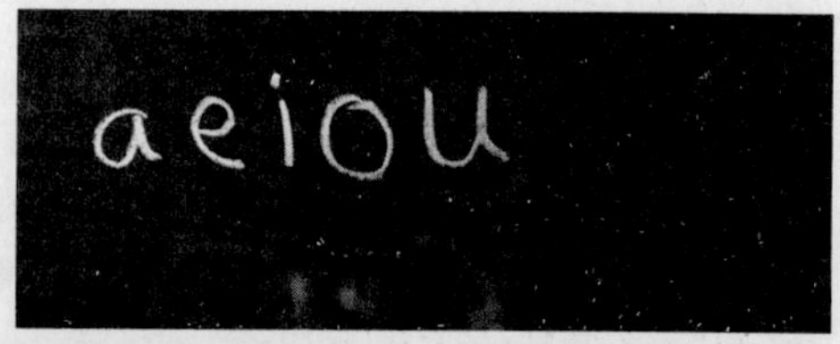

Figure 11.3 Elements of the set of vowels in English alphabet

Some sets of numbers and their notations

N = Set of all natural numbers = {1, 2, 3, 4, 5, ...}

W = Set of all whole numbers = {0, 1, 2, 3, 4, 5, ...}

Z = Set of all integers = {0, ±1, ±2, ±3, ...}

Cardinal Number of a Set

The number of elements in a set A is called its **cardinal number**. It is denoted by $n(A)$.

Example: If $A = \{a, b, c, d\}$, $n(A) = 4$.

Konnect

A set which has finite number of elements is a **finite set** and a set which has infinite number of elements is an **infinite set**.

Examples:

i. Set of consonants in English alphabet is a finite set.

ii. Set of all persons living on the earth is a finite set.

iii. The set of all integers is an infinite set.

Representation of Sets

Sets can be represented by the following methods:

1. **Roster method:** In this method, a set is described by listing out all the elements in the set.

   Examples: (i) Let V be the set of all vowels in English alphabet. Then we represent V as, $V = \{a, e, i, o, u\}$.
   (ii) Let E be the set of all odd natural numbers less than 12. Then we represent the set E as, $E = \{1, 3, 5, 7, 9, 11\}$.

2. **Description method:** In this method, the well-defined description of the elements is enclosed in curly brackets.
   Example: {1, 2, 3, 4, 5} = {The first five natural numbers}

3. **Set-builder method:** In this method, a set is described by using some property common to all its elements.

   Examples: (i) Let V be the set of all vowels in English alphabet. Then we represent the set V as, $V = \{x : x$ is a vowel in English alphabet$\}$
   (ii) Let P be the set of all odd numbers less than equal to 100. Then we represent the set P as, $P = \{x : x \le 100$ and x is an odd number$\}$

Table 11.1 Three methods of representation of a set of natural numbers between 5 and 10

Roster Method	Descriptive Method	Set-builder Method
N = {6,7,8,9}	{Natural numbers between 5 and 10}	$N = \{x : x$ is a natural number, $5 < x < 10\}$

Types of Sets

Following are definitions of different types of sets.

1. **Empty set or Null set:** A set with no elements in it is called an **empty set (or) void set (or) null set**. It is denoted by { } or ϕ (read as 'phi').
   Examples: (i) Set of all whole numbers less than 0.
   (ii) Set of all woman Chief Ministers of Andhra Pradesh.

2. **Singleton set:** A set consisting of only one element is called a **singleton set**.
   Examples: (i) The set of all even prime numbers is a singleton set as 2 is the only even prime number.
   (ii) The set of all the numbers which are neither prime nor composite is a singleton set as 1 is only neither prime nor composite.

3. **Disjoint sets:** Two sets A and B are said to be **disjoint**, if they have no elements in common.
   Examples: (i) Sets $A = \{0, 5, 6, 7, 12\}$ and $B = \{1, 2, 4, 8, 11\}$ are disjoint as they have no elements in common.
   (ii) Sets $A = \{1, 3, 4, 5\}$ and $B = \{3, 5, 8\}$ are not disjoint as they have some common elements such as 3 and 5.

Info Bytes!

There are different types of sets, such as finite, infinite, equal, and equivalent sets. Each has its unique properties and ways to identify them

EXAMPLE 11.1 Are the sets given below equal?
$A = \{x : x \text{ is an even prime}, x > 2\}$
$B = \{\ \}$

SOLUTION

There is no even prime greater than 2.
$\therefore A = \{\ \}$ and $B = \{\ \}$
Hence, A and B are equal sets.

EXAMPLE 11.2 Are the sets given below equal?
$C = \{x : x \in R, 2 < x < 5\}$
$B = \{x : x \in N, 2 < x < 5\}$

SOLUTION

C is an infinite set, since there are infinite real numbers between 2 and 5.
$D = \{3, 4\}$
$\therefore$ C and D are not equal sets.

Operation on Sets

Let us now learn the different types of operations that we can perform on sets.

Union of Sets

Let A and B be two sets. The **union** of A and B, denoted by $A \cup B$, is the set of all those elements which are either in A or in B or in both A and B, i.e., $A \cup B = \{x : x \in A \text{ or } x \in B\}$.

EXAMPLE 11.3 Given $A = \{2, 3, 4, 5, 8, 9, 14\}$ and $B = \{1, 2, 4, 6, 8, 9, 11, 18\}$. Find $A \cup B$.

SOLUTION

$A \cup B = \{2, 3, 4, 5, 8, 9, 14\} \cup \{1, 2, 4, 6, 8, 9, 11, 18\} = \{1, 2, 3, 4, 5, 6, 8, 9, 11, 14, 18\}$

Intersection of Sets

Let A and B be two sets. The **intersection** of A and B, denoted by $A \cap B$, is the set of all those elements which are common to both A and B, i.e., $A \cap B = \{x : x \in A$ and $x \in B\}$.

> **Konnect**
>
> If A and B are disjoint sets, then $A \cap B = \phi$.

EXAMPLE 11.4 Given $A = \{2, 3, 4, 5, 8, 9, 14\}$ and $B = \{1, 2, 4, 6, 8, 9, 11, 18\}$. Find $A \cap B$.

SOLUTION

$A \cap B = \{2, 3, 4, 5, 8, 9, 14\} \cap \{1, 2, 4, 6, 8, 9, 11, 18\} = \{2, 4, 8, 9\}$

Difference of Sets

Let A and B be two sets. The **difference** $A - B$ is the set of all those elements which are in A but not in B, i.e., $A - B = \{x : x \in A$ and $x \notin B\}$.

> **Konnect**
>
> (a) $n(A \cup B) = n(A) + n(B) - n(A \cap B)$
>
> (b) If A and B are disjoint, then $n(A \cup B) = n(A) + n(B)$

EXAMPLE 11.5 Given $A = \{1, 2, 4, 5, 6, 8, 20\}$ and $B = \{2, 3, 4, 5, 9, 20\}$. Find $A - B$ and $B - A$.

SOLUTION

$A - B = \{1, 2, 4, 5, 6, 8, 20\} - \{2, 3, 4, 5, 9, 20\} = \{1, 6, 8\}$

$B - A = \{2, 3, 4, 5, 9, 20\} - \{1, 2, 4, 5, 6, 8, 20\} = \{3, 9\}$

EXAMPLE 11.6 If $n(A) = 10$, $n(B) = 21$ and $n(A \cap B) = 5$, then find $n(A \cup B)$.

SOLUTION

$n(A \cup B) = n(A) + (B) - (A \cap B)$

$= 10 + 21 - 5$

$= 26$

Venn Diagrams

We can also represent sets pictorially by means of diagrams called **'Venn' diagrams**. In Venn diagrams, the universal set is usually represented by a rectangular region and its subsets by closed regions inside the rectangular region. The elements of the set are written in the closed regions.

> **Info Bytes!**
>
> Venn diagrams were introduced by John Venn in 1880, but he himself did not use the term Venn. The first person to use the term 'Venn diagram' was Clarence Lewis in 1918.

Examples:

(i) Let $\mu = \{1, 2, 3, 4, 5, 6, 7, 8, 9\}$, $A = \{1, 2, 4, 6\}$ and $B = \{2, 3, 4, 5\}$.

These sets can be represented in the form of Venn diagram as follows:

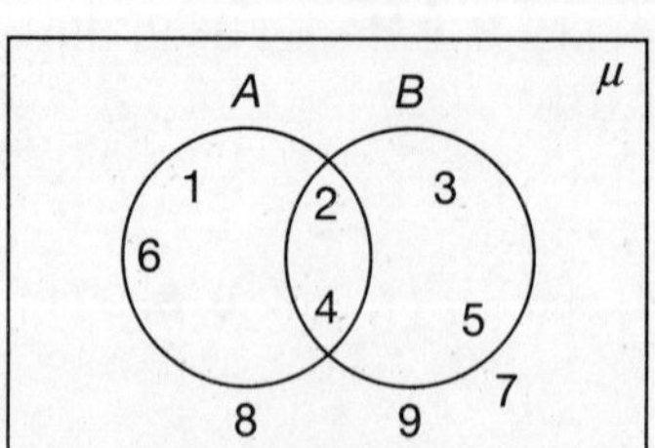

The sets in Venn diagrams can be represented by shaded regions.

(ii) Venn diagram of $A \cup B$, where A and B are two overlapping sets, is

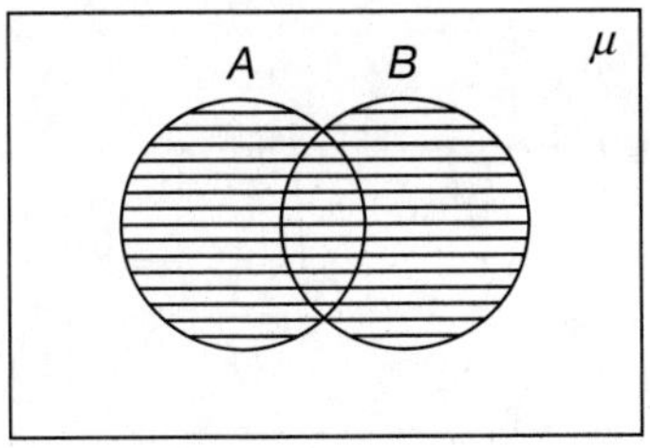

(iii) Let A and B be two overlapping sets. Then, the Venn diagram of $A \cap B$ is

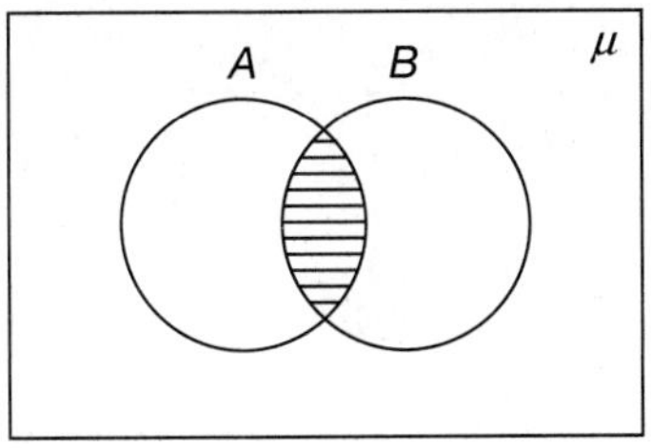

(iv) For a non-empty set A, the Venn diagram of A' is

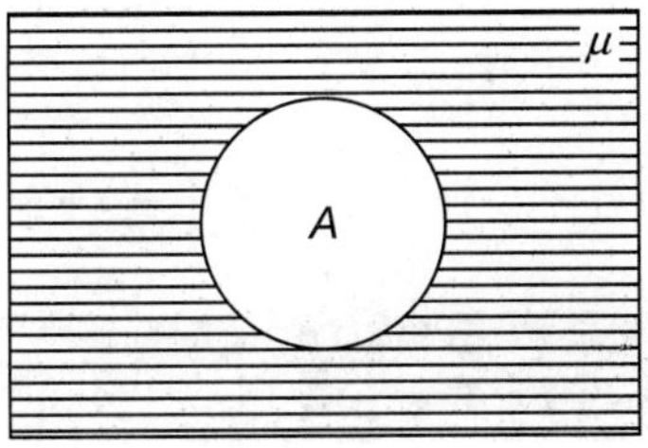

(v) Let A and B be two overlapping sets. The Venn diagram of $A - B$ is

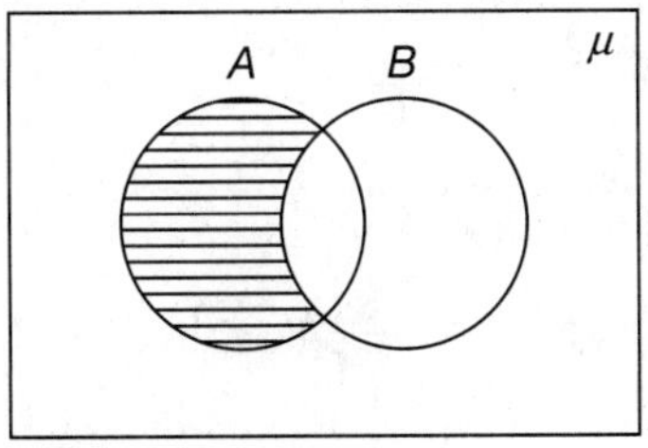

(vi) Let A and B be two sets such that $A \subset B$. This relation can be represented in Venn diagram as follows.

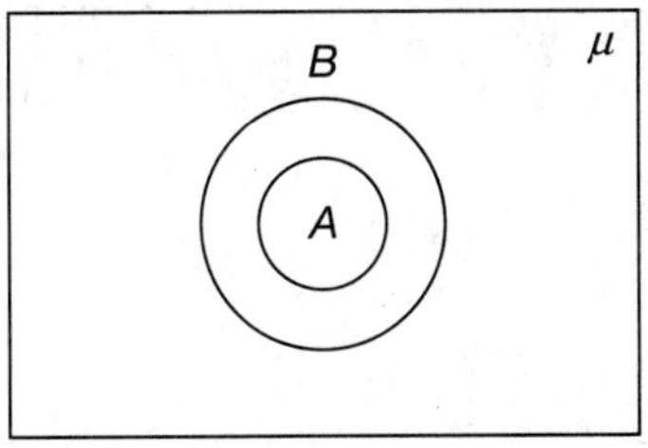

Some Formulae on the Cardinality of Sets

Set $A = \{1, 2, 3, 4, 5, 6, 7\}$ and $B = \{2, 4, 8, 16\}$.

Then, $A \cup B = \{1, 2, 3, 4, 5, 6, 7, 8, 16\}$ and $A \cap B = \{2, 4\}$.

In terms of the cardinal numbers, $n(A) = 7$, $n(B) = 4$, $n(A \cap B) = 2$ and $n(A \cup B) = 9$.

So, $n(A) + n(B) - n(A \cap B) = 7 + 4 - 2 = 9 = n(A \cup B)$.

We have the following formula:

For any two sets A and B, $n(A \cup B) = n(A) + n(B) - n(A \cap B)$.

EXAMPLE 11.7 If $n(A) = 4$, $n(B) = 6$ and $n(A \cup B) = 8$, then find $n(A \cap B)$.

SOLUTION

Given, $n(A) = 4$, $n(B) = 6$ and $n(A \cup B) = 8$

We know that, $n(A \cup B) = n(A) + n(B) - n(A \cap B)$. So, $8 = 4 + 6 - n(A \cap B)$

$\Rightarrow n(A \cap B) = 10 - 8 = 2$

EXAMPLE 11.8 If $n(A) = 8$, $n(B) = 6$ and the sets A and B are disjoint, then find $n(A \cup B)$.

SOLUTION

Given, $n(A) = 8$ and $n(B) = 6$.

A and B are disjoint $\Rightarrow A \cap B = \phi$

$\Rightarrow n(A \cap B) = 0$

$\therefore n(A \cup B) = n(A) + n(B) - n(A \cap B) = 8 + 6 - 0 = 14$

POINTS TO REMEMBER

- ✔ A set is a well-defined collection of objects.
- ✔ The objects in a set are called its elements or members
- ✔ The number of elements in a set A is called its cardinal number.
- ✔ A set with no elements in it is called an empty set (or) void set (or) null set.
- ✔ A set consisting of only one element is called a singleton set.
- ✔ Two sets A and B are said to be disjoint, if they have no elements in common.

DW

PRACTICE QUESTIONS CLASSROOM WING

Very Short Answer Type Questions

Direction for questions from 1 to 5: Select the correct alternative from the given choices.

1. Which of the following is a singleton set?
   (a) The set of all the months in a year having exactly 30 days.
   (b) The set of all the days in a week.
   (c) The set of all the natural satellites of the earth in the solar system.
   (d) The set of all the intersecting points of two parallel lines in a plane.

2. Let A be the set of all triangles in a plane having the sum of three interior angles is greater than 180°, then A is a/an ______set.
   (a) Empty
   (b) Singleton
   (c) Infinite
   (d) None of these

3. Which of the following is an infinite set?
   (a) $\{x: x \text{ is a prime}, x < 10\}$
   (b) $\{x: x$ is a vowel in the word MATHEMATICS$\}$
   (c) $\{x: x \text{ is a natural number}, 2015 < x < 2016\}$
   (d) $\{x: x \in Z, x \text{ is a non-negative integer}\}$

4. Which of the following is an empty set?
   (a) $\{x: x \in N, x \text{ is divisible by } 2\}$
   (b) $\{x: x \in N, x \text{ is the additive inverse of } 2016\}$
   (c) $\{x: x \text{ is a binary digit}\}$
   (d) $\{x: x \text{ is either prime or composite}\}$

5. Which of the following collections is not a set?
   (a) The colours in RAINBOW.
   (b) All good books in a school library.
   (c) The members of your family.
   (d) The principals of your school.

Direction for question 6: Match Column A with Column B.

6. These questions are based on the following data.

$A = \{1,2,3,4,5,6,7,8,9\}, B = \{2,3,5,7\}$,
and $C = \{2,4,6,8,10\}$

Column A	Column B
(i) $n(A \cap B)$	a. 4
(ii) $n(B \cup C)$	b. 5
(iii) $n(A - C)$	c. 6
(iv) $n[(A \cup C) - B]$	d. 7
	e. 8
	f. 9

Direction for questions from 7 to 11: Fill in the blanks.

7. If A and B are disjoint sets, then $n(A \cup B) =$ ______
8. If $A = \{x : x \text{ is prime}\}$ and $B = \{x : x \text{ is even}\}$, then $A \cap B =$ ______
9. If $A \cap B = \phi$, then A and B are called ______ sets.
10. If A and B are two non-empty sets, then the minimum number of elements in $A \cap B$ is ______
11. If all the elements of set A are present in set B, then $A \cup B =$ ______.

Direction for questions from 12 to 15: Select the correct alternative from given choices.

12. If $n(A) = 2016$ and $n(B) = 2017$, then the minimum number of elements in $A \cup B$ is
    (a) 0 (b) 1 (c) 2016 (d) 2017

13. If A is the collection of natural numbers which are less than 2 and $B = \{x: x \in N, x$ is neither prime nor composite$\}$ then $A \cap B =$
    (a) ϕ (b) $\{1\}$
    (c) N (d) None of these

14. If $A = \{x: x \in N, x$ is an additive inverse of 2017$\}$ and $B = \{x: x \in N, x$ is a multiplicative inverse of 2017$\}$. Then $A \cup B =$

(a) ϕ (b) $\{-2017, \frac{1}{2017}\}$

(c) 1 (d) $\{2017, \frac{-1}{2017}\}$

15. If $A = \{x: x \in N, 2015 < x < 2017\}$ $B = \{x: x \in N, x + 1 = 2017\}$, then $A - B =$

(a) ϕ

(b) $\{2016\}$

(c) $\{2015, 2016, 2017\}$

(d) $\{1, 2, 3, \ldots 2017\}$

Direction for question 16: **Match Column A with Column B.**

16.

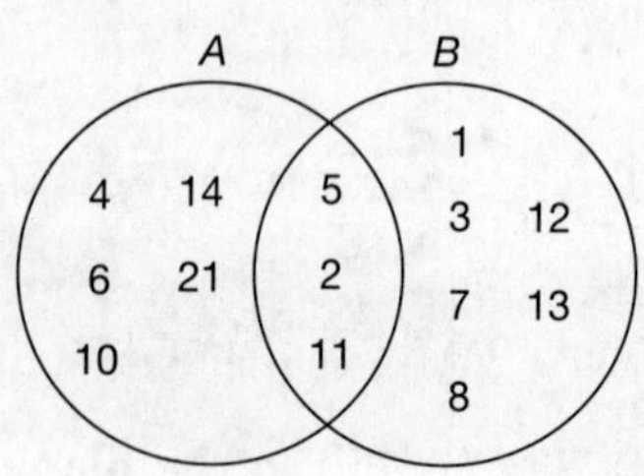

Column A		Column B
(a) $n(A - B)$	(p)	14
(b) $n(A \cup B)$	(q)	3
(c) $n(A \cap B)$	(r)	5
(d) $n(B - A)$	(s)	6

17. If $A = \{4, 8, 12, 16, 20\}$

$B = \{8, 16, 24, 32, 40\}$, then write the correct symbols ($\in$, $\notin$) in the following blanks.

(i) 40 __ A (ii) 8 __ B

(iii) 44 __ A

18. Can the following be called sets?

(i) Consonants in the word SETS

(ii) Names of days of the week that have at least 4 hours of sunshine.

19. If M = {January, March, May, July} and N = {April, June, September, November}, then write the correct symbols ($\in$, $\notin$) in the following blanks.

February __ M

February __ N

Short Answer Type Questions

20. If $A = \{x : x$ is an odd factor of 220$\}$, express A in its Roster form.

21. (a) Describe each of the following sets in the description form.

(i) {A river}

(ii) {Sunday, Monday, Tuesday, Wednesday, Thursday, Friday, Saturday, Sunday}

(b) Describe the following in set builder form.

(i) {2, 4, 6, 8}

(ii) {3, 6, 9, 12, 15, 21…..}

22. Check whether the following sets are equivalent?

(i) $A = \{x: x$ is a letter in the word SOLUTION$\}$

$B = \{$P, R, O, B, L, E, M$\}$

(ii) $C = \{x$: x is either prime or composite, $x < 10\}$

$D = \{1\}$

23. Check whether the following sets are equal?

(i) $A = \{$The set of the first five elements of the periodic table$\}$

$B = \{$H, He, Li, Be, B$\}$

(ii) $C = \{x: x$ is a prime number$\}$

$D = \{x: x$ is an odd number$\}$

24. Classify the following into empty sets or singleton sets.

(i) $A = \{x: x$ is a composite number which is having less than three factors$\}$

(ii) $B = \{x: x \in R, x$ is a multiplicative inverse of 2016$\}$

(ii) $C = \{x: x \in N, x$ is neither prime number nor composite number$\}$

25. If $T - R = \varnothing$, what do you say about the sets T and R?

26. In a class, each student speaks either German or French. If 10 students speak French and 6 students speak only French, then how many students speak both German and French?

27. Let $A = \{x: x \in Z, 2 \leq x \leq 5\}$ and $B = \{x: x \in Z, -2 \leq x < 4\}$. Find the following:

(i) $n(A \cup B)$ (ii) $n(A \cap B)$

(iii) $n(A - B)$ (iv) $n(B - A)$

28. Let $A = \{x: x$ is an even natural number, $x < 10\}$ and $B = \{x: x$ is a factor of 24$\}$

(i) Draw Venn diagrams to represent these sets.

(ii) Find: (a) $A \cup B$ (b) $A \cap B$

29. If $X = \{x : x \geq -5$, where x is a non-negative integer$\}$ and $Y = \{x : x \leq 5$, where x is an integer$\}$, find $X \cap Y$.

30. What is the cardinal number of the Set N of the natural numbers between 10 and 20?

31. What is the cardinal number of a set with the smallest odd number?

Essay Type Questions

32. A = $\{x : x$ is a factor of 36$\}$ and B = $\{y : y$ is a prime factor of 70$\}$. Find the value of $n(A - B)$.

33. If $n(A) = 5$ and $n(B) = 10$, then find the value of $n(A \cap B)$ when the value of $n(A \cup B)$ is maximum.

PRACTICE QUESTIONS COMPETITION WING

Level 1: Apply Your Concepts

Direction for questions from 1 to 5: **Fill in the blanks.**

1. If $A = \{\phi\}$, then $n(A) =$ ______.
2. The set builder form of $A = \{1, 4, 9, 16, 25\}$ is ______.
3. If A and B are two equivalent sets and $n(A) = 2016$, then $n(B) =$ ______.
4. If ϕ is an empty set, then $n(\phi) =$ ______.
5. The set of prime numbers which are having more than two factors is a/an ______ set (empty/singleton).
6. If $n(A) = x$, $n(B) = 2[n(A)]$, $n(A \cup B) = 2017$ and $n(A \cap B) = 1007$. Find the value of x.

   (a) 1008 (b) 2018
   (c) 2017 (d) 2024
7. A and B are any two sets, $n(A) = 17$ and $n(B) = 13$. What is the maximum possible value of $n(A \cup B) - n(A \cap B)$?

   (a) 4 (b) 13
   (c) 17 (d) 30
8. A and B are two equivalent sets, what is the maximum possible value of $n(A \cap B)$?

   (a) $n(A)$ (b) $n(A \cup B)$
   (c) $n(A) + n(B)$ (d) $n(A) - n(B)$

Level 2: Review Your Concepts

9. If $F(n)$ is the set of all the factors of 'n' excluding 1 and $F(16) \cap F(24) = F(x)$, then find the value of x.
10. In a class of 25 students, 18 of them passed in Maths, 14 of them passed in Science and 3 of them failed in both the exams. How many students passed in both the exams?

    (a) 3 (b) 4
    (c) 10 (d) 11
11. A is a set of the factors of 28, B is a set of the factors of 17 and C is a set of the odd multiples of 7 less than 50. Which of the following are singleton sets?

    (A) $A \cap B$ (B) $C \cap B$
    (C) $A \cap C$

    (a) Only (A) and (B)
    (b) Only (B) and (C)
    (c) Only (A) and (C)
    (d) (A), (B) and (C)
12. A is a set of all the prime numbers less than 20, B is a set of all the even natural numbers less than 20 and C is a set of all the odd natural numbers. Which of the following is/are true statements?

    (A) $A \cap B$ is a singleton set.
    (B) B and C are disjoint sets.
    (C) $A \cap C$ is an infinite set.

    (a) Only (B) (b) Both (A) and (B)
    (c) Both (B) and (C) (d) (A), (B) and (C)

Level 3: Assess Your Concepts

13. Write the Roster form of $\{x : 10 \leq x\ 100$, x is a factor of $100\}$. Also find the number of elements in the set.
14. If $F(m)$ is the set of all the multiples of 'm' below 100, and $F(12) \cap F(16) = F(n)$, then find the value of n.
15. Let $A = \{x : x^2 < 100, x \in W\}$ and $B = \{y : y^3\ 1000, x \in N\}$.

    Find:

    (i) $A - B$ (ii) $A - (A - B)$
    (iii) $A \cap B$ (iv) What do you notice?
16. If $P = \{x : x$ satisfies $x^2 - 100 = 0\}$, then express P in its Roster form.
17. If M and N are two non-empty sets and $n(M - N) = 10$, then find the minimum possible number of elements in the set M.
18. A survey was conducted among a group of people, 2000 people like **ragi malt** and 1800 people like **sabja sarabath**. What is the minimum number of people in the group?

AT

ANSWER KEYS

Crossword

Across

2. Set 3. Equivalent sets 5. Cardinal number 9. Infinite set 10. Disjoint sets
11. Elements

Down

1. Over lapping sets 2. Set builder form 4. Equal sets 6. Finite set 7. Roster form
8. Empty set

Classroom Wing

Very Short Answer Type Questions

1. (c) 2. (a) 3. (d) 4. (b) 5. (b)
6. (i) → (a); (ii) → (e); (iii) → (b); (iv) → (c) 7. $n(A) + n(B)$ 8. {2}
9. Disjoint sets 10. 0 11. B 12. (d) 13. (b) 14. (a)
15. (a) 16. (a) → (r); (b) → (p); (c) → (q); (d) → (s) 17. (i) ∉ (ii) ∈ (iii) ∉
18. (i) Yes; (ii) No 19. ∉, ∉

Short Answer Type Questions

20. {1, 5, 11, 55} 22. (i) Yes; (ii) No 23. *A* and *B*
24. (i) Empty set; (ii) Singleton set; (iii) Singleton set 26. 4 27. 8, 2, 2, 4
28. (ii) (a) B; (b) A
29. {0, 1, 2, 3, 4, 5} 30. 9 31. 1 32. 7 33. 0

Essay Type Questions

32. 7 33. 0

Competition Wing

Level 1: Apply Your Concepts

1. 1 2. $A = \{x^2: x \in N, x < 6\}$ 3. 2016 4. 0
5. Empty 6. (a) 7. (d) 8. (a)

Level 2: Review Your Concepts

9. 8 10. (c) 11. (c) 12. (b)

Level 3: Assess Your Concepts

13. 5 14. 48
15. (i) {0}; (ii) {1, 2, 3, 4, 5, 6, 7, 8, 9}; (iii) {1, 2, 3, 4, 5, 6, 7, 8, 9}; (iv) $A - (A - B) = A \cap B$
16. {–10, 10} 17. 10 18. 2000

Hints and Explanations

CLASSROOM WING

Very Short Answer Type Questions

1. (a) All months in a year having exactly 30 days are April, June, September and November.

$\therefore$ It is not a singleton set.

(b) In a week, we have 7 days.

$\therefore$ It is not a singleton set.

(c) The natural satellite of the earth in the solar system is moon.

$\therefore$ It is a singleton set.

(d) Parallel lines in a plane never intersect.

$\therefore$ The set of all intersecting points of two parallel lines in a plane is not a singleton set.

Hence, the correct option is (c).

2. In a plane, there is no triangle, in which the sum of the three interior angles is greater than 180°.

$\therefore$ A is an empty set.

Hence, the correct option is (a).

3. (a) $\{x: x \in N, x \text{ is a prime}, x < 10\}$

$= \{2, 3, 5, 7\}$

It is a finite set.

(b) $\{x: x$ is a vowel in the word MATHEMATICS$\}$

$= \{A, E, I\}$

It is a finite set.

(c) $\{x: x \in N, 2015 < x < 2016\}$

There is no natural number between 2015 and 2016.

$\therefore$ It is an empty set.

$\therefore$ Hence, it is a finite set.

(d) $\{x: x \in Z, x \text{ is a non-negative integer}\}$

$= \{0, 1, 2, 3, \ldots\}$

It is an infinite set.

Hence, the correct option is (d)

4. (a) $\{x: x \in N, x \text{ is divisible by } 2\}$

$= \{2, 4, 6, \ldots\}$

$\therefore$ It is not an empty set.

(b) $\{x: x \in N, x \text{ is an additive inverse of } 2016\}$

Additive inverse of 2016 is but $-2016 \notin N$

$\therefore$ It is an empty set.

(c) Binary digits are 0 and 1.

$\therefore$ Given set is not an empty set.

(d) Except 1, every natural number is either prime or composite.

$\therefore$ Given set is not an empty set.

Hence, the correct option is (b)

5. (a) The collection of colours in a RAINBOW is well-defined. So it is a set.

(b) We cannot say which books are there in our collection. So it is not a well-defined collection.

Hence, it is not a set.

(c) The members of your family is a well-defined collection.

$\therefore$ It is a set.

(d) The collection of principals in your school is a well-defined collection.

$\therefore$ It is a set.

Hence, the correct option is (b).

6. Given that

$A = \{1, 2, 3, 4, 5, 6, 7, 8, 9\}$, $B = \{2, 3, 5, 7\}$,

and $C = \{2, 4, 6, 8, 10\}$

(i) $A \cap B = \{1, 2, 3, 4, 5, 6, 7, 8, 9\} \cap \{2, 3, 5, 7\}$

$= \{2, 3, 5, 7\}$

Hence, $n(A \cap B) = 4$. (i) $\leftrightarrow$ ***a***

(ii) $B \cup C = \{2, 3, 5, 7\} \cup \{2, 4, 6, 8, 10\}$

$= \{2, 3, 4, 5, 6, 7, 8, 10\}$

Hence, $n(B \cup C) = 8$. (ii) $\leftrightarrow$ ***e***

(iii) $A - C = \{1, 2, 3, 4, 5, 6, 7, 8, 9\} - \{2, 4, 6, 8, 10\}$
$= \{1, 3, 5, 7, 9\}$

Hence, $n(A - C) = 5$. (iii) $\leftrightarrow$ ***b***

(iv) $(A \cup C) - B = \{1, 2, 3, 4, 5, 6, 7, 8, 9\}$
$\cup \{2, 4, 6, 8, 10\} - \{2, 3, 5, 7\}$
$= \{1, 2, 3, 4, 5, 6, 7, 8, 9, 10\} - \{2, 3, 5, 7\}$
$= \{1, 4, 6, 8, 9, 10\}$

Hence, $n[(A \cup C) - B] = 6$. (iv) $\leftrightarrow$ ***c***

7. Since A and B are disjoint sets, $A \cap B = \phi$

$n(A \cap B) = 0$

$n(A \cup B) = n(A) + n(B) - n(A \cap B)$

$n(A \cup B) = n(A) + n(B)$

8. $A = \{2, 3, 5, 7, \ldots\}$

$B = \{2, 4, 6, 8, \ldots\}$

$A \cap B = \{2, 3, 5, 7, \ldots\} \cap \{2, 4, 6, 8, \ldots\}$

$A \cap B = \{2\}$

9. If $A \cap B = \phi$, then A and B are called disjoint sets.

10. If A and B are non-empty sets, then minimum number of elements in $A \cap B$ is '0'.

11. If all the elements of set 'A' are present in set 'B', then $A \cup B = B$.

12. Given $n(A) = 2016$ and $n(B) = 2017$. The maximum number of elements in $A \cap B = 2016$.

The minimum of $n(A \cup B) = n(A) + n(B)$ – maximum of $n(A \cap B) = 2016 + 2017 - 2016 = 2017$

Hence, the correct option is (d).

13. $A = \{1\}$

$B = \{1\}$

$A \cap B = \{1\}$

Hence, the correct option is (b).

14. Additive inverse of 2017 is -2017 but $-2017 \notin N$

$\therefore A = \{\ \}$

Multiplicative inverse of 2017 is $\frac{1}{2017}$,

but $\frac{1}{2017} \notin N$

$\therefore B = \{\ \}$

$A \cup B = \{\ \}$

Hence, the correct option is (a).

15. $A = \{2016\}$

$B = \{2016\}$

$A - B = \{\ \}$ or ϕ

Hence, the correct option is (a).

16. $A = \{2, 4, 5, 6, 10, 11, 14, 21\}$

$B = \{1, 2, 3, 5, 7, 8, 11, 12, 13\}$

(a) $A - B = \{4, 6, 10, 14, 21\}$

$n(A - B) = 5 \rightarrow$ (r)

(b) $A \cup B = \{1, 2, 3, 4, 5, 6, 7, 8, 10, 11, 12, 13, 14, 21\}$

$n(A \cup B) = 14 \rightarrow$ (p)

(c) $A \cap B = \{2, 5, 11\}$

$n(A \cap B) = 3 \rightarrow$ (q)

(d) $B - A = \{1, 3, 7, 8, 12, 13\}$

$n(B - A) = (6) \rightarrow$ s

Therefore, the correct match is as follows:

(a) $\rightarrow$ (r), (b) $\rightarrow$ (p); (c) $\rightarrow$ (q); (d) $\rightarrow$ (s)

17. (i) $40 \notin A$

(ii) $8 \in B$

(iii) $44 \notin A$

18. (i) Consonants are S, T; hence, it can be called a set.

(ii) There are no particular days that have four hours of sunshine. Duration of sunshine differs depending on the weather conditions that change daily. Hence, it is not a set.

19. February $\notin$ M

February $\notin$ N

Short Answer Type Questions

20. Given that A = $\{x : x$ is an odd factor of $220\}$.

$220 = 1 \times 220$
$= 2 \times 110$
$= 4 \times 55$
$= 5 \times 44$
$= 10 \times 22$
$= 11 \times 20$

The odd factors of 220 are 1, 5, 11, and 55.

Hence, **A = {1, 5, 11, 55}**.

21. (a) (i) {Indus}

(ii) {The days of a week}

(b) (i) $\{x : x = 2n, n \in N$ and $n \leq 4\}$

(ii) $\{x : x = 3n, n \in N\}$

22. (a) $A = \{S, O, L, U, T, I, N\}$

$n(A) = 7$

$B = \{P, R, O, B, L, E, M\}$

$n(B) = 7$

Since $n(A) = n(B)$,

$\therefore$ A and B are equivalent sets.

(b) $C = \{x: x \in N, x \text{ is either prime or composite}\}$

i.e., C is the collection of all natural numbers except 1, less than 10.

$C = \{2, 3, 4, 5, 6, 7, 8, 9\}$

$n(C) = 8$

$D = \{1\}$

$n(D) = 1$

Since $n(C) \neq n(D)$,

$\therefore$ C and D are not equivalent sets.

23. (i) A is the set of the first five elements of periodic table.

$A = \{H, He, Li, Be, B\}$

$B = \{H, He, Li, Be, B\}$

$\therefore$ A and B are equal sets.

(ii) $C = \{x: x \text{ is prime number}\}$

$D = \{x: x \text{ is odd number}\}$

$C = \{2, 3, 5, 7, 11, \ldots\}$

$D = \{3, 5, 7, 9, \ldots\}$

$2 \in C$ but $2 \notin D$

$\therefore$ C and D are not equal sets.

24. (i) A = Every composite number has at least three factors. There is no composite number having less than three factors.

$\therefore$ A is an empty set.

(ii) The multiplicative inverse of 2016 is $\frac{1}{2016}$.

$B = \left\{\frac{1}{2016}\right\}$

$\therefore$ B is a singleton set.

(iii) In a set of natural numbers, 1 is neither prime nor composite.

$C = \{1\}$

$\therefore$ C is a singleton set.

25. Given that $T - R = \varnothing$.

(i) T and R are equal sets.

(ii) All the elements of the set T are present in the set R.

26. Each student of a class speaks either German or French.

Also, $n(F) = 10$ and $n(F - G) = 6$.

We know that $F - (F - G) = F \cap G$.

$n(F \cap G) = n(F) - n(F - G)$

$= 10 - 6 = 4.$

Hence, the number of students who speak both German and French = **4**.

27. $A = \{2, 3, 4, 5\}$

$B = \{-2, -1, 0, 1, 2, 3\}$

$A \cup B = \{-2, -1, 0, 1, 2, 3, 4, 5\}$

(i) $n(A \cup B) = 8$

$A \cap B = \{2, 3\} \Rightarrow$ (ii) $n(A \cap B) = 2$

$A - B = \{4, 5\} \Rightarrow$ (iii) $n(A - B) = 2$

$B - A = \{-2, -1, 0, 1\}$

(iv) $n(B - A) = 4$

28. (i) $A = \{2, 4, 6, 8\}$

$B = \{1, 2, 3, 4, 6, 8, 12, 24\}$

It is clear that, every element of A is present in B. So we draw two circles such that one is fully contained in the other.

The Venn diagram is as follows:

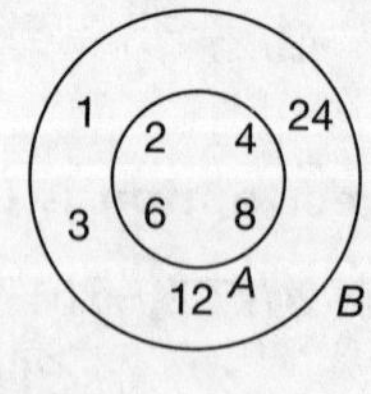

(ii) (a) $A \cup B = \{1, 2, 3, 4, 6, 8, 12, 24\} = B$

(b) $A \cap B = \{2, 4, 6, 8\} = A$

B is a set of all the even natural numbers less than 20 $\Rightarrow$ $B = \{2, 4, 6, 8, 10, 12, 14, 16, 18\}$

C is a set of all the odd natural numbers $\Rightarrow C = \{1, 3, 5, 7...\}$

(A) $A \cap B = \{2\}$ is a singleton set.

(B) $B \cap C = \{\ \} \Rightarrow B$ and C are disjoint sets.

(C) $A \cap C = \{3, 5, 7, 11, 13, 17, 19\}$ is not an infinite set.

Thus, (A) and (B) are true.

Hence, the correct option is (b).

Level 3: Assess Your Concepts

13. $\{x : 10 \le x\ \ 100, x \text{ is an integer}\} = \{10, 11, 12, 13, 14, \ldots 99\}$.

The factors of 100 are: 1, 2, 4, 5, 10, 20, 25, 50 and 100.

$\therefore \{x : 10 \le x\ \ 100, x \text{ is a factor of } 100\} = \{10, 20, 25, 50\}$.

The number of elements in the set = 5.

14. $F(m)$ is the set of all the multiples of 'm' below 100.

$F(12) = \{12, 24, 36, 48, 60, 72, 84, 96\}$.

$F(16) = \{16, 32, 48, 64, 80, 96\}$.

$F(12) \cap F(16) = \{12, 24, 36, 48, 60, 72, 84, 96\} \cap \{16, 32, 48, 64, 80, 96\}$.

$F(12) \cap F(16) = \{48, 96\} = F(48)$.

Given that $F(12) \cap F(16) = F(n)$.

$\therefore n = 48$

15. $A = \{x : x^2 < 100, x \in W\}$
$= \{0, 1, 2, 3, 4, 5, 6, 7, 8, 9\}$.

$B = \{y : y^3\ \ 1000, x \in N\}$
$= \{1, 2, 3, 4, 5, 6, 7, 8, 9, 10\}$.

(i) $A - B = \{0, 1, 2, 3, 4, 5, 6, 7, 8, 9\} - \{1, 2, 3, 4, 5, 6, 7, 8, 9, 10\} = \{0\}$.

(ii) $A - (A - B) = \{0, 1, 2, 3, 4, 5, 6, 7, 8, 9\} - \{0\} = \{1, 2, 3, 4, 5, 6, 7, 8, 9\}$.

(iii) $A \cap B = \{0, 1, 2, 3, 4, 5, 6, 7, 8, 9\} - \{1, 2, 3, 4, 5, 6, 7, 8, 9, 10\} = \{1, 2, 3, 4, 5, 6, 7, 8, 9\}$

(iv) From (b) and (c), $A - (A - B) = A \cap B$.

16. Given that $P = \{x : x \text{ satisfies } x^2 - 100 = 0\}$.

$x^2 - 100 = 0$

$x^2 = 100$.

$x = \pm 10$

Hence, $\boldsymbol{P} = \{-10, 10\}$.

17. Given that M and N are two non-empty sets and $n(M - N) = 10$.

The set consists of the minimum number of elements when M and N are disjoint sets.

Hence, the minimum number of elements in the set M $= n(M - N) = 10$.

18. A survey was conducted in a group of people, 2000 people like ragi malt and 1800 people like sabja sarabath.

$n(R) = 2000$

$n(S) = 1800$

The set R consists of the minimum number of elements when all the elements of S are also the elements of the set R.

Hence, the minimum number of people in the group = **2000**.

